MICHAEL PATRICK ADAMS, PHD, RT(R)
Dean of Health Occupations
Pasco-Hernando Community College

LELAND NORMAN HOLLAND, JR., PHD
Associate Academic Dean,
College of Arts and Sciences
Southeastern University

BRIDGET STIRLING, RN, PHD
Adjunct Professor, UBC Island Medical Progam
University of Victoria

WORKBOOK FOR
PHARMACOLOGY
FOR NURSES CANADIAN EDITION
A PATHOPHYSIOLOGICAL APPROACH

Pearson Canada
Toronto

Copyright © 2010 Pearson Education Canada, a division of Pearson Canada Inc., Toronto, Ontario

Original edition published by Pearson Education, Inc., Upper Saddle River, New Jersey, USA. Copyright © 2008, 2005 Pearson Education, Inc. This edition is authorized for sale only in Canada.

ISBN-13: 978-0-13-175677-9
ISBN-10:   0-13-175677-X

Vice-President, Editorial Director: Gary Bennett
Executive Editor: Michelle Sartor
Senior Developmental Editor: Paul Donnelly
Production Editor: Avivah Wargon
Copy Editor: Kelly Davis
Production Coordinator: Lynn O'Rourke

6   15 14

Printed and bound in Canada.

PEARSON

CONTENTS

PREFACE

Pharmacology is one of the most challenging subjects for those embarking on careers in nursing. It is an interdisciplinary subject borrowing concepts from a wide variety of natural and applied sciences. The purpose of this workbook is to help you—the student—identify the essential content and master the critical concepts found in *Pharmacology for Nurses: A Pathophysiological Approach,* Canadian Edition, by Adams, Holland, Bostwick, and King.

Each chapter includes a variety of questions and activities to help you comprehend difficult concepts and reinforce basic knowledge gained from textbook reading assignments. Highlights of this workbook that will enhance your learning experience include:

- The workbook chapters correlate directly to *Pharmacology for Nurses: A Pathophysiological Approach,* Canadian Edition, which allows you to easily locate information related to each question.
- Thorough assessment of essential information in the textbook is provided through the generous use of multiple choice, fill-in, and matching questions in every chapter.
- Making Connections questions encourage you to recall concepts from previous chapters and apply them to the current chapter, thus promoting retention of information and continuity of learning.
- Dosage calculation problems provide additional practice to assist you in mastering this challenging topic.
- Clinical case studies provide in-depth scenarios to sharpen critical-thinking skills.
- Answers are included in an appendix to provide immediate reinforcement and to permit you to check the accuracy of your work.

It is our hope that this workbook contributes to your success in beginning the study of an exciting and challenging subject.

CHAPTER 1

INTRODUCTION TO PHARMACOLOGY: DRUG REGULATION AND APPROVAL

FILL IN THE BLANK

From the textbook, find the correct word(s) to complete the statement(s).

1. Modern pharmacology began in the early _____.

2. In the early days of pharmacology, _____ had to isolate active agents from scarce _____ to create drugs used to treat clients.

3. In the 20th century, chemists and pharmacologists learned to _____ their own drugs in the laboratory.

4. The central purpose of pharmacology focuses on relieving _____ and improving the _____ .

5. Pharmacology is defined as the study of _____.

6. Therapeutics is the branch of medicine concerned with the prevention of _____ and the treatment of _____.

7. Pharmacotherapeutics is the _____ of drugs for the purpose of disease prevention or treatment and the relief of suffering.

8. A drug is a chemical agent capable of producing _____ responses within the body.

9. _____ are agents naturally produced in animal cells, by microorganisms, or by the body itself.

MATCHING

For questions 10 through 13, match the concept in column I with the agent in column II.

Column I	Column II
10. _____ Biologics	a. Morphine
11. _____ Alternative therapies	b. Hormones
12. _____ Active agent	c. Herbs
13. _____ Non-therapeutic	d. Sunscreen

For questions 14 through 17, match the concept in column I with the definition in column II.

Column I	Column II
14. _____ Health Products and Food Branch	a. Authorization to market a drug
15. _____ Therapeutic Products Directorate	b. Safety of health products
16. _____ Biologics and Genetic Therapies Directorate	c. Regulation of herbal products
	d. Regulation of blood products
17. _____ Natural Health Products Directorate	

MULTIPLE CHOICE

18. Applications to run clinical trials are made to Health Canada after which of the following?

    a. A drug is proven to be effective in animals.

    b. A drug has been shown to be cost-effective.

    c. A drug has demonstrated a desirable effect and is safe for animals.

    d. All of the potential side effects are known.

19. Patent protection gives the right for a manufacturer to sell a drug without competition for how many years?

    a. 10

    b. 15

    c. 20

    d. 25

20. What is the purpose of using a double-blind study method?

    a. To include people with disability

    b. To eliminate bias

    c. To include more participants

    d. To increase bias

21. During a clinical trial, if a drug appears to have dramatic benefits and be without serious side effects, it may

    a. Require no further monitoring

    b. Be shared with competing drug manufacturers

    c. Be immediately approved

    d. Be fast-tracked through the Health Canada approval process

22. What does it mean if a drug receives a DIN?

    a. The drug is authorized to be marketed in Canada.

    b. The drug has no adverse effects.

    c. The drug is highly effective.

    d. Health Canada acknowledges that the drug requires more testing.

23. What activities does the Marketed Health Products Directorate carry out?

    a. Reviews product safety data

    b. Investigates complaints

    c. Monitors product advertising

    d. All of the above

24. What is the purpose of MedEffect?

    a. To monitor the number of prescriptions filled for each medication

    b. To predict the potential effectiveness of each medication

    c. To inform nurses and other healthcare professionals of the availability of new medications

    d. To inform nurses and other healthcare professionals about drug safety concerns.

25. What is the most authoritative source for drugs marketed in Canada?

    a. CPS

    b. Health Canada's Drug Product Database

    c. Nursing Drug Guide

    d. The Internet

26. When compared with brand name drugs, generic drugs cost, on average,

    a. 10% less

    b. 45% less

    c. 10% more

    d. 45% more

27. A client with a life-threatening illness may apply to Health Canada to have access to a drug that is not approved in Canada under which of the following?

    a. Special Access Program

    b. Provincial Health Act

    c. Clinical Trials Application

    d. Health for All Act

CASE STUDY APPLICATIONS

28. Mr. A has a problem with mild constipation. This symptom has just occurred and does not seem to be related to a major illness. He has considered trying OTC drugs such as Ex-Lax or Metamucil. He is also considering some natural alternative therapies.

    a. Using your knowledge of pharmacology, what teaching plan would you implement for Mr. A?

    b. What nursing history is important when answering Mr. A's questions?

29. Ms. B reports to you that she is experiencing a drug reaction. She states that she may have taken a generic medication that does not meet the standard for all pharmaceutical products.

    a. As a nurse, what assessment data are essential in the initial phase of the nurse-client relationship with Ms. B?

    b. What would you teach Ms. B about drug regulations and standards?

CHAPTER 2
DRUG CLASSES AND SCHEDULES

FILL IN THE BLANK

From the textbook, find the correct word(s) to complete the statement(s).

1. With therapeutic classifications, drugs are organized on the basis of their _____ in treating a particular disorder.

2. Drugs organized by _____ classifications are categorized based on how they produce their effects in the body.

3. A _____ drug is the original, well-understood drug model from which other drugs in a particular class have been developed.

4. Three basic types of drug names are _____, _____, and _____.

5. The description given to a drug by the International Union of Pure and Applied Chemistry (IUPAC) is its _____ name.

6. Drugs with more then one active ingredient are called _____.

7. One of the main arguments against substituting generic drugs for brand name drugs is differences in _____.

8. Brand name drugs are usually more _____ than their generic equivalent.

MATCHING

For questions 9 through 12, match the concept in column I with the concept in column II.

Column I

9. _____ Pharmacological classification

10. _____ Therapeutic classification

11. _____ Generic name

12. _____ Trade name

Column II

a. Antihypertensive

b. Calcium channel blocker

c. Brand name

d. Active ingredients

MULTIPLE CHOICE

13. What is the purpose of therapeutic drug classification?

    a. To link the disorder to the drug's clinical usefulness

    b. To clearly state what a drug does chemically

    c. To evaluate the body system affected by the drug

    d. To identify tissue changes that result after the medication is absorbed

14. Who assigns a drug's trade name?
    a. Health Canada
    b. Provincial health authorities
    c. The company marketing the drug
    d. International Union of Pure and Applied Chemistry

15. Which is the key group that makes scheduling recommendations to provincial regulatory authorities?
    a. National Drug Scheduling Advisory Committee
    b. Health Products and Food Branch
    c. International Union of Pure and Applied Chemistry
    d. Office of Controlled Substances

16. What factors are used to determine the schedule under which a drug will be sold?
    a. Potential for dependency
    b. Potential for adverse reactions
    c. Potential for interactions with other drugs
    d. All of the above

17. Which of the following substances requires classification as a scheduled drug?
    a. Vodka
    b. Morphine
    c. Benadryl
    d. Cigarettes

18. Which of the following schedule classifications has the highest potential for abuse?
    a. Schedule I
    b. Schedule II
    c. Schedule III
    d. Schedule IV

19. What term is used to describe the overwhelming feeling that drives a person to use a drug repeatedly?
    a. Addiction
    b. Withdrawal
    c. Dependence
    d. Narcotic

20. What is the main objective of Health Canada's Office of Controlled Substances?
    a. To explain the usefulness of each drug in a way that the public comprehends
    b. To recommend which drugs should be restricted
    c. To work in partnership with the US Drug Enforcement Administration
    d. To ensure that drugs and controlled substances are not diverted for illegal use

CASE STUDY APPLICATIONS

21. You are giving a hospitalized client her morning medications. The client asks you why you are giving the generic form acetaminophen instead of the trade product, Tylenol. The client asks if there is a difference between trade and generic products.

    a.   What is your best reply?

    b.   The client also asks if Tylenol is a controlled substance. How do you respond?

CHAPTER 3
TOXICOLOGY AND EMERGENCY PREPAREDNESS

FILL IN THE BLANK

From the textbook, find the correct word(s) to complete the statement(s).

1. Toxic substances that are stored in tissues prolong _____.

2. Acute toxicity refers to the development of symptoms within _____ hours.

3. The antidote for opioids is _____.

4. Traditional infectious diseases include possible epidemics caused by _____, _____, _____, and _____.

5. The goal of emergency preparedness activities is to make sure that the _____ with the support of _____ is ready and able to respond in the event of an emergency.

6. Anthrax is an example of a category _____ infectious agent.

MATCHING

For questions 7 through 13, match the information in column I with the disease in column II.

Column I

7. _____ Found in contaminated animal products such as wool, hair, bone meal

8. _____ Oral vaccine available

9. _____ Caused by variola virus

10. _____ Genetic code is public information

11. _____ Ciprofloxacin used for prophylaxis

12. _____ Can be manufactured in a simple laboratory

13. _____ Could cause mortality rate of up to 33% if released into unvaccinated population

Column II

a. Anthrax

b. Smallpox

c. Polio

For questions 14 through 21, match the treatment in column I with the chemical agent in column II.

Column I

14. _____ Atropine

15. _____ Give milk to drink

16. _____ Sodium thiosulfate 1% to induce emesis

17. _____ Fresh air and oxygen

18. _____ Rinse nose and throat with 10% solution of sodium bicarbonate

19. _____ Treat skin with borated talcum powder

20. _____ Treat skin with 10% solution of sodium carbonate

21. _____ Oxygen and amyl nitrate

Column II

a. Nerve agents (sarin, soman, tabun)

b. Lewisite

c. Phosgene (gas)

d. Hydrogen cyanide

e. Adamsite

MULTIPLE CHOICE

22. Which of these is *not* an area of concern for possible use by bioterrorists?
    a. Infectious diseases such as anthrax and plague
    b. Incapacitating chemicals such as nerve gas and cyanide
    c. Common drugs such as morphine and strong antibiotics
    d. Nuclear and radiation exposures

23. When do the symptoms of anthrax exposure usually appear?
    a. 1 to 6 days after exposure
    b. 2 to 10 days after exposure
    c. 12 to 24 hours after exposure
    d. 1 week to 1 month after exposure

24. The public is discouraged from using antibiotics prophylactically unless there is a confirmed exposure to anthrax. Which of the following is *not* a rationale for this policy?
    a. Unnecessary use of antibiotics can be expensive
    b. Antibiotics can cause significant side effects
    c. Unnecessary use of antibiotics promotes the development of resistant bacteria
    d. Antibiotic use may inactivate the anthrax vaccine

25. Smallpox vaccine is contraindicated for all of the following persons *except*
    a. A 25-year-old who is HIV positive
    b. An individual who has already been exposed to the disease
    c. A nursing mother
    d. An individual with eczema

26. Exposure to any of the nerve agents does *not* cause which of the following symptoms?

    a. Respiratory failure and convulsions

    b. Severe nausea and vomiting

    c. Increased sweating and salivation

    d. Incontinence of urine and stool

27. Radiation sickness is also known as which of the following?

    a. Acute radiation exposure

    b. Acute radiation syndrome

    c. Nuclear exposure syndrome

    d. Radioisotope syndrome

28. Which of the effects of radiation exposure may be prevented if potassium iodide is used within 3 to 4 hours of exposure to ionizing radiation?

    a. Leukemia

    b. Nausea, vomiting, diarrhea

    c. Thyroid cancer

    d. Bone marrow suppression

29. Which of the following statements regarding the role of the nurse in emergency preparedness is *not* correct?

    a. The nurse must maintain a current knowledge of emergency management.

    b. The nurse must be aware of the early signs and symptoms of chemical and biological agents, and their immediate treatment.

    c. The nurse should be involved in developing emergency plans.

    d. The nurse should prepare for emergency situations by receiving all available vaccines against biological agents.

30. *Bacillus anthracis* can be transmitted in all of the following ways *except*

    a. Bite by an insect that carries the disease

    b. Exposure through an open wound

    c. Contaminated food

    d. Inhalation

MAKING CONNECTIONS

31. A company would like to advertise a drug that claims to protect individuals against smallpox in the event of a bioterrorist act. What agencies are responsible for ensuring that advertisements comply with rules set out by Health Canada?

    a. Local journals and newspapers are self-regulating

    b. Advertising Standards Canada

    c. Pharmaceutical Advertising Advisory Board

    d. Both b and c

CASE STUDY APPLICATIONS

32. During a routine visit to her doctor, Mrs. M asks you where she might be able to get a supply of drugs to prevent anthrax infection. She tells you that she has been following a number of world events in the news that are related to terrorism and war. You note that she becomes agitated while discussing terrorism, wringing her hands and looking distressed. Your nursing diagnosis is "Knowledge deficit related to bioterrorism/anthrax as evidenced by questions voiced and nonverbal anxiety behaviours."

    a.   Your care plan includes interventions relating to client education. What information would you give Mrs. M regarding prophylactic use of antibiotics for bioterrorism agents?

    b.   What information would you give her about the anthrax vaccine?

33. You are asked to assist in the writing of a protocol for the administration of smallpox vaccine to healthcare workers and law enforcement personnel in your area.

    a.   What nursing assessments would be included prior to the administration of the vaccine?

    b.   What information should be included in a pamphlet handed to each person who plans to be vaccinated?

34. Mr. R lives within 2 km of a nuclear power plant. He comes to the doctor's office to request "the pills that make you immune to radiation sickness." As you are aware that nurses play a key role in educating the public about issues of concern for people in your area, you have developed a standard care plan regarding nuclear disaster education.

    a.   What client teaching should you give to Mr. R regarding potassium iodide?

    b.   In evaluating Mr. R's understanding of the information he has been given, you ask him to explain why potassium iodide is effective in preventing thyroid cancer after radiation exposure. What should be his answer?

CHAPTER 4
PHARMACOKINETICS

FILL IN THE BLANK

From the textbook, find the correct word(s) to complete the statement(s).

1. The four main categories used to group processes relating to pharmacokinetics are _____, _____, _____, and _____.

2. The brain and placenta have barriers that prevent some medications from gaining access through normal circulation. These are the _____ and _____ barriers.

3. _____ is a process whereby most medications are deactivated when passing through the liver.

4. A mechanism called the _____ decreases the activity of most medications travelling through the liver.

5. _____ is a process involving the movement of a substance from its site of administration across body membranes to circulating fluids.

6. Four body tissues that have a high affinity for certain medications are _____, _____, _____, and _____.

7. Medications are removed from the body by the process of _____.

8. _____ is the plasma level of a medication that will result in serious adverse effects for the client.

9. The plasma drug concentration between the minimum effective concentration and the toxic concentration is called the _____ of the drug.

10. A _____ dose is a higher amount of drug given to "prime" the client's bloodstream with a level of drug sufficient to quickly induce a therapeutic response.

MATCHING

For questions 11 through 14, match the factors affecting absorption in column I with the absorption/distribution rates shown in column II.

Column I

11. _____ Absence of food in the digestive tract

12. _____ Binding of a drug to plasma proteins

13. _____ Ability to mix with lipids

14. _____ Larger drug particle

Column II

a. Faster absorption/distribution rate

b. Slower absorption/distribution rate

MULTIPLE CHOICE

15. What is the process of moving a medication from its site of administration across one or more body membranes?

    a. Absorption

    b. Distribution

    c. Metabolism

    d. Excretion

16. What process describes how drugs are transported in the body?

    a. Absorption

    b. Distribution

    c. Metabolism

    d. Excretion

17. What are the agents that have no pharmacological activity unless they are first metabolized to their active form by the body?

    a. Inducted enzymes

    b. Conjugates

    c. Prodrugs

    d. Bound plasma proteins

18. The fact that the half-life ($t_{1/2}$) of drug A is longer than that of drug B might be explained by a higher

    a. Metabolic rate for drug A

    b. Rate of elimination for drug B

    c. Potency for drug A

    d. Efficacy for drug B

19. Which of the following refers to the removal of larger drug metabolites from the bloodstream to the urine?

    a. Filtration

    b. Reabsorption

    c. Secretion

    d. Recirculation

20. Which of the following is a true statement regarding the half-life of a medication?

    a. The greater the half-life, the longer the drug takes to be excreted.

    b. The longer the half-life of a drug, the shorter the effect the drug will have on the body.

    c. Half-life and therapeutic range are terms that may be used interchangeably.

    d. When you know the loading dose, you know the half-life of a drug.

21. When a drug is highly bound to protein complexes, what effect does that have for the client?

    a. Drugs bound to protein are not available for distribution to body tissues.

    b. Highly bound drugs reach their target cells very quickly.

   c.   These drugs cross the blood-brain barrier in minutes.

   d.   Protein binding makes the drug more water soluble.

22. Which of the following routes of medication delivery *does not* bypass the first-pass effect?

   a.   Rectal

   b.   Sublingual

   c.   Oral

   d.   Parenteral

23. Which of the following body systems, if altered, could dramatically affect pharmacokinetics?

   a.   Integumentary

   b.   Musculoskeletal

   c.   Sensory

   d.   Renal

24. A process that can prolong the activity of certain drugs (e.g., phenothiazines) is called

   a.   Enterohepatic recirculation

   b.   Integumentary elimination

   c.   Respiratory elimination

   d.   Renal excretion

CASE STUDY APPLICATIONS

25. Mr. P is anxious and has not been able to sleep well for several weeks. He is moderately obese and has a history of hypertension and diabetes. After examination, the healthcare practitioner agrees to provide this client with a drug to treat anxiety.

   a.   What assessment data support the fact that drug distribution could be a problem for this client?

   b.   How will the nurse evaluate the effectiveness of the drugs used to treat anxiety?

   c.   What is the primary site for excretion of this client's medications and therefore the system that must be consistently evaluated by the nurse?

26. Mr. A is 60 years old and has been abusing alcohol for years. He appears to have no major medical problems. His GP has ordered a diagnostic evaluation of his bowel by colonoscopy.

   a.   What elements of the client's history would alert the nurse to possible problems with pharmacokinetics?

   b.   What interventions might the nurse expect during the medication phase of this procedure?

   c.   What system(s) should the nurse assess following the delivery of any medications for this client?

CHAPTER 5

PHARMACODYNAMICS

FILL IN THE BLANK

From the textbook, find the correct word(s) to complete the statement(s).

1. _____ deals with how medications affect body responses.

2. A _____ curve is a graphical representation of the actual number of clients responding to a drug action at different doses.

3. The median effective dose (ED_{50}) is the dose required to produce a specific therapeutic response in _____% of a group of clients.

4. The median lethal dose (LD_{50}) is the dose of drug that will be _____ in 50% of a group of animals.

5. A drug's _____ offers the nurse practical information on the safety of a drug.

6. A drug that is more potent will produce a therapeutic effect at a _____ dose, compared to another drug in the same class.

7. _____ is the magnitude of maximal response that can be produced from a particular drug.

8. _____ refers to a drug's strength at a particular concentration or dose, whereas _____ refers to the effectiveness of a drug in producing a more intense response as the concentration is increased.

9. The classic theory about the cellular mechanism by which most medications produce a response is called the _____ theory.

10. _____ often compete with agonists for receptor binding sites.

MATCHING

For questions 11 through 15, match the factors influencing drug effectiveness in column I with the area of pharmacokinetics or pharmacodynamics in column II.

Column I

11. _____ Concentration (dose) of an administered drug

12. _____ Presence of food in the digestive tract

13. _____ Frequency of drug dosing

14. _____ Age of the client

15. _____ Kidney disease

Column II

a. Pharmacokinetics

b. Pharmacodynamics

MULTIPLE CHOICE

16. Which of the following best explains the pharmacodynamic phase of drug administration?

    a.   The way the drug is absorbed, distributed, and eliminated from the body

    b.   Drug action and the relationship between drug concentration and body responses

    c.   Movement of substances from site of administration across body membranes

    d.   First-pass effect, which determines the frequency of dosing

17. You are giving a drug that is unfamiliar to you. You check the drug guide and determine that the average dose for the drug is 100 mg/day. Which of the following statements best explains what that means to you?

    a.   The 100 mg will be the effective dosing for about 50% of the population.

    b.   The 100 mg is the normal dose, and it should be given twice per day.

    c.   Few clients will respond to the 100 mg dose without side effects.

    d.   Most clients will have a reaction if given more than 100 mg/day.

18. You are explaining to a client the concept of drug potency. Which of the following statements best explains the concept?

    a.   If there are two medications for the same disorder and one has a therapeutic effect at 50 mg and the other at 100 mg, the first one is more potent.

    b.   If there are two medications for the same disorder and one has a therapeutic effect at 100 mg and the other at 50 mg, the first one is more potent.

    c.   Dosing has nothing to do with potency. Site of injection is the most important part of dosing theory.

    d.   Size and weight are what determines drug potency.

19. When drug molecules bind with cell receptors, what occurs?

    a.   Pharmacological effects of agonism or antagonism occur.

    b.   Pharmacogenetics occurs quickly.

    c.   The therapeutic index is increased.

    d.   Potency of the drug is altered.

20. The pharmacist tells you that a drug has a high therapeutic index. Which of the following statements best reflects your understanding of that statement?

    a.   Phase I of the dose-response curve would be low.

    b.   It is therapeutic to give this drug once per day.

    c.   It would take a big error in dosing to create a lethal dose for the client.

    d.   I'd better be really careful—there are a lot of receptors that are sensitive to this drug.

21. Which pharmacological principles will guide your practice as a nurse?

    a.   Future medications may be customized to match the client's genetic makeup.

    b.   If you understand potency and efficacy, you can compare medications.

    c.   As the therapeutic index increases, the safety of the drug increases.

    d.   All of the above are true.

22. You are reviewing the terms "efficacy" and "potency" with a client who is getting medications for cancer. What statement is most correct?

    a. You need to be most interested in the number of milligrams the medication is going to provide. This is called potency.

    b. The number of cancer cells killed is called efficacy. You are most interested in efficacy in the treatment of your disease.

    c. Your cancer is going to require that the fewest number of receptors be affected. So, concentrate on potency.

    d. Cancer is such a genetic issue. It is best to ask questions about dose and drug reactions, not efficacy.

23. The nurse hears in a report that a client had an idiosyncratic reaction to a medication. Which of the following statements best explains what happened to the client?

    a. No response, good or bad, was seen 24 hours after delivery of the medication.

    b. Drug-to-drug interaction occurred and less medication was needed.

    c. An unpredictable and unexplained drug reaction occurred.

    d. An antagonist reaction occurred at the receptor level.

24. Which statement best describes antagonists?

    a. They are sometimes referred to as facilitators of drug action.

    b. They can only produce an effect by interacting with receptors.

    c. They inhibit or block the action of agonist drugs.

    d. They produce the same type of response as an endogenous substance.

25. You are giving two drugs to a client with a heart problem. One drug works at the $beta_1$-adrenergic receptor and the other works at the $beta_2$-receptor. Which of the following statements bests explains how that can be possible?

    a. This is an example of potency and must be questioned.

    b. The graded dose response is the best explanation for this order.

    c. Lethal dose is determined on preclinical trials of beta-receptor drugs.

    d. The drugs can affect the different beta-receptor types in specific ways.

CASE STUDY APPLICATIONS

26. A client with a history of severe migraines is taking an analgesic that is classified as an agonist/antagonist. The client has not asked for the analgesic for 3 hours.

    a. What nursing assessment would you perform before giving this analgesic?

    b. What nursing diagnosis would you consider before giving this analgesic?

    c. What questions would you ask if the migraine headaches are not relieved within 15 minutes?

27. You are a nurse working with clients in an infectious disease clinic. Several of the clients are complaining that their wound infections are not healing quickly enough. You review their medical records.

    a. What information are you looking for related to pharmacotherapy?

    b. What outcomes would you expect to measure for the client in a wound management clinic?

    c. What evaluation would support your recommendation for a medication change?

CHAPTER 6

DRUG ADMINISTRATION THROUGHOUT THE LIFESPAN

FILL IN THE BLANK

From the textbook, find the correct word(s) to complete the statement(s).

1. In order to collaborate effectively with each client, the nurse must consider his or her unique _____, _____, _____, and _____ characteristics.

2. The functional evolution of the physical, psychomotor, and cognitive capabilities of a living being is referred to as _____.

3. The progressive increase in physical size is referred to as _____.

4. The _____ stage is subdivided into the _____ period (conception to 8 weeks) and the _____ period (8 to 40 weeks or birth).

5. By the third trimester of pregnancy, blood flow through the maternal kidneys _____ by 40% to 50%, which may affect drug _____.

6. In older adults, hepatic metabolism _____, which may require a/an _____ in drug dosages for this age group.

7. The _____-aged child begins to refine gross and fine motor skills.

8. The taking of multiple drugs, or _____, in older adults increases the risk for drug interactions and side effects.

MATCHING

For questions 9 through 13, match the pregnancy categories in column I with the descriptions in column II.

Column I

9. _____ Category A

10. _____ Category B

11. _____ Category C

12. _____ Category D

13. _____ Category X

Column II

a. Studies have not shown a risk to the mother or fetus.

b. Use of this drug may cause harm to the fetus, but it may provide benefit to the mother if a safer therapy is not available.

c. Animal studies have shown a risk to the fetus, but controlled studies have not been performed in women.

d. Studies have shown a significant risk to the mother and fetus.

e. Animal studies have not shown a risk to the fetus, or if they have, studies in women have not confirmed this risk.

MULTIPLE CHOICE

14. During the first trimester of pregnancy, what is the primary consideration from a medical, nursing, and pharmacological viewpoint?

    a. Assessing and evaluating each client on an individual basis so that mistaken beliefs can be clarified

    b. Safety of the client and delivery of a healthy baby

    c. Evaluating the knowledge base of the mother in regard to growth and development

    d. A focus on reducing the physical discomforts of the mother

15. The nurse determines that the fetus is at the greatest risk for developmental anomalies during which trimester?

    a. First

    b. Second

    c. Third

    d. Fourth

16. During which trimester do the skeleton and major organs develop?

    a. First

    b. Second

    c. Third

    d. Fourth

17. Health Canada estimates that chemical and drug exposure (including alcohol and tobacco use) accounts for _____ of all fetal malformations.

    a. 1% to 2%

    b. 10% to 12%

    c. 50%

    d. Less than 1%

18. The nurse is providing client education in regard to breastfeeding. The nurse should explore the possibility of postponing pharmacotherapy until the baby

    a. Is 6 months old

    b. Is of preschool age

    c. Is weaned

    d. Has at least doubled its birth weight

19. What is the preferred site for administering an IM injection to an infant?

    a. Deltoid

    b. Dorsogluteal

    c. Gluteus maximus

    d. Vastus lateralis

20. When determining the correct method for calculating a drug amount for infants, what must the nurse consider?

    a.   Development of the immune system

    b.   Development of the nervous system

    c.   Age and size of the infant

    d.   Infant's ability to swallow medications

21. The nurse must be aware that an increased risk of poisoning may occur due to a desire to explore, try new things, and put small objects in the mouth, during which developmental age period?

    a.   School-aged

    b.   Toddler

    c.   Infant

    d.   Preschooler

22. Before administering a drug to an older adult, the nurse should understand that the "average" dose may be affected by which of the following normal consequences of aging?

    a.   Older adults have increased hepatic metabolism.

    b.   Older adults have more rapid gastric motility.

    c.   Older adults have reduced glomerular filtration rates and diminished nephron function.

    d.   Older adults have increased capacity for plasma protein binding.

23. The nurse assumes a key role in the education of the adolescent client in relationship to which of the following?

    a.   Use of vitamins

    b.   Use of herbal remedies

    c.   Use of prescription medications

    d.   Use of tobacco and illicit drugs

24. During which period of adulthood would the nurse expect to offer counselling in relationship to substance abuse and sexually transmitted infections?

    a.   Middle adulthood

    b.   Young adulthood

    c.   Older adulthood

    d.   None of the above

25. During which period of adulthood would the nurse expect to offer counselling in relationship to positive lifestyle modifications?

    a.   Middle adulthood

    b.   Young adulthood

    c.   Older adulthood

    d.   None of the above

26. During which period of adulthood would the nurse expect to offer counselling in relationship to increased potential for adverse reactions to medications related to physiological and biochemical processes?
    a. Middle adulthood
    b. Young adulthood
    c. Older adulthood
    d. None of the above

27. The nurse knows that antidepressants and antianxiety agents are used more frequently by which age group?
    a. Over 65
    b. Over 50
    c. Over 40
    d. Over 30

MAKING CONNECTIONS

28. Drugs with a shorter half-life are preferable for use by lactating women. How is half-life defined?
    a. Drugs that can be cut in half.
    b. The dose at which the medication is lethal in half of the population.
    c. The length of time required for the medication to decrease concentration in the plasma by one-half after administration.
    d. The length of time required for the medication to double in concentration in the plasma after administration.

29. What does the prototype approach to drug therapy consider?
    a. Most popular drug for a particular disorder
    b. Most commonly used drug in a particular class
    c. Representative drug for how other drugs in a particular class work
    d. Drug of choice for a particular disorder

30. About half of all poisonings occur in children less than 6 years old. What centre was established in 1982 to provide a centralized forum for information among poison control centres in Canada?
    a. Health Canada
    b. The Public Health Agency of Canada
    c. The Canadian Network of Toxicology Centres
    d. The Canadian Association of Poison Control Centres

31. While the nurse should recommend that parents of toddlers have a supply of syrup of ipecac in the home, they should be warned *not* to give it unless instructed by a healthcare provider. What is the most important reason for this?

    a.   Parents may not know the right dose to give for the child's age and weight.

    b.   Significant quantities of the toxic substance may have already passed through the stomach.

    c.   The child may aspirate vomit during the ipecac therapy.

    d.   The parents may not seek follow-up care after the child vomits.

CASE STUDY APPLICATIONS

32. Ms. Y, age 19, presents to your clinic 20 weeks pregnant. She has received no prenatal care, has a history of substance abuse, and admits to using tobacco, alcohol, and cocaine during her pregnancy. Based on your knowledge as a nurse, assess for the potential of developmental anomalies for the fetus. Also evaluate the potential for future complications if the substance abuse continues throughout the pregnancy.

    a.   What are the potential anomalies in the fetus at the time of the visit?

    b.   What are the potential complications to the pregnancy?

    c.   State the rationale for the potential anomalies and complications.

33. Mrs. K is a 52-year-old mother with two grown children, six grandchildren, and aging parents with various health problems. She is married and her husband is disabled. Mrs. K also has a full-time job and one part-time job. When she presents to your clinic she is 23 kg overweight and displays signs and symptoms of excessive stress. Evaluate the potential complications from this situation and emphasize changes in your client education.

    a.   What are middle-aged adults sometimes called?

    b.   What options do these adults have to control their lifestyles?

    c.   What health factors are often in place at this time in the life cycle?

34. Mr. Z, age 72, presents with a variety of health problems. He is presently taking 14 different medications prescribed by four different healthcare providers. As the nurse in charge of client education, assess the situation and determine the lifestyle changes that are necessary to ensure optimal health for this client.

    a.   Taking multiple drugs concurrently is known by what term?

    b.   How does this action affect drug interactions and potential for adverse reactions?

    c.   What areas should the nurse assess carefully in this client's health history?

CHAPTER 7

THE NURSING PROCESS IN PHARMACOLOGY

FILL IN THE BLANK

From the textbook, find the correct word(s) to complete the statement(s).

1. A _____ is taken during the initial meeting between a nurse and client.

2. Problem-focused or "_____" history is taken to focus on the symptoms that prompted the client to seek healthcare.

3. Nurses use their skills in _____ during the interview to collect data that are denied or downplayed.

4. The _____ is a systematic method of problem solving with clearly defined steps.

MATCHING

For questions 5 through 11, match the description in column I with the nursing process step in column II.

Column I

5. _____ First step in the nursing process
6. _____ Data that include what the client says
7. _____ Data gathered through diagnostic sources
8. _____ Provide the basis for planning client care
9. _____ Objective measure of goals
10. _____ Links strategies to established outcomes
11. _____ Assessment of goals and outcomes

Column II

a. Evaluation
b. Intervention
c. Nursing diagnoses
d. Objective data
e. Subjective data
f. Assessment
g. Outcomes
h. Planning

MULTIPLE CHOICE

12. Mr. J has just returned from surgery. As the nurse, you are taking vital signs, checking his incision site, and determining if he is in pain. With these actions, what step of the nursing process are you using?

    a. Evaluation

    b. Planning

    c. Assessment

    d. Intervention

13. Mr. J complains of pain in his incision site. As the nurse, you are to administer morphine sulphate 2 mg IV. With these actions, what step of the nursing process are you using?

    a. Evaluation

    b. Planning

    c. Assessment

    d. Intervention

14. Mr. J inquires about the physical therapy he will receive to regain his mobility after his knee replacement surgery. As the nurse, you interact with physical therapy to coordinate his plan of care. With these actions, what step of the nursing process are you using?

    a. Evaluation

    b. Planning

    c. Assessment

    d. Intervention

15. Mr. J received the physical therapy and has regained his mobility after his knee replacement surgery. As the nurse, you interact with physical therapy to determine if he is ready to be discharged from the unit. With these actions, what step of the Nursing Process are you using?

    a. Evaluation

    b. Planning

    c. Assessment

    d. Intervention

16. Ms. L complains of pain in her right hip. As the nurse, you assess the area and observe swelling, redness, and open areas. What type of information have you gathered?

    a. Objective data

    b. Subjective data

    c. Outcomes

    d. Goals

17. Ms. L complains of pain in her right hip. You ask her to describe the nature of the pain and identify the affected area. What type of information have you gathered?

    a. Objective data

    b. Subjective data

    c. Outcomes

    d. Goals

18. Ms. L complains of pain in her right hip. You ask her to estimate the level of pain using a scale from 1 to 10. This information may be used to compare with assessment information gathered at a later date. What type of information have you gathered?

    a. Objective data

    b. Subjective data

    c. Outcomes

    d. Baseline data

19. Mrs. C is recovering from a fracture of the left hip. The interdisciplinary team has established a schedule of physical therapy for her. She will ambulate using a walker with the assistance of one member of the team for 15 m three times a day for 1 week, to be increased to 30 m three times a day for 2 weeks, then to be changed to a quad cane and stand by assist for 2 weeks, and then discharged to home. What type of information has been presented?

    a. Outcomes

    b. Goals

    c. Baseline data

    d. Objective data

20. Mrs. C is recovering from a fracture of the left hip. The interdisciplinary team has established a schedule of physical therapy for her. She is ambulating using a quad cane without assistance. It has been established that she is ready to be discharged to her home. What type of information has been presented?

    a. Outcomes

    b. Goals

    c. Baseline data

    d. Subjective data

21. Using the information in question 20, select the priority nursing diagnosis for the client.

    a. Pain related to hip fracture as evidenced by complaints of pain with ambulation

    b. Immobility related to hip fracture as evidenced by inability to stand or ambulate without assistance

    c. Knowledge deficit related to hospitalization as evidenced by first time in the hospital at 87 years of age

    d. Risk for poor skin integrity related to immobility from hip fracture

22. What is the priority factor in establishing a plan of care for a client who will be on a routine antihypertensive medication at home?

    a. Client education on adverse effects of the medication

    b. Risk for non-adherence

    c. Arranging for the drug to be delivered

    d. Teaching the client to take own blood pressure

23. What factor established from the client's health history would most likely suggest non-adherence with the medication regimen?

    a. Male

    b. Female

c.   Elderly

d.   Lives in a rural area

24. When the nurse educates a client with special needs, which of the following would be appropriate?

a.   Use of special education tools

b.   Use of medical terminology

c.   No client education required

d.   Assigning the task to someone else

MAKING CONNECTIONS

25. Which of the following nursing interventions influences biochemical and psychological responses in the client?

a.   Providing a warm blanket

b.   Administering a medication for pain control

c.   Drinking a carbonated beverage

d.   All of the above

26. How do therapeutic drugs differ from foods, household products, and cosmetics?

a.   Only therapeutic drugs can induce a biological response.

b.   Food, household products, and cosmetics are not traditionally designed for the treatment of disease and suffering.

c.   Drugs may not be considered part of the body's normal activities.

d.   Drugs are narrowly defined.

27. When assessing the ability of elderly clients to take responsibility for their own drug administration, the nurse must consider which of the following:

a.   Does the client have access to medication bottles that she or he is able to open independently?

b.   Which method(s) of teaching will help a client with hearing and visual impairments to understand instructions?

c.   Is the memory of the client impaired, resulting in the need for caregiver assistance, alarmed pill boxes, etc?

d.   All of the above

28. Which term describes how much of a drug is available to produce a biological response?

a.   Volume of distribution

b.   Rate of elimination

c.   Bioavailability

d.   Half-life

29. During the initial health history assessment, the nurse is told that the client is currently breastfeeding a 6-month-old baby. What information about medication administration in the lactating women should the nurse know?

    a. Drugs with high protein-binding ability should be selected.

    b. Drugs with high protein-binding ability should be avoided.

    c. All herbal products are safe for the infant and mother.

    d. None of the above

CASE STUDY APPLICATIONS

30. Ms. P is 15 years old and has just been diagnosed with type 1 diabetes mellitus. She has presented to the emergency department on three occasions with blood glucose over 20 mmol/L. She refuses to follow her prescribed diet and insulin regimen. She states, "My friends and classmates think that I am weird when I don't eat what they do and when I have to give myself a shot." As the nurse, you must remember certain factors related to this age group when establishing your plan of care.

    a. What is the self-image focus at this age?

    b. Would you consider this a special consideration client in regard to client education?

    c. What would be your priority nursing diagnosis?

31. Mrs. G is a 35-year-old Mandarin-speaking migrant worker who does not speak or understand English. She presents to the emergency department with severe abdominal pain and rigidity in the right lower quadrant. As the nurse in charge, you are to take the health history and establish a plan of care.

    a. What would be your priority intervention in this client's plan of care?

    b. What barriers would you expect to encounter when establishing her plan of care?

32. Mr. W is a 25-year-old client with a history of substance abuse. He has been admitted to your area after receiving critical injuries in a car wreck. He is now recovering and has been moved to the acute care ward from the ICU. As the nurse establishing his plan of care, you may encounter barriers in regard to his recovery.

    a. What effect will his substance abuse have on his recovery?

    b. What goals and outcomes will you establish for this client?

CHAPTER 8

PRINCIPLES OF DRUG ADMINISTRATION

FILL IN THE BLANK

From the textbook, find the correct word(s) to complete the statement(s).

1. The _____ route means that the nurse will administer the drug to the client by mouth, under the tongue, or into the rectum.

2. When the nurse places a drug directly onto the skin or associated membranes, this is referred to as the _____ route.

3. The traditional _____ of drug delivery form the operational basis for the safe delivery of medications.

4. Drugs that are swallowed, chewed, or slowly dissolved in the mouth are referred to as _____ medications.

5. _____ administration involves placing drugs under the tongue.

6. _____ and _____ are examples of rectal administration methods.

7. The parenteral route that offers the fastest onset of drug action is the _____ route.

8. Drugs are injected directly into the muscle in the _____ route.

9. One popular method for delivering drugs across the skin at a slow steady rate is the _____ patch.

10. _____ drug delivery methods are useful in treating respiratory and reproductive ailments.

MATCHING

For questions 11 through 19, match the specific drug delivery method in column I with the general route in column II.

Column I

11. _____ Rectal

12. _____ Intravenous (IV)

13. _____ Intramuscular (IM)

14. _____ Oral (PO)

15. _____ Transmucosal

16. _____ Subcutaneous (SC)

17. _____ Transdermal

18. _____ Sublingual

19. _____ Intradermal

Column II

a. Enteral

b. Parenteral

c. Topical

MULTIPLE CHOICE

20. Which of the following orders means to give the medication immediately?
    a. STAT
    b. PRN
    c. OD
    d. ASAP

21. Which of the following orders means to give the medication as required by the patient?
    a. STAT
    b. PRN
    c. OD
    d. ASAP

22. Of the following clients, which would be appropriate for rectal administration?
    a. Unconscious client
    b. Client experiencing nausea or vomiting
    c. Infant who cannot swallow pills
    d. All of the above

23. Which of the following methods is *not* a parenteral method of drug administration *and* avoids the first-pass effect in the liver?
    a. Oral
    b. Intravenous
    c. Intramuscular
    d. Sublingual

24. Which of the following is a major advantage of IV drug administration?

    a.   The duration of drug action can be easily controlled.

    b.   It is relatively free from the possibility of harmful effects.

    c.   A precise concentration of drug can be administered into the bloodstream.

    d.   The onset of drug action can be easily controlled.

25. What is a disadvantage of subcutaneous drug administration?

    a.   The final drug concentration within the bloodstream is unpredictable.

    b.   Drugs cannot be confined to a precise location.

    c.   For safety reasons, clients must be conscious when they receive a subcutaneous injection.

    d.   Pain, swelling, or infection may occur if proper precautions are not taken.

26. If rapid onset of action is critical, which of the following routes would the nurse choose?

    a.   Intravenous

    b.   Intramuscular

    c.   Sublingual

    d.   Rectal

27. Which of the following drug administration methods would the nurse use for the tuberculin test with purified protein derivative (PPD)?

    a.   Topical

    b.   Intradermal

    c.   Subcutaneous

    d.   Intramuscular

28. Implants are generally administered by which drug administration method?

    a.   Intradermal

    b.   Subcutaneous

    c.   Intraperitoneal

    d.   Intramuscular

29. Which of the following intravenous drug administration methods might be used to instil adjunct medications, such as antibiotics and analgesics, over a short time period?

    a.   Intraperitoneal

    b.   Intermittent infusion

    c.   Large-volume infusion

    d.   IV bolus administration

30. What medications are designed to release over an extended period of time?

    a.   Extended-release capsules

    b.   Long-acting medications

    c.   Slow-release medications

    d.   All of the above

31. Which of the following statements is true about IV infusion?
    a. It is the least dangerous method of drug administration.
    b. A flow regulator is always used to regulate drug flow.
    c. Quick delivery of IV drugs is not possible with IV infusion.
    d. Medications are delivered directly into the bloodstream.

32. What is the deepest skin layer?
    a. Epidermis
    b. Dermis
    c. Hypodermis
    d. Muscular layer

33. Which of the following statements is true regarding topical drug applications?
    a. For a local effect, it is necessary to keep drugs from penetrating the skin barrier.
    b. Liquids and liquid mixtures are the most effective physical compositions for topical drug therapy.
    c. In some cases, it is desirable for topical drugs to enter the systemic circulation.
    d. All of the above

34. What is the most common type of drug formulation for eye and ear medications?
    a. Salves
    b. Ointments
    c. Drops
    d. Sprays

CASE STUDY APPLICATIONS

35. Oftentimes, different formulations of medications are available, giving clients more than one option for drug therapy. Birth control is one example. Clients may take birth control pills, receive injections, or take medication via transdermal patches or vaginal inserts. Each method has advantages and disadvantages. Consider a situation in which your client, a 34-year-old working mother, has an active lifestyle and needs a reliable and effective means of birth control.
    a. What assessment data should be gathered?
    b. Outline the client teaching necessary to help her to make the best choice.

36. An elderly man presents with a complaint of nausea and diarrhea. After a thorough assessment, the physician determines that medication might help relieve some of these symptoms and requests the nurse to administer the medication.
    a. In planning drug administration routes, what would you recommend for this client and why?
    b. How will the nurse evaluate effectiveness of this route of administration?

CHAPTER 9
MEDICATION INCIDENTS AND RISK REDUCTION

FILL IN THE BLANK

From the textbook, find the correct word(s) to complete the statement(s).

1. Medication incidents that put clients at risk include _____ and _____.

2. "To do no harm" is the ethical principle of _____.

3. In nursing, standards of care are defined by nurse practice acts and the rule of _____.

4. Incomplete orders should be _____ with the healthcare provider before the drug is _____.

5. Adverse drug reactions can be reported to Health Canada through _____.

MULTIPLE CHOICE

6. Assessment is the most important step of the nursing process in preventing medication errors by which of the following?
   a. Having the client state the outcome of the medication
   b. Obtaining allergy and medication history information
   c. Advising the client to question the nurse about medications
   d. Planning the correct times for the client to take medications

7. Which best describes the reporting of medication errors?
   a. Is voluntary in ethical nursing practice
   b. Must be kept confidential in nursing practice
   c. Is an optional act on the part of the nurse
   d. Is the responsibility of the nurse

8. Practising under stressful work conditions can contribute to an increased risk of which of the following medication incidents?
   a. Giving the wrong drug
   b. Giving the wrong dose
   c. Giving a drug by the wrong route of administration
   d. All of the above

9. The nurse should not use the following abbreviation because it has been found to result in medication errors.

    a. qid

    b. bid

    c. qd

    d. PRN

10. Nurses do not want to do harm and put their clients' safety at risk by committing medication errors. This practice is guided primarily by which ethical principle?

    a. Veracity

    b. Utilitarianism

    c. Non-maleficence

    d. Beneficence

11. A nurse has given an incorrect dose of a medication. She follows the agency protocol by completing an incident report and discussing the incident with the risk manager. The purpose of following this procedure for reporting errors is to

    a. Determine the competence of the nurse

    b. Prevent future medication errors

    c. Determine who is to blame

    d. Gather information for risk management procedures

12. Morphine q4 hours is ordered for a client with terminal cancer who is experiencing severe pain. The nurse records that the client's respirations are 12 per minute and administers the medication as ordered. Twenty minutes later, the client develops respiratory arrest and dies. Which of the following statements provides the most accurate description of the nurse's dilemma?

    a. The nurse should have notified the healthcare provider for a clarification of the order.

    b. The nurse should have reassessed the client in 30 minutes to determine further nursing action.

    c. The nurse should have withheld a dose of the medication because the client's respirations were too slow.

    d. The nurse's intention was to alleviate pain, using a reasonable and prudent manner.

13. What documentation should a nurse *not* include when a medication error occurs?

    a. All nursing interventions taken to protect client safety

    b. An incident report

    c. The factors that contributed to the medication error

    d. Who the nurse believes is responsible for the medication error

14. As the nurses hands the medication cimetidine (Tagamet) to a client, the client states, "Thank you. This is the pill that neutralizes the acid in my stomach so that I don't get heartburn." The nurse will take which step in the nursing process?

    a. Assessment

    b. Planning

   c. Intervention

   d. Evaluation

15. While administering the 10 AM medications, the nurse discovers that the 6 AM intravenous dose was still hanging and never infused. What should be the nurse's first action?

   a. Document this finding on the client's chart

   b. Notify the primary healthcare provider

   c. Complete an incident report

   d. Begin the infusion at once

16. The physician approaches the nurse while she is preparing a medication. The nurse asks the physician to come back in 10 minutes. This is an example of which step in the nursing process?

   a. Assessment

   b. Planning

   c. Intervention

   d. Evaluation

17. When the nurse hands a client his morning medications, he says, "There's a yellow tablet in the cup. The doctor must have ordered a new pill." Which of the following responses is the best reply?

   a. Let me check with the pharmacist to see if that pill is appropriate for you.

   b. Yes. It is the right medication. Would you like some water to take with your pills?

   c. Let me check the doctor's orders and the medication administration record.

   d. Would you like me to check the doctor's orders?

18. A very thin 85-year-old client is on bed rest following surgery for a fractured hip. The nurse is preparing to administer heparin 5000 units IM. Identify which of the following actions the nurse should do.
   i. The nurse grasps the skinfold of the deltoid muscle between her thumb and forefinger.
   ii. The nurse inserts a 1.6 cm (5/8 inch) needle at a 45 degree angle.
   iii. The nurse massages the injection site.
   iv. Prior to administering the medication, the nurse checks the identification band.

   a. i and ii

   b. i, ii, and iii

   c. ii and iv

   d. All of the above

19. A nurse who is doing telephone triage for an outpatient clinic receives a call from a 76-year-old woman who is concerned because she hasn't had a bowel movement in 3 days and reports that "her stomach really hurts." Which of the following responses is correct?

   a. The nurse suggests that she eat foods high in fibre and drink some prune juice.

   b. The nurse suggests that she take a gentle laxative and drink more fluids.

   c. The nurse suggests that she call her primary care provider and have a more complete assessment.

   d. The nurse suggests that she use a glycerine suppository.

20. A client is recuperating after having hip surgery. The doctor orders heparin 5000 units subcutaneously every 12 hours to prevent thromboemboli. What is the correct method of administration?

    a. Use a 26 gauge needle and insert at a 90 degree angle.

    b. Use a 22 gauge needle and insert at a 90 degree angle.

    c. Use a 25 gauge needle and insert at a 45 degree angle.

    d. Use a 22 gauge needle and the Z-track method of administration.

21. A nurse administers a doctor's order for 150 mg of medication, when the usual dosage is 75 mg. When the nurse manager discusses the incident with the nurse, the nurse states that the dosage administered is what the doctor ordered. Which of the following statements is the correct one for the nurse manager to tell the nurse?

    a. It is not your fault. The doctor ordered the wrong dosage.

    b. This was a serious error. You must have misread the order.

    c. It is your responsibility to know the correct dosage. If the dosage seemed incorrect, it was your responsibility to call the physician.

    d. Did you ask the physician why the dosage was higher than usual?

22. The nurse is preparing to administer a dose of an enteric-coated tablet to a client. The client states that he is unable to swallow a pill. What is the correct action for the nurse to take?

    a. Instruct the client to place the tablet on the back of his tongue and give him large amounts of water immediately.

    b. Leave the tablet at the bedside and instruct the client to take it later.

    c. Crush the tablet and mix it in applesauce. Then administer the tablet in applesauce to the client.

    d. Return to the medication room with the medication and notify the healthcare provider.

23. The specific details of an incident report should be written

    a. In a factual and objective manner

    b. In a factual and subjective manner

    c. With the permission of the client

    d. In a compassionate and apologetic manner

24. Tetracycline 500 mg bid by mouth has been ordered for Mr. J, a 36-year-old forest ranger who has been diagnosed with Lyme disease. He tells you that antibiotics often give him indigestion, so you give him a glass of milk to take with his medication. What should you have known to avoid a medication error?

    a. He should be receiving 500 mg qid.

    b. This medication should be given intravenously to be effective.

    c. Sulfa drugs are more effective in the initial treatment of Lyme disease.

    d. Milk products inhibit the absorption of tetracycline.

25. Sulfasalazine (Azulfidine) has been ordered for Ms. T, who has ulcerative colitis. She also takes a beta-blocker for hypertension and reports an allergy to eggs, peanuts, and Aspirin. The order is for 2 g given four times a day. The nurse gives the client 500 mg at 0930 for the morning dose. What medication error has occurred?

   a. The medication should have been given before breakfast.

   b. The dose was too high. The maximum dosage is 1 g every 12 hours.

   c. People who are allergic to salicylates should not receive sulfasalazine.

   d. Beta-blockers are contraindicated for people who are on sulfasalazine.

MAKING CONNECTIONS

26. In Canada, the Code of Ethics for Registered Nurses is published by

   a. Food and Drug Administration (FDA)

   b. Canadian Nurses Association (CNA)

   c. Public Health Agency of Canada (PHAC)

   d. Health Canada

27. All narcotics are assigned a schedule or classification by law. In which schedule will you find morphine sulfate?

   a. Schedule I

   b. Schedule II

   c. Schedule III

   d. Schedule IV

28. What does it mean when a drug is classified as being teratogenic?

   a. It is safe for the mother in the first trimester of pregnancy.

   b. It is safe for the mother in the last trimester of pregnancy.

   c. Harmful effects on the fetus may occur at high doses.

   d. It is not safe for the fetus and may cause abnormalities if given.

29. Which of the following is a normal change in physiology that occurs with aging?

   a. Absorption of drugs is more rapid.

   b. Cardiac output is higher, distributing drugs more rapidly.

   c. Hepatic function decreases, slowing drug metabolism.

   d. Immune function increases, reducing the need for prophylactic antibiotics.

30. There is an increase in the risk of medication incidents in older adults for which of the following reasons?

   a. Dosages are based on weight.

   b. Older adults are often taking multiple medications.

   c. Older adults may have normal age-related changes in pharmacokinetics.

   d. b and c

CASE STUDY APPLICATIONS

31. An elderly client refuses an antihypertensive drug after breakfast. You note that this has happened 3 days in a row. The client's blood pressure has risen 40 mm Hg, and the client complains of an occipital headache.

    a. What step of the nursing process is utilized in this scenario? What type of data are described in this process?

    b. In developing your plan of care for this client, what ethical principle would you include in your interventions?

32. While you are preparing drugs for your client, you note that he has been receiving an anticoagulant daily, but the order reads for it to be given every other day.

    a. What would be an appropriate nursing diagnosis for this client?

    b. What nursing interventions would be included in the plan of care?

33. A 34-year-old woman with a diagnosis of bipolar disorder is admitted to the behavioural health unit and is reporting fine hand tremors, nausea, slurred speech, and dizziness. The medications that she has been taking are lithium carbonate 300 mg bid and risperidone 0.5 mg at 10 AM and hs. Since it is time for her next dose of lithium, you administer the medication before proceeding with the nursing assessment. While gathering information for the assessment, the client tells you that she has recently been taking a diuretic because of fluid retention before her menstrual period.

    a. What further information and assessments are indicated at this time?

    b. Should you have delayed the next dose and contacted the healthcare provider? Why?

    c. The healthcare provider orders an increase of lithium to 300 mg tid. What should you do?

    d. State two possible nursing diagnoses and their desired outcomes.

    e. What teaching would be indicated for this client?

34. Ferrous sulfate is ordered at 10 AM, 2 PM, and 7 PM. However, the client is scheduled for physical therapy at 9 AM. The nurse decides to give the medication at 8 AM with breakfast since he knows that administering iron supplements with food reduces gastric irritation. However, the medication is charted as if it were given at 10 AM.

    a. Is this considered a medication error?

    b. What is the best way for the nurse to handle this situation?

CHAPTER 10

PSYCHOSOCIAL AND CULTURAL INFLUENCES ON PHARMACOTHERAPY

FILL IN THE BLANK

From the textbook, find the correct word(s) to complete the statement(s).

1. The recipient of care must be regarded in a _____ context for health to be affected in a positive manner.

2. To deliver the highest quality of care, the nurse must fully recognize the _____ and _____ of the client.

3. Strong _____ or religious beliefs may greatly influence a person's perception of illness and the preferred modes of treatment.

4. Culturally competent nursing requires knowledge of the _____, _____, and _____ of various people.

5. _____ focuses on specific diseases, their causes and treatments.

MATCHING

For questions 6 through 12, match the definition in column I with the key term in column II.

Column I

6. _____ Change in enzyme structure and function due to mutation in DNA

7. _____ Science that deals with normal and abnormal processes and their impact on behaviour

8. _____ Study of human behaviour within the context of groups and societies

9. _____ Incorporates the capacity to love, to convey compassion, to enjoy life, and to find peace of mind and fulfillment

10. _____ Community of people having a common history and similar genetic heritage

11. _____ Beliefs, values, customs, and religious rituals shared by a group of people

12. _____ Each person viewed as an integrated whole

Column II

a. Culture

b. Ethnic

c. Genetic polymorphism

d. Holistic

e. Psychology

f. Sociology

g. Spirituality

MULTIPLE CHOICE

13. The client's psychosocial history is essential in the initial assessment. It includes all of the following *except*
    a. Religious beliefs
    b. Sexual practices
    c. Previous illnesses
    d. Use of alcohol, tobacco, or illegal drugs

14. Which of the following clients is least likely to be compliant with a medication regimen?
    a. The client who trusts the nurse
    b. The client who is aware of possible severe side effects associated with a medication
    c. The client who has high expectations regarding the results of taking a medication
    d. The client who has received limited information about a medication

15. Which of the following statements is *not* true about functional illiteracy?
    a. Functional illiteracy can lead to misunderstanding of the importance of pharmacotherapy.
    b. Functional illiteracy can lead to poor adherence.
    c. Functional illiteracy is rare in Canada.
    d. Functional illiteracy is more prevalent in older adults.

16. Community-related variables that influence pharmacotherapy include all of the following *except*
    a. Access to healthcare
    b. Alternative therapies
    c. Literacy
    d. Spiritual beliefs

17. Which of the following statements by the nurse will ensure that the client understands the instructions given?
    a. "Mrs. J, do you understand how to take your meds?"
    b. "Mrs. J, you take this drug at 8 AM and 8 PM. Call the doctor if you have any problems."
    c. "Mrs. J, could you explain to me how you will take your medication at home?"
    d. "Mrs. J, here are some printed instructions on how to use your prescription meds."

18. What is the study of changes in enzyme structure and function caused by mutations in DNA?
    a. Pharmacogenetics
    b. Eugenics
    c. Polymorphisms
    d. Acetylation

19. Which of the following drugs would have the least effect on a person of African Canadian descent because of enzyme polymorphisms?
    a. Isoniazid
    b. Propranolol

   c.   Procainamide

   d.   All of the above

20. Which of the following statements regarding women's health is *false*?

   a.   Women seek healthcare earlier than men.

   b.   Women have a higher incidence of Alzheimer's disease than men.

   c.   Women do not seek medical attention for potential cardiac problems as readily as men.

   d.   Women do not like to use antihypertensive medications because of side effects.

21. Since the late 1990s, Health Canada has had formalized policies that require the inclusion of which groups of people in drug development research studies?

   a.   People of both genders

   b.   Children

   c.   Octogenarians

   d.   People who are functionally illiterate

22. The Human Integration Pyramid model includes all of the following categories *except*

   a.   Age corollaries

   b.   Cultural and ethnic perspectives

   c.   Genetic predisposition

   d.   Financial status

MAKING CONNECTIONS

23. All of the following are examples of culturally based nonverbal communication behaviours *except*

   a.   Use of personal space

   b.   Eye contact

   c.   Fluency in the client's primary language

   d.   Hand gestures

24. The nurse should have open communication about the potential side effect of impotency in men using certain types of antihypertensives. Checking in with these clients on how things are going in this respect is a part of which step in the nursing process?

   a.   Evaluating

   b.   Planning

   c.   Implementing

   d.   Nursing diagnosis

25. An older client states that she is taking 15 minims of a certain medication. The nurse understands this to mean 1 mL. The 15 minims is an example of what type of measurement system?

    a. Metric

    b. Apothecary

    c. Household

    d. Centigrade

26. Ms. T is a young functionally illiterate woman in her first trimester of pregnancy. She has been told not to use a drug the physician called "teratogenic." She asks you what this means. You tell her that it is a substance

    a. That could produce dependency

    b. That will harm her developing baby

    c. Used to induce labour

    d. That cannot be obtained over the counter

27. Some cultures in East Africa believe that medications are more effective if delivered by the parenteral method of drug delivery. Which of the following methods of medication administration would that include?

    a. Oral

    b. Sublingual

    c. Intramuscular

    d. Vaginal

CASE STUDY APPLICATIONS

28. Mrs. B has come in for her monthly prenatal checkup. During your assessment she confides that her husband is an alcoholic. His parents were both alcoholics as well. Mrs. B tearfully asks you whether this is a genetic condition and what the chances are that her child will have a problem with alcohol abuse.

    a. What other assessments must you make?

    b. How will you answer her question?

    c. What other interventions might you include in your care plan for helping Mrs. B deal with this situation?

29. Mr. F, age 50, has been admitted to the hospital with a diagnosis of accelerated hypertension. He informs you that he quit taking his medications several weeks ago. During your initial assessment you determine that Mr. F has excellent prescription drug insurance coverage.

    a. What other factors related to use of his medications must be assessed in this situation?

    b. You determine that Mr. F has little knowledge regarding his medications and plan client teaching as one of your primary nursing interventions. What information do you need to give Mr. F regarding the use of his antihypertensives?

30. Ms. L has been admitted to your floor with multiple compression fractures of her lumbar vertebrae. On your initial assessment she is obviously in pain—her face is pale, diaphoretic, and drawn. She is gripping the side rail with her hand. When you offer her a narcotic for pain relief she refuses, saying, "It's not God's will for us to use medicines that cloud the mind so that we can't think about His goodness to us."

   a. What other modes of treatment could you include in your care plan that Ms. L might find more compatible with her religious beliefs?

   b. What other assessments should you make on Ms. L in order to help her further?

   c. Are there any medications she might be willing to consider if you offered them?

CHAPTER 11
NATURAL HEALTH PRODUCTS AND ALTERNATIVE THERAPIES

FILL IN THE BLANK

From the textbook, find the correct word(s) to complete the statement(s).

1. Many people think that the advantage of natural substances over synthetic medications is that they have more _____ than synthetic medications.

2. From the perspective of pharmacology, the value of complementary and alternative medicine (CAM) therapies lies in their ability to _____ the need for _____.

3. The nurse should not be _____ when the client requests alternative treatment.

4. An herb is technically a botanical without any _____ such as _____ or _____.

5. When collecting herbs for use at home, it is essential to know which portion of the plant contains the _____.

6. The _____ is responsible for defining NHPs and determining licensing requirements.

MATCHING

For questions 7 through 16, match the example in column I with the therapy in column II.

Column I

7. _____ Faith and prayer

8. _____ Yoga

9. _____ Biofeedback

10. _____ Nutritional supplements

11. _____ Homeopathy

12. _____ Acupuncture, Chinese herbs

13. _____ Chiropractic

14. _____ Music, dance

15. _____ Shamans

16. _____ Massage

Column II

a. Biological-based therapy

b. Alternate healthcare systems

c. Manual healing

d. Mind-body interventions

e. Spiritual

MULTIPLE CHOICE

17. Common characteristics of CAM systems include all of the following *except*

    a. They consider the health of the whole person.

    b. They promote disease prevention, self-care, and self-healing.

    c. They recognize the role of spirituality in health and healing.

    d. They provide inexpensive supplements and substitutes for expensive traditional drugs.

18. With the rise of the pharmaceutical industry in the late 1800s, interest in herbal medicine began to wane because of what reason?

    a. Herbs became very expensive.

    b. Herbs were no longer readily available in the environment.

    c. Synthetic drugs could be standardized and produced more cheaply.

    d. Herbs were proven to be ineffective against most diseases.

19. Which of the following is *not* a major factor contributing to the recent increase in popularity of botanicals?

    a. Many herbs have been clearly demonstrated to be more effective than available drugs.

    b. Herbal products are more widely available to the public.

    c. The herbal industry has aggressively marketed its products.

    d. Herbal products cost considerably less than most prescription medicines.

20. The nurse should understand that which of the following statements regarding herbs is *false*?

    a. Herbs may contain dozens of active chemicals.

    b. The chemicals in herbs may not have the same activity if they are isolated from each other.

    c. Herbal preparations are standardized, and the exact quantities of active chemicals are known.

    d. The strength of an herbal preparation may vary depending on where it was grown and how it was stored.

21. Which of the following statements regarding herbal products is true?

    a. Herbal products are always organic.

    b. Herbal products are 100% safe.

    c. Herbal products are potentially harmful.

    d. Herbal products are all standardized.

22. What are specialty supplements?

    a. Herbs used in food preparation

    b. Synthetic forms of traditional medicine

    c. Herbal dietary products used to enhance a wide variety of body functions

    d. Non-herbal dietary products used to enhance a wide variety of body functions

23. The nurse is teaching a client about how to properly read labels on herbal products. The nurse should explain that which of the following statements would most likely *not* be allowed on the label of a dietary supplement?

    a. Helps promote a healthy immune system

    b. May reduce pain and inflammation

    c. Reduces blood pressure and the risk of stroke

    d. May improve cardiovascular function

24. The nurse is advising the client about the proper use of herbal and dietary supplements. What is the responsibility of the nurse in regard to recommending herbal products?

    a. Seek to dissuade the client from using them because they are not "scientific"

    b. Be aware of the latest medical information on herbal products, including interactions and side effects

    c. Inform the client that he or she can trust the labelling on herbal products because the Canadian government has a rigorous testing program before the product is marketed

    d. Tell the client to seek information on herbal products from a practitioner of alternative medicine rather than a physician, because the physician has no knowledge of these products

25. The nurse should know that which popular herb is used for its possible benefit in treating depression?

    a. Aloe

    b. Astragalus

    c. St. John's wort

    d. Ginger

26. The client asks the nurse which herb may have beneficial effects on the immune system. The nurse should know that which of the following popular herbs is used for this purpose?

    a. Black cohosh

    b. Echinacea

    c. Ginkgo

    d. Kava kava

27. While assessing a new client, the nurse discovers that he is taking saw palmetto daily. The nurse should know that this popular herb is taken for what potential effect?

    a. Relief of urinary problems related to enlarged prostate

    b. Reduction of stress and promotion of sleep

    c. Reduction of blood cholesterol levels

    d. Treatment of constipation

28. Mrs. B has insulin-dependent diabetes. She has come to the doctor complaining of frequent hypoglycemic episodes. She tells you that she is taking all of the following dietary supplements. Which one needs to be considered as a possible cause of her hypoglycemia?

    a. Ginger

    b. Ginkgo biloba

    c.   Echinacea

    d.   Garlic

29. The nurse should know that an herbal infusion consists of which of the following?

    a.   Extract of active ingredients using organic solvents, forming a highly concentrated liquid or solid

    b.   Fresh or dried herb soaked in hot water for at least 15 minutes

    c.   Herb soaked in alcohol, which remains as part of the liquid

    d.   Herb that is ground and formed into tablets or capsules

MAKING CONNECTIONS

30. Which of the following distinguishes a conventional drug from a natural alternative agent?

    a.   A natural alternative agent is obtained from a natural source.

    b.   A conventional drug is routinely used by healthcare providers.

    c.   A conventional drug is chemically produced.

    d.   A natural alternative must be tested by Health Canada.

31. Which of the following statements best describes an advantage of prescription drugs over OTC drugs?

    a.   OTC drugs do not require a physician's order.

    b.   Prescription drugs ensure that harmful reactions, ineffective treatment, or a progressive disease state will not occur.

    c.   Only clients authorized to receive prescription drugs will take these medications.

    d.   The healthcare provider can maximize therapy by ordering the amount and frequency of the drug to be dispensed.

32. The nurse reads an order for rectal chlorpromazine 50 mg q6h. Which of the following is a rationale for administering a drug by the rectal route?

    a.   The client is unconscious.

    b.   The client is experiencing nausea or vomiting.

    c.   The client is an infant who cannot swallow pills.

    d.   All of the above

33. Which of the following statements is true regarding adverse effects and CAM?

    a.   CAM may reduce the need for medications, leading to fewer adverse effects.

    b.   All adverse effects will be reported and monitored.

    c.   CAM does not cause adverse effects.

    d.   All of the above

34. The client who is most likely to benefit from a prescription drug is the one who

    a.   Has prescription drug coverage through an insurance company

    b.   Sees the physician regularly and follows the directions for using the drug

    c.   Is not aware that the drug can cause serious side effects

    d.   Uses herbal supplements and goes to the doctor only when these fail to work

CASE STUDY APPLICATIONS

35. Mr. S, age 78, is being discharged from your unit on Lanoxin and Coumadin. Your care plan includes client education regarding these drugs. You have included his wife in the teaching session, and she mentions that she believes his problems can be corrected by using naturally grown herbs rather than drugs. Mr. S states, "I'm going to do what the doctor says, but a few weeds can't hurt me. I'll take them to keep her happy."

    a. What further assessments are indicated in this situation?

    b. Your care plan has been altered to give additional information on herbal preparations to this couple. What information must you give to Mr. and Mrs. S regarding the use of herbs while on Coumadin and Lanoxin?

    c. What other information regarding the use of herbal products should be given to this client?

36. Mrs. R comes to your mental health outpatient clinic with new symptoms, including agitation, headache, and dizziness. You note on assessment that she is also profusely diaphoretic. Mrs. R has been treated for depression with Prozac, an SSRI. During your assessment she confides that she has been using St. John's wort with her prescription drugs. She asks if her prescription can be changed to something that "works better."

    a. What is a likely cause of Mrs. R's symptoms?

    b. Your initial plan of care is for client education regarding drug-herb interactions. What other antidepressants might interact unfavourably with St. John's wort?

37. Mr. K, a 42-year-old teacher, has been using Echinacea regularly, yet he now has the flu. During your assessment you note that he has rheumatoid arthritis, for which he is taking methotrexate. He is upset that he has become ill and feels that the advertisements in nutrition magazines and on television may have misled him into buying useless products. He asks your advice regarding the value of alternative therapies.

    a. Your nursing interventions call for monitoring specific lab values in view of Mr. K's use of Echinacea and methotrexate. Which lab values would you monitor, and why?

    b. Your care plan includes client education regarding the uses of alternative therapies. What information should be included?

    c. During a team conference, a colleague suggests that a goal for Mr. K's care should be "discontinues use of all supplements and uses only prescription drugs." Explain why you might disagree with her suggestion, and write an improved goal.

CHAPTER 12

SUBSTANCES OF ADDICTION

FILL IN THE BLANK

From the textbook, find the correct word(s) to complete the statement(s).

1. _____ is the self-administration of a drug in a manner that does not conform to the norms within ones society.

2. Three substances that come from natural sources and are frequently abused are _____, _____, and _____.

3. The risk of addiction to prescription drugs is based on _____ and _____.

4. Two categories used to classify substance dependence are _____ and _____.

5. _____ occurs when a person has an overwhelming desire to take a drug and cannot stop.

6. Psychological dependence may develop after one dose of _____.

7. It is common to treat alcohol withdrawal with a short-acting _____.

8. Opioid withdrawal can be treated with _____.

9. After several months of pain therapy, a client must increase the dose of the pain medication. The best description of this situation is that the client has developed _____ to the pain medication.

10. Signs of physical discomfort after drug use is discontinued are referred to as classic _____ symptoms.

MATCHING

For questions 11 through 18, match the drug/substance in column I with the group name in column II.

Column I

11. _____ Lysergic acid diethylamide (LSD)

12. _____ Diazepam

13. _____ Alprazolam (Xanax)

14. _____ Methadone (Dolophine)

15. _____ Dextroamphetamine (Dexedrine)

16. _____ Methylphenidate (Ritalin)

17. _____ Heroin

18. _____ MDMA (Ecstasy)

Column II

a. Hallucinogen

b. CNS stimulant

c. CNS depressant

d. Opioid

For questions 19 through 23, match the withdrawal symptoms in column I with the drug classification in column II.

Column I

19. _____ Depression

20. _____ Dilated pupils

21. _____ Goose bumps

22. _____ Increased appetite

23. _____ Yawning

Column II

a. Opioid

b. Nicotine

c. Cocaine

For questions 24 through 27, match the drug/substance in column I with the source in column II.

Column I

24. _____ Opium

25. _____ MDMA

26. _____ Cocaine

27. _____ LSD

Column II

a. Natural

b. Synthetic

MULTIPLE CHOICE

28. All abused substances affect which body system?

    a. Cardiovascular

    b. Nervous

    c. Digestive

    d. Respiratory

29. You are working with a client who has a diagnosis of alcoholism. What organ is most likely to be malfunctioning in this client?

    a. Lungs

    b. Bowels

    c. Liver

    d. Kidneys

30. A client is admitted with liver failure. What nursing action is most appropriate prior to delivery of medications for this client?

    a. Check drug dosing because of issues related to metabolism

    b. Request increase in blood clotting drugs because of liver dysfunction

    c. Hold all nutritional supplements until liver disease is resolved

    d. Expect increase in drug dosing of antibiotics because of immune compromise

31. Repeated use of caffeine products can create which of the following effects?
    a.   Decreased stomach acid
    b.   Decreased blood pressure
    c.   Increased fatigue
    d.   Increased urination

32. What drug was once used for bronchodilation but has been discontinued because of psychotic episodes in some clients?
    a.   Cocaine
    b.   LSD
    c.   Phencyclidine
    d.   Amphetamine

33. Which of the following statements about addiction is *not* correct?
    a.   Addiction is most likely a neurobiological problem linked closely to the client's psychological state and social setting.
    b.   In some cases, addiction may begin with the client's medical need for the treatment of an illness.
    c.   The therapeutic use of narcotics and sedatives creates large numbers of addicted clients.
    d.   Attempts to predict a client's addictive tendency using psychological profiles or genetic markers have largely been unsuccessful.

34. Which of the following drugs was once used as a local anesthetic?
    a.   Amphetamine
    b.   Ketamine
    c.   Phencyclidine
    d.   Cocaine

35. What is the term for when a person has an overwhelming desire to take a drug and cannot stop?
    a.   Addiction
    b.   Dependence
    c.   Tolerance
    d.   Withdrawal

36. What term describes when an individual adapts to a drug over a short time and requires higher and higher doses to produce the same effect?
    a.   Conditioning
    b.   Withdrawal
    c.   Immunity
    d.   Tolerance

37. When taking sedatives for extended periods at high doses, clients can develop

   a. Tolerance

   b. Physical dependence

   c. Psychological dependence

   d. All of the above

CASE STUDY APPLICATIONS

38. A 28-year-old client is admitted to the hospital with pneumonia. During your assessment of the social history, you learn the client has a job, is self-reliant, and smokes marijuana every other night, but does not drink alcohol. The client claims "smoking a joint now and then doesn't hurt anybody."

   a. Based on your understanding of marijuana, what would you teach this client regarding the long-term effects of marijuana?

   b. Describe the psychological effects of marijuana and explain how dependence might develop in this case.

   c. Compare the risks of smoking marijuana to those of smoking tobacco products.

39. A client admitted for recurrent bladder infections describes a 15-year history of drinking beer and wine in moderate amounts. The client gives a family history of paternal alcoholism. The client asks, "What kinds of factors are linked with addiction? Is it genetic, or is there some other reason why people become addicted?"

   a. What would you include in the teaching plan to answer the client's questions?

   b. What assessment data are important when you admit this client?

   c. What nursing diagnoses and what client outcomes would you write in relation to the alcohol consumption?

CHAPTER 13

DRUGS AFFECTING THE AUTONOMIC NERVOUS SYSTEM

FILL IN THE BLANK

From the textbook, find the correct word(s) to complete the statement(s).

1. The two primary divisions of the nervous system are the _____ nervous system, made up of the brain and spinal cord, and the _____ nervous system, made up of sensory and motor pathways.

2. The _____ nervous system provides involuntary control over smooth muscle, cardiac muscle, and glands.

3. The sympathetic nervous system produces the _____ response; the parasympathetic nervous system produces symptoms called the _____ response.

4. _____ is the main neurotransmitter responsible for sympathetic nervous transmission; _____ is the main neurotransmitter responsible for parasympathetic nervous transmission.

5. Sympathetic nerves are often called _____, a term coming from the word "adrenaline"; parasympathetic nerves are called _____.

6. Increased heart rate, bronchodilation, decreased motility in the GI tract, mydriasis, and decreased secretions from glands are physiological responses associated with inactivation of the _____ nervous system or activation of the _____ nervous system.

7. _____-blockers, primarily used for hypertension, comprise the most commonly prescribed autonomic medications.

8. A class of drugs named after the fight-or-flight response and primarily used for increasing the heart rate, dilating the bronchi, and drying secretions resulting from colds is _____ drugs.

9. _____ drugs, named after the rest-and-digest response, are commonly used to stimulate the urinary or digestive tracts following general anesthesia.

MATCHING

For questions 10 through 14, match the physiological responses in column I with the autonomic receptor class in column II.

Column I

10. _____ Cause dry mouth, constipation, urinary retention, and increased heart rate

11. _____ Relax vascular smooth muscle and dry nasal secretions

12. _____ Cause bronchodilation

13. _____ Lower blood pressure without affecting the heart

14. _____ Decrease heart rate

Column II

a. Beta$_1$-blockers

b. Alpha$_1$-blockers

c. Beta$_2$-agonists

d. Alpha$_2$-agonists

e. Cholinergic (muscarinic) blockers

For questions 15 through 19, match the peripheral nervous system drug in column I with the indication in column II.

Column I

15. _____ Atropine

16. _____ Bethanechol (PMS-Bethanechol)

17. _____ Prazosin (Minipress)

18. _____ Doxazosin (Cardura)

19. _____ Albuterol (Ventolin)

Column II

a. Myasthenia gravis

b. GI stimulation following surgery

c. Pupil dilation during an eye exam

d. Asthma inhaler

e. Hypertension

For questions 20 through 24, match the drug in column I with the classification in column II.

Column I

20. _____ Scopolamine (Hyoscine)

21. _____ Phenylephrine (Neo-Synephrine)

22. _____ Bethanechol (PMS-Bethanechol)

23. _____ Propranolol (Inderal)

24. _____ Dobutamine (Dobutrex)

Column II

a. Parasympathomimetic

b. Anticholinergic

c. Sympathomimetic

d. Adrenergic antagonist

MULTIPLE CHOICE

25. A client is discharged with a newly prescribed antagonist for control of hypertension. The nurse gives discharge instructions. It is inappropriate to include which of the following instructions prior to the client's leaving?

    a.   Report any difficulty with urination to the nurse.

    b.   Take the medication for the first time directly prior to getting into bed.

    c.   Monitor BP and pulse daily (giving parameters that need to be reported).

    d.   Return for lab tests to monitor renal function.

26. An adrenergic antagonist is *most directly* related to which of the following?

    a.   Stimulation of the sympathetic nervous system

    b.   Inhibition of the parasympathetic nervous system

    c.   Stimulation of the parasympathetic nervous system

    d.   Inhibition of the sympathetic nervous system

27. How does bethanechol (PMS-Bethanechol) exert its effects?

    a.   Stimulates cholinergic receptors

    b.   Blocks cholinergic receptors

    c.   Blocks beta-receptors

    d.   Stimulates alpha-receptors

28. What drugs block the action of norepinephrine at alpha- and beta-receptors?

    a.   Parasympathomimetics

    b.   Parasympatholytics

    c.   Sympathomimetics

    d.   Sympatholytics

29. A nurse is to give adrenergic therapy in the form of parenteral phenylephrine. What safety precaution would be especially necessary with this drug?

    a.   Monitor IV insertion sites throughout the infusion

    b.   Monitor temperature of client q1h during the infusion

    c.   Monitor for CNS depression

    d.   Monitor for hypotension throughout the infusion

30. Cholinergics should *not* be used for clients diagnosed with which of the following?

    a.   Bradycardia

    b.   Hypotension

    c.   Urinary obstruction

    d.   All of the above

31. How does propranolol (Inderal) exert its effects?
    a.   Stimulates cholinergic receptors
    b.   Blocks cholinergic receptors
    c.   Blocks beta-receptors
    d.   Stimulates alpha-receptors

32. Pseudoephedrine has been ordered for a client with nasal congestion. The nurse knows that the drug can cause which of the following side effects?
    a.   Hypertension, insomnia, and tachycardia
    b.   Drowsiness and dry mouth
    c.   Increased heart rate and abdominal cramps
    d.   Dilated pupils and orthostatic hypotension

33. An anticholinergic may be used in treatment of peptic ulcers. What action makes this drug useful in this condition?
    a.   Decreases gastric emptying time
    b.   Decreases gastric acid secretions
    c.   Decreases intestinal motility
    d.   Relaxes gastric smooth muscles

34. The parasympathetic nervous system produces symptoms called the
    a.   Fight-or-flight response
    b.   Rest-and-digest response
    c.   Cholinergic blockers
    d.   Adrenergic blockers

35. Epinephrine is a non-selective adrenergic agonist. What is the disadvantage of this non-specific action?
    a.   It causes more autonomic side effects.
    b.   This drug cannot be used for nervous system conditions.
    c.   It will not cross the blood-brain barrier.
    d.   It can only be given by SC injection.

36. Homeostasis is achieved when
    a.   The most potent dose of a given drug is given
    b.   A proper balance of the two autonomic branches is achieved
    c.   There are little or no adverse effects
    d.   All of the above

37. Neostigmine (Prostigmin) is an example of which of the following?
    a.   Indirect-acting cholinergic
    b.   Direct-acting cholinergic
    c.   Indirect-acting anticholinergic
    d.   Direct-acting anticholinergic

38. Which of the following drugs would dry up body secretions?
    a.   Bethanechol (PMS-Bethanechol)

    b.   Metoprolol (Lopresor)

    c.   Atropine

    d.   Doxazosin (Cardura)

39. Atropine is usually not prescribed for any client with glaucoma. The nurse knows the contraindication is due to which of the following effects of atropine?
    a.   Increase in intraocular pressure

    b.   Decrease in lacrimation

    c.   Decrease in lateral movement of the eyes

    d.   Increase in difficulty with night vision due to papillary constriction

MAKING CONNECTIONS

40. Which cholinergic has been used in bioterrorism?
    a.   Phenylephrine

    b.   Pilocarpine

    c.   Sarin

    d.   Bethanechol

41. When a drug is referred to as an agonist, it can do which of the following?
    a.   Be a facilitator of an action

    b.   Be an inhibitor of an action

    c.   Have a potentiated action

    d.   Make one drug interact with another drug

42. What are the most commonly abused adrenergics?
    a.   Amphetamines

    b.   Proventil

    c.   Sudafed/pseudoephedrine

    d.   Marijuana

43. What is an example of a CNS stimulant that is often used illegally?
    a.   Propoxyphene (Darvon)

    b.   Flurazepam (Dalmane)

    c.   Heroin

    d.   Cocaine

44. The nurse is to administer the anticholinergic Atrovent using the "five rights." While the facility that the nurse works in requires clients to wear ID bracelcts, this client does not have one. To give medications to a client without an ID bracelet may put the nurse at risk of violating which of the following rights?

    a. Right medication

    b. Right time of delivery

    c. Right client

    d. Right route

CALCULATIONS

45. You are doing the following calculation to ensure that you will have enough medication on hand to last until the next pharmacy delivery. The physician has ordered metaproterenol sulfate 20 mg qid. The pharmacy sent metaproterenol syrup 10 mg/5 cc.

    The client should receive _____ cc per day.

46. The physician orders 0.3 mg atropine sulfate SC q4h. The pharmacy sends atropine sulfate 0.6 mg/mL.

    The nurse should administer _____ mL SC q4h.

CASE STUDY APPLICATIONS

47. Mr. Z, age 80, was diagnosed with COPD and hypertension. The client was given Inderal to treat the hypertension. The nurse assesses the following medications that he is also taking: Benadryl for itching and sneezing due to allergies, Minipress bid for hypertension, and Ventolin inhaler PRN for wheezing.

    a. Identify three potential nursing diagnoses that could occur because of drug interactions when these medications are given concurrently. Explain why these interactions would occur.

    b. What nursing interventions can be carried out to decrease the risk of the problems created by these interactions?

48. Ms. W, a 73-year-old woman diagnosed with glaucoma, presents at the clinic where you work. She was recently prescribed pilocarpine (Salagen) and took her first dose yesterday. She quietly admits that she very nearly didn't make it in to the clinic bathroom in time. She states, "I was worried the whole time I was driving over here that I might urinate on myself ."

    a. What teaching needs are apparent by this brief conversation?

CHAPTER 14

DRUGS FOR ANXIETY AND INSOMNIA

FILL IN THE BLANK

From the textbook, find the correct word(s) to complete the statement(s).

1. Excessive anxiety that is difficult to control and lasts for 6 months or more is referred to as
    _____.

2. Two important sets of brain structures are associated with anxiety. The one connected with emotion is
    the _____ system; the other, projecting from the brainstem and connected with alertness,
    is the _____ system.

3. _____ are classes of drugs prescribed to relax clients. Classes of drugs used to help clients
    sleep are _____.

4. Diazepam (Valium) reduces anxiety by binding to a receptor in the brain referred to as the
    _____ channel molecule.

5. The drug class usually prescribed for short-term insomnia caused by anxiety is _____.

6. _____ are a class of drugs that reduce anxiety, cause drowsiness, and promote sleep when
    administered at higher doses.

7. _____ is a fatal symptom often associated with an overdose of barbiturates or other CNS
    depressants.

8. Schedule _____ is the level assigned to many benzodiazepines; Schedule
    _____ is the level assigned to some barbiturates.

9. _____ have an ability to reduce anxiety symptoms by altering levels of norepinephrine and
    serotonin in the brain.

MATCHING

For questions 10 through 14, match the descriptions in column I with the drug classification in column II.

Column I

10. _____ Beginning in the early 1900s, the drug classification that has been used to control seizures, insomnia, and anxiety

11. _____ Class of drugs that act by binding GABA, intensifying the effect, without causing respiratory depression unless taken with other CNS depressants

12. _____ Class containing older agents rarely prescribed for anxiety and insomnia because of the availability of safer agents

13. _____ Introduced in the 1960s, now one of the most frequently prescribed classes in medicine

14. _____ A chemical related to tryptophan, sold OTC in many countries but banned in Canada

Column II

a. Benzodiazepines

b. Barbiturates

c. Non-benzodiazepine, non-barbiturate sedatives

d. Melatonin

e. Antidepressants

For questions 15 through 20, match the drug in column I with the class name and most appropriate use in column II.

Column I

15. _____ Secobarbital (Novo-Secobarb)

16. _____ Zopiclone (Imovane)

17. _____ Lorazepam (Ativan)

18. _____ Alprazolam (Xanax)

19. _____ Phenobarbital (PMS-Phenobarbital)

20. _____ Triazolam (Halcion)

Column II

a. Benzodiazepine, used for anxiety and panic

b. Benzodiazepine, with a half-life of 10–16 hours

c. Long-acting barbiturate, used for sedation

d. Barbiturate, used for short-term sedation

e. Non-barbiturate CNS depressant, used for short-term relief of insomnia

f. Hypnotic agent for sedation, peaks within 2 hours

MULTIPLE CHOICE

21. What term describes episodes of immediate and intense apprehension, fearfulness, or terror?
    a. Anxiety
    b. Panic
    c. Phobia
    d. Posttraumatic stress

22. Which are the drugs of choice for treating generalized anxiety and insomnia?
    a. Antidepressants
    b. Barbiturates
    c. Mood disorder drugs
    d. Benzodiazepines

23. Benzodiazepines have several uses. Which would be an *inappropriate* use?
    a. Long-term administration to treat phobias, OCD, and PTSD
    b. Treatment of anxiety that interferes with daily activities of living
    c. Short-term treatment of generalized anxiety disorder
    d. Short-term treatment of insomnia caused by anxiety

24. Which of the following terms may be used to describe benzodiazepines?
    a. Sedative
    b. Hypnotic
    c. Tranquilizer
    d. All of the above

25. Which were the first drugs used for anxiety treatment?
    a. Antidepressants
    b. Mood disorder drugs
    c. Barbiturates
    d. Benzodiazepines

26. CNS depressants include which of the following drug classes?
    a. Benzodiazepines
    b. Barbiturates
    c. Non-barbiturate, non-benzodiazepine sedatives
    d. All of the above

27. Which statement is true about re-establishing a healthy sleep regimen?
    a. Drinking alcohol close to bedtime helps one sleep.
    b. Eating a moderate meal close to bedtime helps one sleep.
    c. Supplements are often recommended for insomnia.
    d. Sedatives and hypnotics may be useful for insomnia if taken long term.

28. Which of the following best describes rebound insomnia?
    a. A time during which insomnia and symptoms of anxiety may worsen
    b. A worsening of insomnia due to drug dependency
    c. More common in younger clients
    d. Develops from short-term use of insomnia medication

29. Zopiclone (Imovane) is contraindicated with which of the following?

    a. Insomnia

    b. Severe sleep apnea

    c. Anxiety

    d. All of the above

30. Which of the following is true regarding sleep stages and patterns?

    a. Drugs for insomnia generally do not affect sleep stages.

    b. Clients with normal sleep patterns move from non-REM to REM sleep about every 90 minutes.

    c. REM sleep is the deepest stage of sleep.

    d. The most significant type of sleep with respect to the effect of hypnotic drugs is REM sleep.

31. Sleep deprivation has been linked to which of the following?

    a. Decreased risk of type 2 diabetes

    b. An increase in fearfulness, irritability, paranoia, and emotional disturbance

    c. Less daydreaming or fantasizing throughout the day

    d. Better judgment and less impulsive thinking

32. Which of the following best describes phenobarbital?

    a. Is a short-acting barbiturate and thus more useful for brief medical procedures

    b. Stimulates liver enzymes and thus may increase its own metabolism with repeated dosing

    c. Is mainly limited in drug therapy to induction of sleep

    d. Does not affect levels of folate (B_9) or vitamin D in the body

33. Benzodiazepines must be given with caution when given parenterally because of what risk?

    a. Seizures

    b. CNS excitation

    c. Respiratory depression

    d. Dependence

34. Which of the following best describes buspirone (BuSpar)?

    a. Is a benzodiazepine

    b. Rarely interacts with other CNS depressants

    c. Is the most highly addictive CNS depressant

    d. All of the above

MAKING CONNECTIONS

35. A client is experiencing extreme anxiety in a dental chair due to an impending tooth extraction. Which route of administration should the dentist use to give the most rapid onset of action of a drug for anxiety?

    a. Oral

    b. IV

    c. IM

    d. Rectal

36. A client tells you that she has returned from another country where she purchased melatonin OTC for insomnia. Which client teaching would be appropriate?

    a. Melatonin can increase ovulation in women trying to conceive.

    b. Melatonin can be taken safely during pregnancy.

    c. Melatonin is safe for everyone and has been approved for use by Health Canada.

    d. Melatonin is banned in Canada due to several safety concerns.

37. Which of the following drug delivery methods is *not* a parenteral method of drug delivery *and* avoids the first-pass effect in the liver?

    a. Oral

    b. Intrathecal

    c. Intramuscular

    d. Sublingual

38. One reason the first-pass effect is so important is that drugs absorbed at the level of the digestive tract do which of the following?

    a. Are circulated directly back to the heart

    b. Are distributed to the rest of the body and target organs

    c. Have ultimately more bioavailability than they would if absorbed at a different location

    d. Are routed through the hepatic portal circulation

39. Compared to middle-aged clients, younger and elderly clients metabolize drugs

    a. More slowly

    b. More rapidly

    c. At the same rate

CALCULATIONS

40. A physician orders lorazepam 1.5 mg IV bolus. The pharmacy supplies 0.001 g/mL of lorazepam. The nurse should administer _____ mL IV bolus as ordered.

41. The physician orders diazepam 1 mg solution PO. The oral solution is 5 mg/mL. The nurse should administer _____ mL/dose.

CASE STUDY APPLICATIONS

42. Mr. L is a 38-year-old client who is to have a short surgical procedure during which he will be given lorazepam IV. The nurse knows that lorazepam is a benzodiazepine used as pre-anesthetic.

    a.   What does the nurse need to assess prior to giving lorazepam?

    b.   What interventions would the nurse use to maintain the client's safety during the procedure?

    c.   What would the nurse use to evaluate the effectiveness of these interventions?

43. Mrs. D has not slept in weeks. She is troubled about a new job and feels that if she can just get through a couple more weeks, things might start to become a little easier. One thing that would definitely help Mrs. D is a good night's sleep.

    a.   What nursing diagnosis would you identify for this client?

    b.   What nursing interventions would be used to assist this client?

    c.   What would the nurse teach the client regarding available pharmacological interventions?

CHAPTER 15

DRUGS FOR SEIZURES

FILL IN THE BLANK

From the textbook, find the correct word(s) to complete the statement(s).

1. Seizures can result from _____ situations or occur on a _____ basis as with epilepsy.

2. Five possible causes of seizures include _____, _____, _____, _____, and _____.

3. Because antiseizure drugs are mostly pregnancy category D and may decrease the effectiveness of oral contraceptives, clients should use _____.

4. Antiseizure drugs may cause _____ deficiency, which can cause neural tube defects in a fetus.

5. Clients who have seizures may have a lower tolerance to environmental triggers such as _____ deprivation and exposure to _____ or _____ lights.

6. _____ seizures occur in 0.5% of _____-month-old to _____-year-old children during an illness and last 1 to 2 minutes. Prevention is best carried out by controlling _____.

7. Of the major antiseizure medications, _____ is a drug of choice for tonic-clonic and partial seizures.

8. _____ seizures occur only on one side of the brain and continue for a short distance before they stop; _____ seizures may travel throughout the brain.

9. Of the most popular antiseizure medications, the drug of choice for absence seizures is _____.

10. Two popular benzodiazepines used to treat status epilepticus are _____ and _____.

11. _____ is an emergency type of generalized tonic-clonic seizure that is prolonged and usually affects _____, causing hypoxia.

12. Treatment of status epilepticus includes providing antiseizure medications while maintaining the client's _____.

13. The goal of antiseizure medications is to prevent _____ or repeated firing and therefore to _____ neuronal activity.

14. Once seizures are controlled, drug therapy continues for some time. After _____ years, the medications may be withdrawn slowly, one at a time, over several _____.

MATCHING

For questions 15 through 21, match the signs and symptoms in column I with the type of seizure in column II.

Column I

15. _____ In adults, this seizure may be preceded by an aura. Muscles then become tense, and a rhythmic jerking motion develops.

16. _____ This seizure is marked by major muscle groups contracting quickly, making a jerking motion. Clients appear unsteady and clumsy and may fall from a sitting position or drop whatever they are holding.

17. _____ This seizure usually starts with a blank stare. Clients may become disoriented and not pay attention to verbal commands or act as if they have a psychiatric illness. After the seizure, clients do not remember what happened.

18. _____ Clients may feel for a brief moment that their precise location is vague and out of sorts. Often clients will hear and see things that are not there or may smell or taste things and have an upset stomach. Parts of the body such as the arms, legs, or face may start twitching. Symptoms are often not dramatic and may occur without loss of consciousness.

19. _____ This type of seizure occurs most often in children. Clients develop a blank stare without having twitching facial or body movements. This seizure lasts for only a few seconds. Clients then quickly recover and engage in normal activities.

20. _____ This is a medical emergency brought on by repeated seizures and convulsions. Steps must be taken to ensure the airway remains open.

21. _____ Clients often stumble or fall for no apparent reason. Episodes are very short, lasting only a matter of seconds. After the seizure, clients return to normal activities without difficulty.

Column II

a. Simple partial seizure

b. Complex partial seizure

c. Absence seizure

d. Atonic seizure

e. Myoclonic seizure

f. Generalized tonic-clonic seizure

g. Status epilepticus

For questions 22 through 27, match the drug in column I with the pharmacological category in column II.

Column I

22. _____ Phenobarbital (PMS-Phenobarbital)

23. _____ Clonazepam (Rivotril)

24. _____ Phenytoin (Dilantin)

25. _____ Gabapentin (Neurontin)

26. _____ Carbamazepine (Tegretol)

27. _____ Ethosuximide (Zarontin)

Column II

a.   Drugs acting through a GABA receptor

b.   Drugs delaying an influx of sodium across neuronal membranes

c.   Drugs delaying an influx of calcium across neuronal membrane

MULTIPLE CHOICE

28. What common concern occurs with phenobarbital (PMS-Phenobarbital)?
    a.   Irregular heartbeat
    b.   Blood cell reactions
    c.   Hypotension
    d.   Vitamin D and folate deficiency

29. What is the main advantage of using carbamazepine (Tegretol) for partial seizures?
    a.   Category C status
    b.   Dual use for the treatment of trigeminal neuralgia
    c.   Causes less drowsiness
    d.   Dual use for the treatment of bipolar disorder

30. An influx of sodium or calcium into the neuron _____ neuronal activity, whereas an influx of chloride _____ neuronal activity.
    a.   Suppresses, enhances
    b.   Enhances, suppresses
    c.   Enhances, has no effect on
    d.   Suppresses, has no effect on

31. Valproic acid (Depakene) belongs to which group?
    a.   Hydantoins
    b.   Barbiturates
    c.   Succinimides
    d.   Phenytoin-like agents

32. Which antiseizure medication might produce psychotic behaviour symptoms?
    a. Ethosuximide (Zarontin)
    b. Phenobarbital (PMS-Phenobarbital)
    c. Lorazepam (Ativan)
    d. Gabapentin (Neurontin)

33. Which is the most potent benzodiazepine used for the treatment of convulsions?
    a. Clonazepam (Rivotril)
    b. Clorazepate (Apo-Clorazepate)
    c. Diazepam (Valium)
    d. Lorazepam (Ativan)

34. Which medication is used as a specific benzodiazepine receptor antagonist that can be administered to reverse CNS depression?
    a. Flumazenil
    b. Felbamate
    c. Divalproex
    d. Lamotrigine

35. What is the major issue to consider when initiating antiseizure therapy?
    a. Avoiding kidney and liver toxicity
    b. Medication adherence
    c. Maintaining proper drug levels in the bloodstream
    d. All of the above

36. Why should women of childbearing age be counselled regarding antiseizure medications?
    a. The medications are teratogenic.
    b. They interfere with oral contraceptives.
    c. They produce folic acid deficiency.
    d. All of the above

37. Clients taking barbiturates for seizures must be monitored for respiratory depression in the presence of which of the following?
    a. Oral administration
    b. Non-opiate analgesics
    c. Chronic respiratory dysfunction
    d. All of the above

38. A client is admitted with an overdose of Diazepam (Valium). Which of the following drugs would the nurse need to have on hand?

    a.   Diphenhydramine

    b.   Flumazenil

    c.   Epinephrine

    d.   Atropine

39. The nurse should teach the client taking benzodiazepines that the drug can do which of the following?

    a.   Cause sedation when first started

    b.   Be safely stopped abruptly

    c.   Increase the amount of digoxin needed

    d.   Be potentiated by smoking, nicotine patches, or chewing tobacco

40. A client taking phenytoin (Dilantin) chronically for seizures should be encouraged to maintain good oral hygiene and visit the dentist every 6 months. Phenytoin does which of the following?

    a.   Causes cavities

    b.   Causes gingival hyperplasia

    c.   Causes mouth cancers

    d.   Builds up tartar on the teeth

MAKING CONNECTIONS

41. Although phenobarbital (PMS-Phenobarbital) is an antiseizure medicine, it is also classified as which of the following?

    a.   Benzodiazepine

    b.   Category I drug

    c.   Sympathomimetic

    d.   Sedative-hypnotic

42. Which term describes a craving to continue drug use despite its negative effects?

    a.   Tolerance

    b.   Physical dependence

    c.   Psychological dependence

    d.   Resistance

43. When is a client who is undergoing alcohol withdrawal most likely to experience seizures?

    a.   Immediately after the client has stopped drinking

    b.   1 to 3 days after the client has stopped drinking

    c.   5 to 7 days after the client has stopped drinking

    d.   During an episode of delirium tremens

44. Which of the following drugs is *not* used to treat convulsions?

    a.   Buspirone (BuSpar)

    b.   Phenobarbital (PMS-Phenobarbital)

    c.   Gabapentin (Neurontin)

    d.   Carbamazepine (Tegretol)

45. What is the most important reason why benzodiazepines are *not* used for chronic seizure control?

    a.   Tendency for the client to develop tolerance to the drug

    b.   Psychological addiction

    c.   Respiratory depression that occurs with chronic use

    d.   No antidote exists

CALCULATIONS

46. The physician orders phenobarbital elixir 60 mg PO bid. The pharmacy fills the prescription with phenobarbital elixir 20 mg/5 mL.

    The client's care provider should be instructed to administer _____ mL/dose.

47. The physician orders Carbamazepine (Tegretol) 1200 mg per day in four divided doses.

    The nurse would give _____ mg/dose.

CASE STUDY APPLICATIONS

48. A nurse is preparing for a client who is coming to the ER with status epilepticus. The physician has ordered Dilantin by IV drip as soon as the client arrives.

    a.   What evidence (assessment data) would support a nursing diagnosis of "risk for injury"?

    b.   What interventions would provide safety for the client during Dilantin administration?

49. A male client has been placed on Dilantin for newly diagnosed epilepsy. He has generalized tonic-clonic seizures. He has asked how long it will take to manage his seizures and what side effects can occur. He also wants to know what foods or drugs to avoid while on this medication.

    a.   Which nursing diagnosis would be first priority for this client?

    b.   What interventions would be helpful for this diagnosis?

CHAPTER 16

DRUGS FOR EMOTIONAL AND MOOD DISORDERS

FILL IN THE BLANK

From the textbook, find the correct word(s) to complete the statement(s).

1. The two major types of mood disorders are _____ and _____.

2. _____ is the most common mood disorder in Canada.

3. The three major classes of antidepressants are _____, _____, and _____.

4. _____ are drugs of choice for simple depression.

5. _____ produce fewer cardiovascular side effects and therefore are less dangerous than the MAO inhibitors.

6. Clients taking _____ for bipolar disorder should be placed on a low-sodium diet to increase its effectiveness.

7. The inability to focus or pay attention is one of the main symptoms of _____.

8. _____ are the class of drugs most widely prescribed for attention deficit-hyperactivity disorder (ADHD).

9. Drugs for bipolar disorder are called _____ because they have the ability to modulate extreme shifts in emotion between _____ and _____.

MATCHING

For questions 10 through 21, match the drug in column I with the primary indication/class in column II.

Column I

10. _____ Lithium (Carbolith)

11. _____ Venlafaxine (Effexor)

12. _____ Paroxetine (Paxil)

13. _____ Amitriptyline (Elavil)

14. _____ Phenelzine (Nardil)

15. _____ Methylphenidate (Ritalin)

16. _____ Dextroamphetamine (Dexedrine)

17. _____ Tranylcypromine (Parnate)

18. _____ Imipramine (Tofranil)

19. _____ Bupropion (Wellbutrin)

20. _____ Fluoxetine (Prozac)

21. _____ Sertraline (Zoloft)

Column II

a. ADHD/CNS stimulant

b. Depression/TCA

c. Depression/MAO inhibitor

d. Depression/SSRI

e. Depression/atypical/SNRI

f. Bipolar disorder

For questions 22 through 26, match the definition in column I with the term in column II.

Column I

22. _____ Enzyme that breaks down catecholamine neurotransmitters in the synapse

23. _____ Accumulation of serotonin when taking two drugs that reduce serotonin uptake

24. _____ Condition exhibiting signs of both clinical depression and mania

25. _____ The class of drug that is closely related to methylphenidate

26. _____ Chemical found in foods that cannot be ingested by clients on MAO inhibitors because of high risk of severe hypertension

Column II

a. Amphetamines

b. Bipolar disorder

c. Monoamine oxidase

d. Tyramine

e. Serotonin syndrome

MULTIPLE CHOICE

27. What is the most common age range for the diagnosis of ADHD?

   a. 0 to 3 years

   b. 3 to 7 years

   c. 10 to 13 years

   d. 15 to 18 years

28. Which medication has *not* been useful in stabilizing emotions in mood disorders such as bipolar disorder?

    a. Lithium (Carbolith)

    b. Carbamazepine (Tegretol)

    c. Valproic acid (Depakene)

    d. Metoprolol (Lopresor)

29. Lithium is used with other medications during phases of bipolar disorder. The nurse knows that which of these medications would *not* be used with lithium?

    a. Tricyclic antidepressants

    b. Benzodiazepines

    c. SSRI antidepressants

    d. Diuretics

30. Your client receives a prescription for lithium (Carbolith). Which of the following points should be included in your teaching?

    a. Consume sufficient quantities of dietary salt

    b. Increase fluid intake by 1 to 1.5 L per day

    c. Limit or eliminate caffeine intake

    d. All of the above

31. A client is discharged from hospital after being given fluoxetine (Prozac) for depression. The nurse should instruct the client to do which of the following?

    a. Call back if there is no improvement in 24 hours

    b. Call back if any nausea, drowsiness, or dizziness occurs

    c. Start the Prozac before stopping the current MAO inhibitor

    d. Expect to see improvement in mood, appetite, and energy within 1 to 3 weeks

32. Methylphenidate (Ritalin) produces its effects by activating what portion of the brain?

    a. Cerebellum

    b. Hypothalamus

    c. Pituitary

    d. Reticular activating system

33. When sending a client home on imipramine (Tofranil), which of the following is important for the nurse to teach the client?

    a. St. John's wort may be used concurrently with no anticipated interaction.

    b. Photosensitivity is not a problem with Tofranil.

    c. This drug should not be stopped abruptly.

    d. Use of this drug with other CNS depressants is permitted.

34. Which of the following is *not* a common symptom of clinical depression?

    a. Lack of energy

    b. Sleep disturbances

    c. Hallucinations

    d. Feelings of despair or guilt

35. In assessing a client, the nurse should know that rapid shifts in emotion from profound depression to euphoria and hyperactivity are characteristic of which of the following?

    a. Psychosis

    b. Bipolar disorder

    c. Schizophrenia

    d. ADHD

36. Which of the following would *least* likely be used to treat clinical depression?

    a. Monoamine oxidase inhibitors

    b. Tricyclic antidepressants

    c. Selective serotonin reuptake inhibitors

    d. Phenothiazines

37. How does phenelzine (Nardil) produce its therapeutic effects?

    a. Inhibits the reuptake of norepinephrine into presynaptic nerve terminals

    b. Irreversibly inhibits monoamine oxidase (MAO) and intensifies the effects of norepinephrine in the synapse

    c. Selectively inhibits the reuptake of serotonin into presynaptic nerve terminals

    d. Interferes with the binding of dopamine to receptors located in the limbic system

38. How do tricyclic antidepressants produce their therapeutic effects?

    a. Inhibit the reuptake of both serotonin and norepinephrine into presynaptic nerve terminals

    b. Irreversibly inhibit monoamine oxidase (MAO) and intensify the effects of norepinephrine in the synapse

    c. Selectively inhibit the reuptake of serotonin into presynaptic nerve terminals

    d. Interfere with the binding of dopamine to receptors located in the limbic system

39. How does fluoxetine (Prozac) produce its therapeutic effects?

    a. Inhibits the reuptake of both serotonin and norepinephrine into presynaptic nerve terminals

    b. Irreversibly inhibits monoamine oxidase (MAO) and intensifies the effects of norepinephrine in the synapse

    c. Selectively inhibits the reuptake of serotonin into presynaptic nerve terminals

    d. Interferes with the binding of dopamine to receptors located in the limbic system

40. Why are the selective serotonin reuptake inhibitors (SSRIs) generally preferred over other classes of antidepressants?

   a.   More efficacious

   b.   Produce fewer sympathomimetic and anticholinergic side effects

   c.   Do not produce sexual dysfunction

   d.   Cause more extrapyramidal effects

41. The nurse should teach clients taking fluoxetine to avoid foods high in which amino acid, because it is a chemical precursor for serotonin synthesis?

   a.   Histidine

   b.   Tyramine

   c.   Lysine

   d.   Tryptophan

MAKING CONNECTIONS

42. Typical oral doses are 1 mg for risperidone and 50 mg for clozapine. Which of the following may you correctly conclude from this information?

   a.   Risperidone is more efficacious.

   b.   Clozapine is more efficacious.

   c.   Risperidone is more potent.

   d.   Clozapine is more potent.

43. Thorazine is available by both IM and oral routes. Which would be expected to have a faster onset of action?

   a.   IM

   b.   Oral

44. In assessing a new client, the nurse should know that panic attacks, phobias, and obsessive-compulsive disorder are usually treated with which of the following?

   a.   Antipsychotic drugs

   b.   Antianxiety drugs

   c.   Drugs for bipolar disorder

   d.   Antidepressants

45. "Speedball" is the street name for a drug combination containing methylphenidate (Ritalin) and which of the following?

   a.   Heroin

   b.   Marijuana

   c.   LSD

   d.   Cocaine

46. Methylphenidate is a Schedule II drug. What does this mean?

    a. It may adversely affect the fetus.

    b. It has no therapeutic use.

    c. It has a low abuse potential.

    d. It has a high potential for physical and psychological dependence.

CALCULATIONS

47. The physician orders lithium carbonate 1.2 g PO daily in four divided doses. The pharmacy supplies 300 mg lithium carbonate capsules.
The nurse should instruct the client to take _____ capsule(s) per dose.

48. The physician orders fluoxetine 45 mg PO daily. The pharmacy fills the prescription with fluoxetine oral solution of 20 mg/5 mL.
The client should be instructed to take _____ mL per day.

CASE STUDY APPLICATIONS

49. A client who has bipolar disorder has been started on lithium. He is also on paroxetine (Paxil), digoxin (Lanoxin), furosemide (Lasix), and potassium supplements for depression, hypertension, and HF. He has also been on a low-sodium diet.

    a. During the first 3 weeks on lithium, what would the nurse identify as the priority nursing diagnosis?

    b. What assessments would the nurse make in identifying this diagnosis?

    c. What is the client's goal for the first 3 weeks of therapy?

50. A client, Mrs. C, is started on sertraline (Zoloft) for depression. Upon admission to hospital, she is assessed as having episodes of crying, feelings of guilt, insomnia, and suicidal ideation. The nurse needs to monitor the client for drug effectiveness, side effects, and potential problems.

    a. Discuss what goals might be assigned to the client and how these goals could be evaluated.

CHAPTER 17

DRUGS FOR PSYCHOSES

FILL IN THE BLANK

From the textbook, find the correct word(s) to complete the statement(s).

1. The most common type of psychosis is _____.

2. Acute psychosis develops in _____, whereas chronic psychoses develop over _____.

3. Atypical antipsychotic drugs are effective for both _____ and _____ symptoms of psychosis.

4. The majority of psychoses have no known _____. The six identifiable causes are _____, _____, _____, _____, _____, and _____.

5. Positive symptoms include _____, _____, _____, and _____.

6. Negative symptoms include a lack of _____, _____, _____, and _____.

7. Proper diagnosis of positive and negative symptoms is important for selection of the appropriate _____ drugs.

8. Symptoms of schizophrenia are thought to be associated with the _____ receptors in the basal nuclei.

9. Medications that block 65% of D_2-receptors will reduce symptoms of _____. Blocking more than 80% will likely cause _____ symptoms.

MATCHING

For questions 10 through 19, match the drug in column I with the primary indication/class in column II.

Column I

10. _____ Haloperidol (Haldol)

11. _____ Thioridazine (Apo-Thioridazine)

12. _____ Chlorpromazine (Apo-Chlorpromazine)

13. _____ Promazine (Apo-Promazine)

14. _____ Olanzapine (Zyprexa)

15. _____ Loxapine succinate (Apo-Loxapine)

16. _____ Clozapine (Clozaril)

17. _____ Pimozide (Orap)

18. _____ Thiothixene (Navane)

19. _____ Risperidone (Risperdal)

Column II

a. Psychosis/phenothiazine

b. Psychosis/non-phenothiazine

c. Psychosis/atypical

For questions 20 through 28, match the characteristic in column I with the term in column II.

Column I

20. _____ A condition in which the client exhibits symptoms of both schizophrenia and mood disorders

21. _____ Firm ideas and beliefs not founded in reality

22. _____ Symptoms that are added to normal behaviour

23. _____ A term meaning "antipsychotic medications"

24. _____ An extreme suspicion that one is being followed, or that others are trying to harm oneself

25. _____ Symptoms that subtract from a normal behaviour

26. _____ Seeing, hearing, or feeling something that is not there

27. _____ A class of drug that might be used to decrease extrapyramidal effects

28. _____ A movement disorder brought on by medication effects

Column II

a. Paranoid

b. Delusions

c. Hallucinations

d. Positive symptoms

e. Negative symptoms

f. Schizo-affective disorder

g. Neuroleptics

h. Anticholinergics

i. Extrapyramidal effects

MULTIPLE CHOICE

29. Which class of drugs tends to produce severe side effects such as muscle twitching, compulsive motor activity, and a Parkinson-like syndrome?

    a. Barbiturates

    b. Phenothiazines

    c. Benzodiazepines

    d. Serotonin reuptake inhibitors

30. Delusions, hallucinations, disordered communication, and difficulty relating to others are symptoms closely associated with which of the following?

    a. Clinical depression

    b. Bipolar disorder

    c. Schizophrenia

    d. ADHD

31. Which of the following best describes extrapyramidal side effects?

    a. Paranoid delusions

    b. Profound depression

    c. Seizures

    d. Distorted body movements and muscle spasms

32. Like many antipsychotics, chlorpromazine (Apo-Chlorpromazine) usually takes how long before its therapeutic effect is achieved?

    a. 2 to 3 days

    b. 2 to 3 weeks

    c. 7 to 8 weeks

    d. More than 6 months

33. Many of the major effects of chlorpromazine (Apo-Chlorpromazine) can be attributed to which of the following?

    a. Inhibiting the reuptake of both serotonin and norepinephrine into presynaptic nerve terminals

    b. Irreversibly inhibiting monoamine oxidase (MAO) and intensifying the effects of norepinephrine in the synapse

    c. Selectively inhibiting the reuptake of serotonin into presynaptic nerve terminals

    d. Interfering with the binding of dopamine to receptors located throughout the brain

34. Why are atypical antipsychotics sometimes preferred over phenothiazines?

    a. They produce no major adverse effects.

    b. They can treat both positive and negative symptoms of psychosis.

    c. They are much more efficacious.

    d. They can improve symptoms within a few days of initial administration.

35. Non-phenothiazine agents differ from phenothiazine agents in what way?

    a. Non-phenothiazines do not produce as many anticholinergic side effects as phenothiazines.

    b. Non-phenothiazines cause less sedation and fewer anticholinergic side effects than phenothiazines.

    c. Phenothiazines do not produce as many side effects as non-phenothiazines.

    d. Phenothiazines cause less sedation and anticholinergic side effects than non-phenothiazines.

36. Clients on clozapine (Clozaril) must watch carefully for signs of agranulocytosis, which include which of the following?

    a. Dizziness and drowsiness

    b. Appetite increase

    c. Fever and sore throat

    d. Bruises and bleeding

37. A client who is on a phenothiazine complains of having elevated temperature, sweating, and "not feeling well." What possible indication should the nurse assess the client for?

    a. Agranulocytosis

    b. Neuroleptic malignant syndrome

    c. Infection that may decrease potency of the medication

    d. Dystonic reaction

38. For a client who has problems with daily adherence, a drug is available that lasts for 3 weeks. Which drug would be a good choice for this client?

    a. Haloperidol (Haldol LA)

    b. Olanzapine (Zyprexa)

    c. Chlorpromazine (Apo-Chlorpromazine)

    d. Clozapine (Clozaril)

MAKING CONNECTIONS

39. A client has been prescribed an antipsychotic drug that has a high degree of anticholinergic side effects. Anticholinergic effects include which of the following?

    a. Nervousness and tremors

    b. Restlessness and constant movement of legs

    c. Drying of mouth, sedation, and urinary retention

    d. Headaches, skin rashes, and hallucinations

40. The atypical antipsychotics bind to serotonergic and cholinergic sites throughout the brain. The nurse understands that this would affect which neurotransmitters?

    a. Acetylcholine and serotonin

    b. Serotonin and dopamine

    c. Serotonin and norepinephrine

    d. Acetylcholine and norepinephrine

41. Benzodiazepines are often given with antipsychotic drugs. Which benzodiazepine side effects would create a problem when given with these medications?

    a.   Drowsiness and dry mouth

    b.   Lowered seizure threshold

    c.   Hypotension and respiratory depression

    d.   Bone marrow depression

42. Clients on herbal supplements must be warned about interactions with other prescribed medications. What herbal preparations are sometimes taken to treat mental illness?

    a.   Tryptophan

    b.   St. John's wort

    c.   Kava

    d.   All of the above

43. Schizo-affective disorder is treated with antipsychotic medications and may require antidepressants. Which of the following medications is an antidepressant?

    a.   Diazepam (Valium)

    b.   Phenytoin (Dilantin)

    c.   Chlorpromazine (Apo-Chlorpromazine)

    d.   Paroxetine (Paxil)

CALCULATIONS

44. The physician orders fluphenazine HCl (Apo-Fluphenazine) 15 mg SC. The pharmacy supplies fluphenazine HCl 25 mg/mL.

    The nurse would administer _____ mL SC.

45. A client has an order for quetiapine fumarate (Seroquel) 200 mg/day in divided dosages bid. Seroquel comes in 50 mg tablets.

    The nurse would give the client _____ tablets per dose.

CASE STUDY APPLICATIONS

46. Mrs. S has been taking chlorpromazine (Apo-Chlorpromazine) for about a year. She has been having problems with orthostatic hypotension and akathisia and has needed to take Cogentin to avoid dystonic reactions. The physician has decided to change her to clozapine (Clozaril). The client asks the nurse about the advantages and disadvantages of the new drug. The nurse has chosen knowledge deficit as the nursing diagnosis for this client.

    a.   What interventions would be used for this diagnosis?

    b.   How would the nurse evaluate the outcome of the interventions?

47. Ms. G was recently diagnosed with schizophrenia. She was prescribed Haloperidol (Haldol) while hospitalized and has had hallucinations and delusions.

    a.   What assessments would the nurse need to complete during the first 3 weeks that the client is on this medication?

CHAPTER 18

DRUGS FOR DEGENERATIVE DISEASES OF THE NERVOUS SYSTEM

FILL IN THE BLANK

From the textbook, find the correct word(s) to complete the statement(s).

1. Drug therapy of Parkinson's disease focuses on restoring _____ function and also blocking the effect of _____ within the same area of the brain.

2. _____ is a degenerative disorder characterized by progressive memory loss, confusion, and inability to think or communicate effectively.

3. _____ is responsible for 65% of all dementia.

4. Alzheimer's clients experience a dramatic loss of their ability to perform tasks that require _____ as a neurotransmitter.

5. Parkinson's disease could be related to a _____ link because many clients have a family history of the disorder.

6. Extensive treatment with certain _____ medications may induce Parkinson-like syndrome or _____ symptoms.

7. Side effects of drugs used to treat Parkinsonism include _____ and _____. Signs of toxicity include _____ and _____.

8. When treating Alzheimer's disease, the goal of pharmacotherapy is to improve the function in three domains: _____, _____, and _____.

9. _____ can only be used in the early stages of Alzheimer's disease because they are only effective in the presence of _____ neurons.

MATCHING

For questions 10 through 19, match the drug in column I with the primary classification in column II.

Column I

10. _____ Biperiden hydrochloride (Akineton)

11. _____ Carbidopa-levodopa (Sinemet)

12. _____ Rivastigmine tartrate (Exelon)

13. _____ Pergolide (Permax)

14. _____ Benztropine mesylate (Apo-Benztropine)

15. _____ Donepezil hydrochloride (Aricept)

16. _____ Bromocriptine (Parlodel)

17. _____ Amantadine (Symmetrel)

18. _____ Procyclidine (PMS-Procyclidine)

19. _____ Galantamine (Reminyl)

Column II

a.   Dopaminergic drug

b.   Cholinergic blocking drug

c.   Cholinergic drug (AchE inhibitor)

For questions 20 through 28, match the characteristic in column I with the drug in column II.

Column I

20. _____ Decreases effect of dopaminergics

21. _____ Antioxidant possibly useful in Alzheimer's disease

22. _____ Approved in Europe for dementia; can react with anticoagulants

23. _____ Antiviral that releases dopamine from its nerve terminals

24. _____ Acetylcholinesterase inhibitor used for AD and associated with weight loss

25. _____ Drug of choice for Parkinsonism

26. _____ Inhibits enzymes that destroy levodopa or dopamine

27. _____ Dopamine agonist that activates the dopamine receptors

28. _____ Carbidopa added to levodopa to make more levodopa available to enter the CNS

Column II

a.   Levodopa

b.   Sinemet

c.   Selegiline hydrochloride

d.   Bromocriptine

e.   Amantadine

f.   rivastigmine tartrate (Exelon)

g.   Ginkgo biloba

h.   Donepezil

i. Pyridoxine

MULTIPLE CHOICE

29. Parkinson's disease is a degenerative disorder of the nervous system caused by the death of neurons that produce which of the following?

    a. Dopamine

    b. Norepinephrine

    c. Acetylcholine

    d. Serotonin

30. A client is admitted with a new diagnosis of Parkinson's disease. If he is in the early stages, what would usually *not* be seen on assessment?

    a. Tremor

    b. Muscle rigidity and weakness

    c. Bradykinesia

    d. Dementia

31. What is the relationship between acetylcholine and dopamine in the area of the brain that affects balance, posture, and involuntary muscle movement?

    a. Both dopamine and acetylcholine stimulate this region.

    b. Both dopamine and acetylcholine inhibit this region.

    c. Dopamine stimulates and acetylcholine inhibits this region.

    d. Dopamine inhibits and acetylcholine stimulates this region.

32. What class of drugs may induce artificial Parkinsonism by interfering with the same neural pathway and functions modified by a lack of dopamine?

    a. Phenothiazines

    b. Tricyclic antidepressants

    c. MAO inhibitors

    d. Benzodiazepines

33. A client develops EPS after taking phenothiazines. The nurse would expect an order for which medication to counteract the EPS?

    a. Diphenhydramine (Benadryl)

    b. Procyclidine (PMS-Procyclidine)

    c. Levodopa

    d. Donepezil hydrochloride (Aricept)

34. Which drug has been prescribed more extensively than any other drug for clients with Parkinson's disease?

    a. Carbidopa-levodopa (Sinemet)

    b. Benztropine (Apo-Benztropine)

    c. Levodopa

    d. Donepezil hydrochloride (Aricept)

35. A client is started on levodopa for Parkinson's disease. What type of side effects would be expected?

    a.   Sleep disorders such as insomnia

    b.   Sedation

    c.   Involuntary muscle movements

    d.   Seizures

36. If a client is unable to tolerate dopaminergic medications, which class of drugs would likely be prescribed?

    a.   Cholinergic drugs

    b.   Anticholinergic drugs

    c.   Antipsychotic drugs

    d.   Selective serotonin reuptake inhibitors (SSRIs)

37. What normally causes vascular dementia?

    a.   Multiple strokes

    b.   Multiple heart attacks

    c.   Too little blood flow to the brain

    d.   Lack of sufficient neurotransmitters in certain areas of the brain

38. Amyloid plaques and neurofibrillary tangles within the brain are diagnostic signs of which of the following?

    a.   Parkinson's disease

    b.   Tardive dyskinesia

    c.   Vascular dementia

    d.   Alzheimer's disease

39. Acetylcholine inhibitors enhance the action of what chemical in the brain?

    a.   Dopamine

    b.   Norepinephrine

    c.   Acetylcholine

    d.   Serotonin

40. Drugs that inhibit the enzyme acetylcholinesterase (AchE) will do which of the following?

    a.   Increase levels of dopamine

    b.   Decrease levels of dopamine

    c.   Increase levels of acetylcholine

    d.   Decrease levels of acetylcholine

41. When a client takes phenothiazines for an extended time, what conditions would the nurse expect to see?

    a.   Parkinsonism

    b.   Hypertensive crisis

    c.   Decreased muscle rigidity

    d.   Bruising and bleeding from the gums

MAKING CONNECTIONS

42. An anticholinergic drug is one that blocks the effects of which of the following?
    a.   Epinephrine

    b.   Norepinephrine

    c.   Acetylcholine

    d.   Serotonin

43. Succinimides, barbiturates, and benzodiazepines are used to treat what disorder?
    a.   Anxiety

    b.   Seizures

    c.   Sleep disorders

    d.   Mood disorders

44. What is the result of combining levadopa and carbidopa?
    a.   There is no change in the effectiveness of either drug.

    b.   They nullify each other's effect.

    c.   The combination makes less levadopa available to enter the CNS.

    d.   The combination makes more levadopa available to enter the CNS.

45. Which type of drug is given to discourage tardive dyskinesia in clients being treated for psychosis?
    a.   Cholinergic

    b.   Anticholinergic

    c.   Dopaminergic

    d.   Selective serotonin reuptake inhibitor

46. Antipsychotic medications have actions that decrease which of the following in the brain?
    a.   Dopamine

    b.   Acetylcholine

    c.   Norepinephrine

    d.   Acetylcholinesterase

CALCULATIONS

47. A client has an order for bromocriptine (Parlodel) 100 mg per day. The drug is available in 25 mg tablets. You order the medications weekly. You have 25 tablets left. Do you need to reorder today or can you wait until next week?

48. A client has an order for trihexyphenidyl hydrochloride 7.5 mg per day. He is to take it tid. He should take _____ mg/dose.

CASE STUDY APPLICATIONS

49. Mr. H is a 30-year-old client who was recently diagnosed with early Parkinson's disease. He has been quite upset and depressed about the diagnosis and has lost interest in most of his usual activities and hobbies. His wife reports that his tremors and involuntary movements have worsened. He has been taking the following medications for 6 months: levodopa (2 g/day) and sertraline (Zoloft). He now has benztropine mesylate added to his medications.

    a.   What is the nursing diagnosis that best describes problems related to his condition and his new medication?

    b.   What goal would relate to the diagnosis?

50. Mr. B has been brought to your facility by his wife. He was diagnosed last year with Alzheimer's disease. His confusion has become increasingly worse. He has been restless, agitated, and experiencing hallucinations. This past year he has been taking moderate doses of amitriptyline (Elavil) and alprazolam (Xanax). The client is now placed on donepezil (Aricept) for a trial. During the first 4 weeks of the treatment with this AchE inhibitor, monitoring for adverse reactions and effectiveness is the responsibility of the nurse.

    a.   What would be the priority nursing diagnosis for this situation?

    b.   What interventions would be included?

CHAPTER 19

DRUGS FOR THE CONTROL OF PAIN

FILL IN THE BLANK

From the textbook, find the correct word(s) to complete the statement(s).

1. The two main classes of pain medication are the _____ and _____.

2. All non-steroidal anti-inflammatory drugs (NSAIDs) have _____ and _____ activity, as well as analgesic properties.

3. The type of headache characterized by tightening of the muscles of the head and neck area due to stress is called a _____ headache.

4. A sensory cue that precedes a migraine is called an _____.

5. NSAIDs act by inhibiting pain mediators at the _____ level.

6. The sensation of pain may be increased by _____, _____, and _____.

7. Successful choice of pain therapy is dependent on the _____ and _____ of the pain.

8. The goals of pharmacotherapy for migraine are to _____ the migraine in progress and to _____ migraines from occurring.

9. Two major drug classes used for migraine headaches include _____ and _____. Both of these are _____ agonists.

10. Triptans are 5-HT selective and are thought to act by constricting _____. They are available to be administered _____, _____, or _____.

MATCHING

For questions 11 through 22, match the drug in column I with the class in column II.

Column I

11. _____ Naloxone (Narcan)

12. _____ Meperidine (Demerol)

13. _____ Celecoxib (Celebrex)

14. _____ Oxycodone hydrochloride (OxyContin)

15. _____ Zolmitriptan (Zomig)

16. _____ Naltrexone (ReVia)

17. _____ Ibuprofen (Advil, Motrin)

18. _____ Ergotamine tartrate

19. _____ Methadone hydrochloride (Metadol)

20. _____ Naproxen (Naprosyn)

21. _____ Propranolol hydrochloride (Inderal)

22. _____ Amitriptyline hydrochloride (Elavil)

Column II

a. NSAID

b. Opioid; moderate efficacy

c. Opioid; high efficacy

d. Opioid blocker

e. Antimigraine agent

For questions 23 through 28, match the description in column I with the related term in column II.

Column I

23. _____ Natural or synthetic chemicals providing pain relief

24. _____ Dull, throbbing, or aching pain

25. _____ Caused by injury to tissues

26. _____ Sharp localized pain

27. _____ Caused by injury to nerves

28. _____ Natural chemicals that relieve pain

Column II

a. Nociceptor pain

b. Neuropathic pain

c. Somatic pain

d. Visceral pain

e. Opiates

f. Opioids

MULTIPLE CHOICE

29. Painful disorders having a strong inflammatory component, such as arthritis, are treated most effectively with which of the following?

    a. NSAIDs

    b. Acetaminophen (Tylenol)

    c. Opioids

    d. Herbal supplements

30. When asked why NSAIDs are better than acetaminophen for arthritis, the healthcare provider responds, "Compared to Aspirin, acetaminophen has _____."
    a. Less analgesic activity
    b. No antipyretic activity
    c. Less anti-inflammatory activity
    d. The same effect on blood coagulation

31. Which of the following would be best used to treat mild to moderate pain due to inflammation?
    a. Oxycodone (OxyContin)
    b. Meperidine (Demerol)
    c. Ibuprofen (Advil)
    d. Acetaminophen (Tylenol)

32. Why are selective COX-2 inhibitors often prescribed over ASA?
    a. They are more effective at relieving severe pain.
    b. They are more effective at relieving dull, throbbing pain.
    c. They are less expensive.
    d. They cause fewer side effects.

33. ASA is an abbreviation that refers to which of the following?
    a. Any NSAID
    b. Aspirin
    c. Opioid analgesics
    d. COX-2 inhibitors

34. A healthcare provider sees an order for ASA 325 mg once daily. The healthcare provider knows this medication is given at this dose level for what reason?
    a. To prolong clotting times
    b. To fight infections
    c. To relieve pain
    d. To decrease inflammation

35. When a healthcare provider is asked to explain why Tylenol is used more often than Aspirin, the response is that Aspirin can cause which of the following?
    a. Dependence
    b. Increased platelet adhesiveness
    c. GI bleeding
    d. CNS depression

36. A mother asks why Aspirin should not be given to children and teens. The appropriate reaction by the healthcare provider is based on the actions of Aspirin, which can cause which of the following?
    a. Anticoagulant activity
    b. Reduced incidence of strokes

    c.   Reduced risk of colorectal cancer

    d.   Increased risk of Reye's syndrome

37. Which of the following medications is part of a therapeutic strategy to reduce dependence for people who are addicted to heroin?

    a.   Methadone

    b.   Oxycodone

    c.   Morphine

    d.   Meperidine

38. Why are opioids often used for pain relief following tooth extractions?

    a.   They help the client sleep.

    b.   They do not prolong bleeding time.

    c.   They can be taken once a day.

    d.   They are more efficacious than other analgesics.

39. A healthcare provider knows that the therapeutic effects of opiates do *not* include which of the following?

    a.   Treatment of respiratory depression

    b.   Treatment of diarrhea

    c.   Relief of severe pain

    d.   Suppression of cough reflex

40. A client comes to the ER with an overdose of morphine. What would the priority nursing assessment include?

    a.   Dilated pupils

    b.   Depressed respiration

    c.   Hypertension

    d.   Diarrhea

41. For an overdose of opiates, what would the healthcare provider need to have on hand to counteract the effects?

    a.   Dextroamphetamine (Dexedrine)

    b.   Phenytoin (Dilantin)

    c.   Naloxone (Narcan)

    d.   Nifedipine (Adalat)

42. A client comes to the ER with a history of severe headaches. She reports that she often sees an aura prior to the onset of the headache. What does the aura indicate about the client?

    a.   The client has taken an overdose of ASA.

    b.   The client has taken an overdose of opioids.

    c.   The client may be experiencing migraine headaches.

    d.   The client has a high fever.

43. What is the mechanism of action of sumatriptan (Imitrex) and other triptans?
    a. Affects mu receptors
    b. Causes vasoconstriction of cranial arteries
    c. Blocks prostaglandin synthesis
    d. Blocks COX-2

MAKING CONNECTIONS

44. Besides an antimigraine agent, what is another use for amitriptyline (Elavil)?
    a. Anticonvulsant
    b. Sedative hypnotic
    c. Antipsychotic
    d. Antidepressant

45. Ergotamine is a category X drug, which means what about the drug?
    a. Has a high risk of physical and psychological dependence
    b. Should never be taken during pregnancy
    c. Has no therapeutic use
    d. Is very toxic to the client

46. Phenobarbital (PMS-Phenobarbital) is a sedative-hypnotic that is also prescribed for which of the following?
    a. Migraines
    b. Marijuana addiction
    c. Seizures
    d. Clinical depression

47. Where would an intrathecal injection of morphine be administered?
    a. Spinal subarachnoid space
    b. Brain
    c. Joint
    d. Abdominal cavity

48. Which of the following steps in pharmacokinetics occurs first?
    a. Metabolism
    b. Absorption
    c. Distribution
    d. Excretion

CALCULATIONS

49. The physician orders ibuprofen 400 mg PO tid. The pharmacy sends ibuprofen suspension 100 mg/5 mL. The client should receive _____ mL per dose.

50. The physician orders naloxone HCl 0.4 mg IV bolus now. The pharmacy supplies naloxone 0.02 mg/mL. The nurse should administer _____ mL IV bolus now.

CASE STUDY APPLICATIONS

51. Mr. T arrives in your office complaining of severe pain in his joints. You are asked to assess this client's complaints and recommend a course of treatment. He is 75 years old and, other than anxiety and insomnia, appears to be in good health. Mr. T is interested in non-pharmacological control of his pain. He admits to being reluctant to take the oxycodone that the physician ordered, because he does not want to "become a crazy addict." The nurse has chosen knowledge deficit for a nursing diagnosis.

    a. What interventions would be appropriate for this situation?

    b. What outcomes would be evaluated for this client?

52. Ms. M has been experiencing migraine headaches for 2 years. She is now seeking medical assistance because they have become more frequent and painful. She states that it takes six Aspirin to relieve the pain once the migraine has started. She has a history of chronic heart failure and hypertension. She has heard that drugs used for migraines are addictive and is interested in a non-pharmacological solution. The following medications are being taken: Oxycodone terephthalate (Percocet), given prn; Verapamil (Isoptin); Digoxin (Lanoxin).

    a. The nurse chooses "altered comfort: pain" as the diagnosis. What interventions can be used for this nursing diagnosis?

    b. What client goals would be included in the care for this client?

CHAPTER 20

DRUGS FOR LOCAL AND GENERAL ANESTHESIA

FILL IN THE BLANK

From the textbook, find the correct word(s) to complete the statement(s).

1. Local anesthesia is loss of _____ to a relatively small part of the body without loss of _____.

2. The direct injection of a local anesthetic into tissue immediate to a surgical site is called _____ anesthesia.

3. The goal of general anesthesia is to provide rapid and complete loss of _____.

4. The two major ways to induce general anesthesia are by using _____ agents and _____ agents.

5. Opioids are sometimes given as preoperative medications to counteract _____.

6. _____ depress all nervous activity of the brain, while _____ depresses only specific areas.

7. In applying local anesthesia, the method employed depends on _____ and _____ of desired anesthetics.

8. In the area where the local anesthetic is applied, _____ and _____ will temporarily diminish.

9. Drug classes used as adjuncts to anesthesia include _____, _____, _____, and _____.

10. The advantage of _____ anesthesia is that the dose of anesthetic can be _____, thus making the procedure safer for the client.

MATCHING

For questions 11 through 23, match the drug in column I with the classification in column II.

Column I

11. _____ Droperidol (Inapsine)

12. _____ Benzocaine (Solarcaine)

13. _____ Bupivacaine (Marcaine)

14. _____ Enflurane (Ethrane)

15. _____ Succinylcholine chloride (Quelicin)

16. _____ Lidocaine (Xylocaine)

17. _____ Prilocaine (Citanest)

18. _____ Fentanyl citrate (Duragesic)

19. _____ Promethazine (Phenergan)

20. _____ Ketamine (Ketalar)

21. _____ Isoflurane (Forane)

22. _____ Pentobarbital (Nembutal)

23. _____ Tubocurarine

Column II

a.   Ester-type local anesthetic

b.   Amide-type local anesthetic

c.   Inhaled anesthetic

d.   Intravenous anesthetic

e.   Adjunct to anesthesia

For questions 24 through 32, match the characteristic in column I with the drug or class in column II.

Column I

24. _____ Prolongs duration of local anesthetic agents

25. _____ Most commonly used topical anesthetics

26. _____ May be prescribed for cardiac dysrhythmias

27. _____ Type of anesthesia most commonly used during labour and delivery

28. _____ Most commonly used injectable local anesthetic

29. _____ Most commonly used local anesthetic

30. _____ Most abused anesthetic agent

31. _____ Major depolarizing neuromuscular blocker

32. _____ Most widely used inhalation anesthesia

Column II

a.   Epinephrine

b.   Epidural

c.   Amides

d.   Benzocaine

e.   Lidocaine

f.   Isoflurane (Forane)

g.   Succinylcholine

h.   Nitrous oxide

MULTIPLE CHOICE

33. Epinephrine is often added to a local anesthetic. The nurse must monitor for which factors when caring for the client who is due to receive epinephrine in the anesthetic?
    a. Side effects of increased heart rate and BP
    b. History of cardiac conditions
    c. Vital signs
    d. All of the above

34. Which of the following is *not* a major route for applying local anesthetics?
    a. Epidural
    b. Spinal
    c. Nerve block
    d. Inhalation

35. In administering general anesthetics using balanced anesthesia, the nurse would expect which medication to be administered first?
    a. IV anesthesia
    b. Inhalation anesthesia
    c. Analgesics
    d. Neuromuscular blocking agents

36. Nitrous oxide can be administered safely in clients with which of the following?
    a. Myasthenia gravis
    b. Increased anxiety related to pain or procedures
    c. Increased intracranial pressure
    d. Cardiac disease

37. An alkaline substance such as sodium hydroxide is sometimes added to a vial of anesthetic solution for what reason?
    a. To provide the environment needed for absorption
    b. To prolong the duration of anesthetic action
    c. To increase the effectiveness of the anesthetic in regions with extensive local infection or abscesses
    d. To decrease the potential for anaphylaxis

38. Which of the following is a potential early adverse effect from local anesthetics?
    a. Hypertension
    b. Myocardial infarction
    c. Flushing
    d. Restlessness or anxiety

39. Which stage of general anesthesia is called surgical anesthesia because it is the stage in which most surgery occurs?
    a. Stage 1
    b. Stage 2
    c. Stage 3
    d. Stage 4

40. The *primary* reason nitrous oxide is used in dentistry is that it provides which of the following?
    a. Potent analgesia
    b. Sedation/relaxation
    c. Anti-inflammatory properties
    d. Anti-infective properties

41. Inhaled general anesthetics produce their effect by preventing the flow of which of the following into neurons of the CNS?
    a. Carbohydrates
    b. Lipids
    c. Sodium
    d. Calcium

42. Which of the following is a potential early adverse effect from nitrous oxide?
    a. Restlessness or anxiety
    b. Dysrhythmia
    c. Hypertension
    d. Mania

43. What is the major depolarizing neuromuscular blocker used during surgery?
    a. Succinylcholine
    b. Acetylcholine
    c. Promethazine (Phenergan)
    d. Bethanechol (Urecholine)

44. Which of the following is a parasympathomimetic sometimes administered to stimulate the smooth muscle of the bowel and urinary tract following surgery?
    a. Succinylcholine
    b. Acetylcholine
    c. Promethazine (Phenergan)
    d. Bethanechol (Urecholine)

45. Halothane hepatitis can be prevented by using halothane (Fluothane)
    a. In those clients presently not pregnant
    b. Only once in any 21-day period

    c.   With caution in clients with diminished hepatic function

    d.   With caution in clients with high blood pressure or irregular heartbeats

MAKING CONNECTIONS

46. In addition to its use as an injected anesthetic, what is lorazepam (Ativan) also used to treat?

    a.   Depression

    b.   Anxiety

    c.   Loss of appetite

    d.   Bipolar disorder

47. Where are sublingual medications administered?

    a.   Into a body cavity

    b.   Into the subarachnoid spinal space

    c.   Into a vein or artery

    d.   Under the tongue

48. Which of the following is a hallucinogen?

    a.   Psilocybin

    b.   Cocaine

    c.   Heroin

    d.   Marijuana

49. Before administering an opioid, which of the following should be checked?

    a.   Blood pressure

    b.   Respiration rate

    c.   Body temperature

    d.   Pulse rate

50. Adrenergic blockers produce a response similar to that of which of the following?

    a.   Sympathetic stimulation

    b.   Parasympathetic stimulation

    c.   Dopaminergic inhibition

    d.   Serotonin inhibition

CALCULATIONS

51. Atropine grains 1/6 SC is ordered. Availability is 15 mg/mL.

    The nurse should administer _____ mL.

52. Lidocaine (Xylocaine) 100 mg is ordered IM STAT. Availability is an ampule with 200 mg/2 cc.

    The nurse should administer _____ mL.

CASE STUDY APPLICATIONS

53. Ms. K is to undergo a procedure that requires general anesthesia. She asks the nurse what she can expect from the medications. She also queries what will happen before and after the procedure.

    a. Identify the nursing diagnosis.

    b. Describe interventions that would be appropriate for this client.

54. Mrs. B is to have a minor procedure on her foot during which local anesthesia is to be used. She is anxious and asks how this procedure is done. She asks what type of effect the anesthesia will have and how long the anesthesia will last. Mrs. B has rapid speech and talks in a pressured speech pattern. She is tremulous and seems to be restless, scanning the room frequently.

    a. Identify the nursing diagnosis.

    b. What assessment data would cause the nurse to have picked this diagnosis?

    c. Describe interventions that would be appropriate for this client.

    d. Identify the goal(s) for this client.

    e. How would each goal be evaluated by the nurse?

CHAPTER 21

DRUGS FOR HYPERTENSION

FILL IN THE BLANK

From the textbook, find the correct word(s) to complete the statement(s).

1. As cardiac output increases, the blood pressure _____.

2. Angiotensin II raises blood pressure by _____.

3. Calcium channel blockers cause the smooth muscle in arterioles to_____, thus_____ blood pressure.

4. ACE inhibitors such as captopril (Capoten) reduce blood pressure by lowering levels of _____ and _____.

5. _____ is a condition that occurs when the heart rate increases due to the rapid fall in blood pressure created by a drug.

6. The side effects of adrenergic blockers are generally quite predictable since they are usually extensions of the _____ response.

7. _____ act on the kidney and are often first-line medications for the treatment of hypertension.

MATCHING

For questions 8 through 16, match the drug in column I with the classification in column II.

Column I

8. _____ Clonidine (Catapres)

9. _____ Captopril (Capoten)

10. _____ Atenolol (Tenormin)

11. _____ Furosemide (Lasix)

12. _____ Nifedipine (Adalat, Apo-Nifed)

13. _____ Lisinopril (Prinivil, Zestril)

14. _____ Hydralazine (Apo-Hydralazine)

15. _____ Metoprolol (Lopresor)

16. _____ Hydrochlorothiazide (HCTZ, Urozide)

Column II

a. Diuretic

b. Calcium channel blocker

c. ACE inhibitor or angiotensin II receptor blocker

d. Beta$_1$-blocker

e. Alpha$_1$-blocker

f. Centrally acting alpha$_2$-agonist

g. Direct vasodilator

MULTIPLE CHOICE

17. Which of the following lowers blood pressure primarily by increasing the renal excretion of sodium and water?

    a. Doxazosin (Cardura)

    b. Furosemide (Lasix)

    c. Verapamil (Isoptin, Apo-Verap)

    d. Quinapril (Accupril)

18. Which of the following is a cardioselective $beta_1$-blocker?

    a. Propranolol (Inderal)

    b. Doxazosin (Cardura)

    c. Ipratropium (Atrovent)

    d. Atenolol (Tenormin)

19. Beginning at 115/75 mm Hg, the risk of cardiovascular disease _____ with each increment of 20/10 mm Hg.

    a. Reduces

    b. Halves

    c. Doubles

    d. Triples

20. Which of the following is *not* a primary factor responsible for blood pressure?

    a. Venous pressure

    b. Cardiac output

    c. Resistance of the small arteries

    d. Blood volume

21. The average person maintains a volume of approximately how much blood?

    a. 4 L

    b. 4.5 L

    c. 5 L

    d. 5.5 L

22. When developing a plan of care, the nurse should know that which drug class is *not* commonly used to treat hypertension?

    a. Calcium channel blockers

    b. Angiotensin-converting enzyme inhibitors

    c. Direct-acting vasodilators

    d. Sodium channel blockers

23. Which are first-line drugs for treating mild to moderate hypertension because they act on the kidney tubule to block reabsorption of sodium?

    a. Diuretics

    b. Calcium channel blockers

    c. Direct vasodilators

    d. Alpha-blockers

24. The nurse should carefully monitor for hyperkalemia when clients are taking which drug?

    a. Diuretic

    b. Calcium channel blocker

    c. Direct vasodilator

    d. Alpha-blocker

25. Calcium channel blockers used for hypertension act by blocking calcium ion channels in which of the following?

    a. Skeletal muscle

    b. Vascular smooth muscle

    c. Central nervous system

    d. Kidney

26. Blood pressure is regulated by a cluster of neurons called the

    a. Medulla oblongata

    b. Vasomotor centre

    c. Neurotransmitters

    d. Neutrons

27. Which of the following drug classes are used to treat chronic hypertension?

    a. Calcium channel blockers

    b. Diuretics

    c. NSAIDs

    d. Both a and b

28. Nitroprusside (Nitropress, Nipride) is an example of which class of drug?

    a. Direct-acting vasodilators

    b. Calcium channel blockers

    c. Diuretics

    d. ACE inhibitors

29. The nurse is treating a client having a hypertensive emergency. The nurse should know that which of the following drugs is used to lower high blood pressure within minutes?

    a. Hydralazine (Apo-Hydralazine)

    b. Nitroprusside (Nitropress, Nipride)

   c. Doxazosin (Cardura)

   d. Prazosin (Minipress)

30. In response to falling blood pressure, what does the kidney release?

   a. Renin

   b. Aldosterone

   c. Angiotensin

   d. Potassium

31. In asthma clients, the nurse should monitor carefully for signs and symptoms of bronchoconstriction when using which class of antihypertensives?

   a. Alpha-blockers

   b. Calcium channel blockers

   c. ACE inhibitors

   d. Beta-blockers

MAKING CONNECTIONS

32. The nurse is treating a client who experienced a myocardial infarction 2 months ago. The nurse should know that which of the following is *not* given to prevent thrombus formation?

   a. Thrombolytics

   b. Aspirin

   c. Heparin

   d. Warfarin

33. Which of the following routes for hydromorphone should be used to achieve the most rapid onset of action?

   a. PO 8.0 mg

   b. SC 1.5 mg

   c. IV 0.80 mg

   d. Rectal 3.0 mg

34. For hypertension, the nurse administers an average daily dose of 5.0 mg enalapril and 10.0 mg fosinopril. From this information, what may the nurse correctly conclude?

   a. Enalapril is twice as efficacious as fosinopril.

   b. Enalapril will likely produce fewer side effects than fosinopril.

   c. Enalapril is more potent than fosinopril.

   d. The onset of action for fosinopril will take longer than that of enalapril.

35. Atropine is a prototype for which drug class?

   a. Sympathomimetics

   b. Beta-adrenergic blockers

   c. Parasympathomimetics

   d. Cholinergic blockers

36. Which of the following drugs is often combined in cartridges with local anesthetics?

   a. Epinephrine

   b. Atropine

   c. Heparin

   d. Acetaminophen

CALCULATIONS

37. Furosemide 15 mg is ordered. The bottle reads 20 mg/2 mL.

   How much furosemide will the nurse draw up in the syringe?

38. A cardiac client has Cardizem 60 mg qid ordered. The bottle reads diltiazem HCl (Cardizem) 120 mg/tablet.

   How many tablets will the nurse administer?

CASE STUDY APPLICATIONS

39. Mr. H, age 50, has presented with a blood pressure of 170/100 mm Hg during the last two visits to his doctor. Hydrochlorothiazide (HCTZ, Urozide) was prescribed for him about 1 year ago. Other than some anxiety, he offers no complaints and other vital signs are normal. His blood lipids are elevated, he is 9 kg overweight, and he smokes a pack of cigarettes a day; otherwise he appears healthy.

   a. What assessment data help you understand the contributing factors for Mr. H's hypertension?

   b. You suspect that Mr. H has not been taking his medication. What nursing diagnoses would you identify? What outcomes would you select for the diagnoses?

   c. Assuming Mr. H has been taking his hydrochlorothiazide, what is the next logical pharmacological option for him?

40. Ms. F is a 75-year-old client who has been taking enalapril (Vasotec) and chlorothiazide (Diuril) for hypertension for the past 2 years. She is very compliant; she takes walks daily, watches her salt intake, and eats plenty of potassium-rich foods such as bananas. Two weeks ago, her physician increased her dose of enalapril and switched her to spironolactone (Aldactone) instead of chlorothiazide. She is now in the office complaining that she gets dizzy and falls over every morning when she gets out of bed and that she feels like her heart is racing when she walks. Although her blood pressure is normal, she wants to be switched back to her previous medications.

   a. What assessment data lead you to understand the potential cause of her dizziness? What teaching might be done to help solve this problem?

   b. Results of Ms. F's ECG are normal. Can you recognize anything in her history that might be responsible for her heart complaints? What assessment information would help you define her problem?

   c. Is it necessary to change Ms. F's medication, or is it possible that her complaints could be resolved through client teaching?

CHAPTER 22
DRUGS FOR LIPID DISORDERS

FILL IN THE BLANK

From the textbook, find the correct word(s) to complete the statement(s).

1. The general term that means high levels of lipids in the blood is _____.

2. Cholesterol contributes to the fatty _____ that narrows arteries.

3. The three basic types of lipids are _____, _____, and _____.

4. Lipoproteins consist of various amounts of _____, _____, and _____ plus a protein carrier.

5. The _____ class of antihyperlipidemics interferes with a critical enzyme in the synthesis of cholesterol.

MATCHING

For questions 6 through 9, match the drug in column I with the primary class in column II.

Column I

6. _____ Cholestyramine (Novo-Cholamine, PMS-Cholestyramine)

7. _____ Nicotinic acid

8. _____ Gemfibrozil (Lopid)

9. _____ Atorvastatin (Lipitor)

Column II

a. HMG-CoA reductase inhibitor

b. Bile acid resin

c. Fibric acid agent

d. None of the above

MULTIPLE CHOICE

10. Drugs that lower lipids are intended to reduce the likelihood of which of the following?
    a. Dysrhythmias
    b. Colon cancer
    c. Coronary artery disease
    d. Obesity

11. LDL transports cholesterol from the liver to the tissues and organs, where it is used to do which of the following?
    a. Provide energy for cells
    b. Build plasma membranes or synthesize steroids

    c.   Make bile

    d.   Make HDL

12. LDL is often called what type of cholesterol, because the lipoprotein contributes significantly to plaque deposits?

    a.   Good

    b.   Bad

    c.   High

    d.   Low

13. What happens to the cholesterol component of HDL after it is transported to the liver?

    a.   It is used to make LDL.

    b.   It is used to build plasma membranes.

    c.   It is used as an energy source.

    d.   It is broken down to become part of bile.

14. Which of the following is *not* a lifestyle change that should be considered by clients with high blood lipid levels?

    a.   Maintain weight at an optimum level

    b.   Implement a medically supervised exercise plan

    c.   Reduce sources of stress

    d.   Limit soluble fibre in the diet to 2 g or less per day

15. Which of the following should be monitored carefully during the first few months of therapy with statins?

    a.   Blood pressure

    b.   Sleep patterns

    c.   Cardiac function

    d.   Liver function

16. Bile acid resins act by doing which of the following?

    a.   Inhibiting HMG-CoA reductase

    b.   Increasing excretion of cholesterol in the feces

    c.   Decreasing production of HDL

    d.   Decreasing absorption of dietary lipids

17. Which of the following is *not* true regarding cholestyramine (Novo-Cholamine, PMS-Cholestyramine)?

    a.   It is not absorbed or metabolized once it enters the intestine.

    b.   It acts by inhibiting cholesterol biosynthesis.

    c.   Its most frequent side effects are constipation, bloating, gas, and nausea.

    d.   It should not be taken at the same time as other medications.

18. Which of the following is a B complex vitamin?
    a.   Nicotinic acid
    b.   Gemfibrozil (Lopid)
    c.   Lovastatin (Advicor, Apo-Lovastatin, Mevacor)
    d.   Colestipol (Colestid)

19. Which of the following best describes the use of nicotinic acid in treating hyperlipidemia?
    a.   It should never be used in clients with hypercholesterolemia.
    b.   It should never be used in clients with a history of heart failure.
    c.   It should never be used with other antihyperlipidemics because their effects may cancel each other.
    d.   It is most often used in lower doses in combination with a statin.

20. Which of the following should be taken separately from other medications because it may interfere with drug absorption?
    a.   Nicotinic acid
    b.   Gemfibrozil (Lopid)
    c.   Cholestyramine (Novo-Cholamine, PMS-Cholestyramine)
    d.   Fluvastatin (Lescol)

MAKING CONNECTIONS

21. Which of the following best describes concerns associated with phenelzine (Nardil)?
    a.   It should not be taken concurrently with MAO inhibitors.
    b.   Clients must avoid foods containing tyramine.
    c.   It may affect the therapeutic outcome of some antiseizure mediations.
    d.   It may potentiate the effects of anticholinergic drugs.

22. Which of the following is *not* a therapeutic effect of ASA?
    a.   Increase in PT time
    b.   Prevention of heart attack
    c.   Relief of severe pain
    d.   Reduction of inflammation

23. Which of the following medications is used primarily for insomnia therapy?
    a.   Triazolam (Halcion)
    b.   Pentobarbital sodium (Nembutal)
    c.   Alprazolam (Xanax)
    d.   Lorazepam (Ativan)

24. Which of the following is true regarding category D drugs?
    a. They may be safely used in pregnant clients.
    b. Animal studies indicate some risk, but the drug appears to be safe for humans.
    c. They should only be used in pregnant clients if the potential benefit justifies the potential risk to the fetus.
    d. They should not be used in pregnant clients under any circumstance.

25. Which of the following is used to treat seizures?
    a. Thiopental sodium (Pentothal)
    b. Fluoxetine (Prozac)
    c. Valproic acid (Depakote)
    d. Haloperidol (Haldol)

CALCULATIONS

26. The physician orders simvastatin (Zocor) 40 mg qhs. The drug is supplied as 40 mg scored tablets.
    How many tablets will the nurse give the client, and at what time?

27. The nurse practitioner orders gemfibrozil (Lopid) 1.2 g daily in two divided doses. The pharmacy sends several 600 mg scored tablets.
    How many tablets will the nurse give the client, and at what time?

CASE STUDY APPLICATIONS

28. Mr. S is a 57-year-old obese client who has a history of two heart attacks over the past 3 years. He has been treated with antihypertensives for a 3-year history of hypertension. LDL cholesterol was recently measured at 4.9 mmol/L, and his serum triglyceride level was 3 mmol/L. The client does not smoke and walks 0.5 km twice a week.
    a. What data can you identify from the initial assessment that would support a nursing diagnosis of "deficient knowledge: disease process and lifestyle implications of coronary heart disease"?
    b. Does the clinical history warrant the implementation of antihyperlipidemic therapy? Why?
    c. As you evaluate this client's history, what lifestyle suggestions might you offer?

29. Ms. G is a 35-year-old client who is 11 kg overweight. She exercises regularly and has been taking atorvastatin (Lipitor) 40 mg/day for the past 2 years. Although her blood lipid profile was normal 12 months ago, her total cholesterol to HDL ratio has slowly risen to 4.2 (ideal is less than 4.0).
    a. How do you evaluate this change in lipid level?
    b. What teaching plan would you implement to help the lipid levels return to normal?

CHAPTER 23

DRUGS FOR ANGINA PECTORIS, MYOCARDIAL INFARCTION, AND CEREBROVASCULAR ACCIDENT

FILL IN THE BLANK

From the textbook, find the correct word(s) to complete the statement(s).

1. Acute chest pain on physical exertion or emotional stress is characteristic of _____.

2. Atherosclerosis is due to a buildup of fatty, fibrous material called _____ in the walls of arteries.

3. The type of angina pectoris that is predictable in its frequency and duration is called _____ angina.

4. Drug therapy of stable angina usually begins with _____.

5. Long-acting nitrates are often delivered through a _____ to decrease the frequency and severity of anginal episodes.

6. After a clot in the coronary artery has been successfully dissolved, therapy with _____ is often initiated to prevent the formation of additional thrombi.

MATCHING

For questions 7 through 13, match the drug in column I with the classification in column II.

Column I

7. _____ Diltiazem (Cardizem, Novo-Diltiazem)

8. _____ Isosorbide dinitrate (Isordil, Novo-Sorbide, Cedocard SR)

9. _____ Metoprolol (Apo-Metoprolol, Lopresor)

10. _____ Atenolol (Apo-Atenolol, Tenormin)

11. _____ Nifedipine (Adalat, Apo-Nifed)

12. _____ Nitroglycerin (Nitrostat, Nitro-Dur, Nitrogard SR)

13. _____ Amlodipine (Norvasc, Caduet)

Column II

a. Organic nitrate

b. Beta-blocker

c. Calcium channel blocker

d. ACE inhibitor

e. Analgesic

MULTIPLE CHOICE

14. Which of the following drug classes is frequently prescribed for clients with angina pectoris?
    a. Calcium channel blockers
    b. ACE inhibitors
    c. HMG-CoA reductase inhibitors
    d. Cardiac glycosides

15. Which of the following best explains the mechanism by which organic nitrates terminate variant angina?
    a. Direct vasodilation of coronary arteries
    b. Slowing of heart rate
    c. Stronger force of myocardial contraction
    d. Dilation of peripheral veins, reducing preload

16. What is the condition of having a reduced blood supply to myocardial cells?
    a. Myocardial infarction
    b. Angina pectoris
    c. Myocardial ischemia
    d. Stroke

17. In assessing a client with chest pain, the nurse knows that angina is most often preceded by which of the following?
    a. An aura
    b. Physical exertion or emotional excitement
    c. A sensation that the heart has skipped a beat
    d. Severe pain down the left arm

18. The pharmacological goals for the treatment of angina are usually achieved by which of the following?
    a. Reducing cardiac workload
    b. Increasing heart rate
    c. Increasing force of myocardial contraction
    d. Increasing amount of blood entering the heart

19. Nitrates reduce the amount of blood returning to the heart, thus decreasing which of the following?
    a. Heart rate
    b. Conduction velocity
    c. Ischemia
    d. Cardiac output

20. In addition to causing a reduction in the amount of blood flow, organic nitrates have what other ability?
    a. Inhibit alpha$_1$-adrenergic receptors in arterioles
    b. Dilate the coronary arteries

    c.   Terminate dysrhythmias

    d.   Remove plaque from coronary arteries

21. Organic nitrates are classified based on whether they are one or the other of which of the following?

    a.   Parenteral or oral

    b.   High or low potency

    c.   Short or long acting

    d.   Sedating or non-sedating

22. What percentage of clients die within the first year following a CVA?

    a.   10%

    b.   20%

    c.   30%

    d.   40%

23. A client is receiving nitroglycerin. The nurse should monitor for the most common side effect, which is

    a.   Headache

    b.   Drowsiness

    c.   Nausea/vomiting

    d.   Hypotension

24. What is the primary mechanism by which beta-adrenergic blockers decrease the frequency of angina attacks?

    a.   Dilating the coronary arteries

    b.   Increasing the heart rate

    c.   Increasing the strength of contraction of the myocardium

    d.   Reducing cardiac workload

25. Which of the following is true regarding the effect of atenolol (Apo-Atenolol, Tenormin) on the heart?

    a.   Selectively blocks $beta_1$-receptors

    b.   Non-selective $beta_1$- and $beta_2$-blocker

    c.   Selectively blocks $beta_2$-receptors

    d.   Has no effect on beta-receptors

26. What is the primary mechanism by which calcium channel blockers decrease the frequency of angina attacks?

    a.   Slowing conduction through the SA node

    b.   Increasing the heart rate

    c.   Increasing the strength of contraction of the myocardium

    d.   Reducing cardiac workload

27. Calcium channel blockers are useful in treating variant angina because they do which of the following?

    a.   Lower blood pressure

    b.   Slow the heart rate

    c.   Slow conduction across the myocardium

    d.   Relax arterial smooth muscle in the coronary arteries

28. Which of the following agents has the ability to inhibit the transport of calcium ions into myocardial cells and the ability to relax both coronary and peripheral blood vessels?

    a.   Atenolol (Apo-Atenolol, Tenormin)

    b.   Diltiazem (Cardizem, Novo-Diltiazem)

    c.   Nitroglycerin

    d.   Reteplase (Retavase)

29. Which of the following is *not* a goal for the pharmacotherapy of acute MI?

    a.   Restore blood supply to the damaged myocardium as quickly as possible

    b.   Increase myocardial oxygen demand with organic nitrates or beta-blockers

    c.   Prevent associated dysrhythmias with antidysrhythmics

    d.   Reduce post-MI mortality with ASA and ACE inhibitors

30. In treating a client with a recent MI, the nurse knows that the function of thrombolytic therapy is to do which of the following?

    a.   Restore blood supply to the damaged myocardium

    b.   Decrease myocardial oxygen demand

    c.   Control dysrhythmias

    d.   Reduce acute pain associated with MI

31. The nurse is administering a thrombolytic drug. The nurse should monitor for which primary adverse effect of thrombolytics?

    a.   Hypertension

    b.   Prolonged prothrombin time

    c.   Excessive bleeding

    d.   Dysrhythmia

32. The nurse should know that reteplase (Retavase) is most effective if given within what time frame after the onset of MI symptoms?

    a.   30 minutes

    b.   1 hour

    c.   6 hours

    d.   12 hours

33. Following an acute MI, metoprolol (Lopresor) is infused slowly until which of the following occurs?

    a.   The clot dissolves completely.

    b.   Blood pressure falls to 100/70 mm Hg.

    c.   A target heart rate of 60 to 90 beats per minute is reached.

    d.   The pain is relieved.

34. Unless contraindicated, 160 to 324 mg of ASA is administered as soon as possible following a suspected MI in order to do which of the following?
    a. Restore blood supply to the damaged myocardium
    b. Decrease myocardial oxygen demand
    c. Reduce post-MI mortality
    d. Reduce acute pain associated with MI

35. Why is captopril (Capoten) prescribed for clients who have experienced a recent MI?
    a. To restore blood supply to the damaged myocardium
    b. To increase myocardial oxygen demand
    c. To reduce post-MI mortality
    d. To reduce acute pain associated with MI

36. Why does the nurse administer opioids such as morphine sulfate to an MI client?
    a. To restore blood supply to the damaged myocardium
    b. To decrease myocardial oxygen demand
    c. To reduce post-MI mortality
    d. To reduce acute pain associated with MI

MAKING CONNECTIONS

37. Chest pain may be caused by diverse situations, unrelated to cardiac pathology. These include which of the following?
    a. Gallstones and peptic ulcer disease
    b. Pneumonia and muscular skeletal injuries
    c. Certain cancers
    d. All of the above

38. What is the classification of nitrous oxide?
    a. IV anesthetic
    b. Gas
    c. Volatile agent
    d. Local anesthetic

39. Which drug would the nurse administer sublingually to terminate angina pain?
    a. Atenolol
    b. Diltiazem
    c. Nitroglycerin
    d. ASA

40. The antidysrhythmic action of lidocaine (Xylocaine) is due to blockade of which of the following?

    a. Sodium channels

    b. Calcium channels

    c. Beta-adrenergic receptors

    d. Potassium channels

41. Which of the following blocks impulses from the parasympathetic nervous system?

    a. Sympathomimetic

    b. Beta-adrenergic blocker

    c. Cholinergic blocker

    d. Calcium channel blocker

CALCULATIONS

42. A nitroglycerin solution of 50 mg/250 mL D5W is infused at 15 gtt/min. The IV set calibration is 60 gtt/mL.

    How many µg/min are infused?

43. A client has an IV drip of Cardizem 125 mg/100 mL D5W. The doctor orders Cardizem 10 mg/hr.

    How many drops per minute will the nurse give if a microdrip is used?

CASE STUDY APPLICATIONS

44. Mr. M is a 70-year-old, 127 kg client admitted through the ER for a possible stroke. His physical exam reveals that he is alert, with a regular pulse of 76, BP 190/110 mm Hg, respirations 24/min, and slurred speech. He has significant weakness in the left arm, left hand, and left leg. CT scan confirms a recent CVA. His social history includes occasional alcohol use and smoking two packs of cigarettes per day for 50 years. He is a retired accountant, is married, and has seven adult children and 16 grandchildren. During hospitalization, he was given reteplase (Retavase), furosemide (Lasix), and heparin. He was discharged with the following medications: hydrochlorothiazide (Urozide), diltiazem (Cardizem), and warfarin (Coumadin).

    a. After analysis of the admission data, what risk factors have likely contributed to this client's stroke?

    b. What presenting symptoms help the nurse to confirm the diagnosis of stroke?

    c. After you review the medications, what rationale supports the delivery of Retavase, Lasix, and heparin?

    d. You are preparing to begin discharge teaching. What rationale will you give Mr. M for the use of hydrochlorothiazide, diltiazem, and warfarin?

45. Mrs. R is a 72-year-old client who has been treated several times for chronic heart failure, hypertension, and angina. Her current complaint is the frequency and intensity of her anginal pain. She has chest pain with minor exertion and headaches with the use of PRN nitroglycerin. Her current medications are isosorbide dinitrate, nitroglycerin, atenolol, and amlodipine. Physical exam reveals that the client is alert and oriented, with BP 164/92 mm Hg, pulse 66 regular, respirations 28, cool skin, equal strength in all extremities, edema in lower extremities, and a weight gain of 3 kg in 3 weeks.

   a.   After analysis of this client's situation, what nursing diagnoses can you identify?

   b.   What assessment data support the possibility of side effects from Norvasc?

   c.   Why do you think the nitrates are not relieving Mrs. R's pain?

CHAPTER 24

DRUGS FOR HEART FAILURE

FILL IN THE BLANK

From the textbook, find the correct word(s) to complete the statement(s).

1. As more stretch is applied to myocardial fibres, they will contract with greater force. This is known as the _____ law.

2. As a general rule, if the heart rate is less than _____ beats per minute, digoxin (Lanoxin) should not be taken.

3. The two most important variables that affect cardiac output are _____ and _____.

4. When a medication has a positive inotropic effect, it has the ability to _____ the _____ of the myocardial contraction.

5. Cardiac glycosides cause the heart to beat more _____ and more _____.

6. If a client has taken an overdose of digoxin, the nurse will prepare to give _____ to treat this life-threatening problem.

7. Blocking phosphodiesterase has the effect of _____ the amount of calcium available for myocardial contraction.

MATCHING

For questions 8 through 16, match the drug in column I with the classification in column II.

Column I

8. _____ Lisinopril (Prinivil, Zestril)

9. _____ Hydralazine (Apo-Hydralazine)

10. _____ Carvedilol (Coreg)

11. _____ Fosinopril (Monopril)

12. _____ Digoxin (Lanoxin)

13. _____ Quinapril (Accupril)

14. _____ Triamterene (Apo-Triazide)

15. _____ Enalapril (Vasotec)

16. _____ Isosorbide dinitrate (Isordil, Coronex)

Column II

a. Diuretic

b. Cardiac glycoside

c. ACE inhibitor

d. Beta-blocker

e. Direct vasodilator

f. Phosphodiesterase inhibitor

MULTIPLE CHOICE

17. The primary action of digoxin (Lanoxin) that makes it very effective at treating heart failure is its ability to do which of the following?
    a. Dilate the coronary arteries
    b. Increase impulse conduction across the myocardium
    c. Decrease blood pressure
    d. Increase cardiac contractility/output

18. Blood electrolyte levels are critical to safe digoxin therapy. The nurse must carefully monitor for which of the following that may predispose the client to digoxin toxicity?
    a. Hypokalemia
    b. Hyperkalemia
    c. Hypocalcemia
    d. Hypercalcemia

19. What is the best definition of heart failure?
    a. Enlargement of the heart
    b. Inability of the heart to beat in a coordinated manner
    c. Inability of the ventricles to pump sufficient blood
    d. Congestion in the lungs caused by damage to the myocardium

20. What is the amount of blood pumped by each ventricle per minute called?
    a. Preload
    b. Afterload
    c. Stroke volume
    d. Cardiac output

21. What is the correct definition of preload?
    a. Amount of blood pumped by each ventricle per minute
    b. Degree to which the heart fibres are stretched just prior to contraction
    c. Pressure in the aorta that must be overcome for blood to be ejected from the heart
    d. Ability to increase the strength of contraction

22. Which of the following drug classes was first derived from the common plant known as the purple foxglove?
    a. Cardiac glycosides
    b. ACE inhibitors
    c. Phosphodiesterase inhibitors
    d. Beta-adrenergic blockers

23. When monitoring clients on cardiac glycosides, the nurse knows that these drugs help the heart to beat more forcefully. They also cause which of the following?

    a.   A faster heart rate

    b.   A slower heart rate

    c.   No change in cardiac output

    d.   Diminished cardiac output

24. Digoxin (Lanoxin) acts by which of the following?

    a.   Blocking beta-adrenergic receptors in the heart

    b.   Stimulating beta-adrenergic receptors in the heart

    c.   Inhibiting Na^+, K^+-ATPase

    d.   Stimulating Na^+, K^+-ATPase

25. The nurse should monitor for which of the following adverse effects in a client taking digoxin for HF?

    a.   Increased heart rate

    b.   Increased cardiac output

    c.   Increased urine production

    d.   Decreased peripheral edema

26. What is potentially the most serious adverse effect of pharmacotherapy with digoxin?

    a.   Permanent visual disturbances

    b.   Hyperkalemia

    c.   Hypotension

    d.   Dysrhythmias

27. Which drug class has largely replaced the cardiac glycosides as first-line drugs in the therapy of heart failure?

    a.   Direct vasodilators

    b.   ACE inhibitors

    c.   Phosphodiesterase inhibitors

    d.   Beta-adrenergic blockers

28. The primary action of the ACE inhibitors that benefits a client with HF is a decrease in which of the following?

    a.   Peripheral resistance / blood pressure

    b.   Cardiac output

    c.   Heart rate

    d.   Urine output

29. By what mechanism does isosorbide dinitrate (Isordil, Coronex) benefit clients with HF?

    a.   Lowering arterial blood pressure

    b.   Increasing urine output

   c. Reducing venous return, causing a decrease in cardiac workload

   d. Slowing the heart rate, causing a reduction in cardiac workload

30. In addition to heart failure, what is hydralazine (Apo-Hydralazine) also prescribed for?

   a. Coagulation disorders

   b. Hypertension

   c. Stroke

   d. Glaucoma

31. In addition to heart failure, what are diuretics also commonly prescribed for?

   a. Minor depression

   b. Coagulation disorders

   c. Hypertension

   d. Dysrhythmias

32. By what mechanism do diuretics such as furosemide (Lasix) improve the symptoms of heart failure?

   a. Blockading beta-adrenergic receptors

   b. Causing the heart to beat with more strength

   c. Reducing fluid / plasma volume

   d. Slowing heart rate, thus reducing cardiac workload

33. The nurse must carefully monitor for which of the following serious side effects of furosemide (Lasix) therapy?

   a. Electrolyte imbalances

   b. Dysrhythmias

   c. Reflex tachycardia

   d. Hypertension

34. What is the primary use of the phosphodiesterase inhibitors in HF clients?

   a. Cause a rapid reduction in fluid / plasma volume

   b. Cause the heart to beat faster

   c. Rapidly lower blood pressure

   d. Increase the force of contraction and increase cardiac output

35. How do beta-adrenergic blockers such as carvedilol (Coreg) improve symptoms of HF?

   a. Increase heart rate

   b. Decrease heart rate

   c. Cause the heart to contract with more force

   d. Lower blood pressure and reduce cardiac workload

MAKING CONNECTIONS

36. Which of the following drug classes is *not* used for hypertension?
    a.   Sodium channel blockers
    b.   ACE inhibitors
    c.   Adrenergic blockers
    d.   Diuretics

37. The nurse should teach clients to eat plenty of bananas during pharmacotherapy with thiazide diuretics, to obtain an adequate amount of which of the following?
    a.   Selenium
    b.   Calcium
    c.   Potassium
    d.   Chloride

38. The nurse is asked to administer carvedilol (Coreg) 6.25 mg bid. What does the term "bid" mean?
    a.   Twice a week
    b.   Twice a day
    c.   Before bedtime
    d.   Before breakfast

39. Which of the following drug classes does *not* have significant potential for abuse by clients?
    a.   Barbiturates
    b.   Benzodiazepines
    c.   Opioids
    d.   Anticholinergics

40. Which drug class is used to dry secretions, treat asthma, and prevent motion sickness?
    a.   Anticholinergics
    b.   Cholinergics
    c.   Parasympathomimetics
    d.   Alpha-blockers

CALCULATIONS

41. A client is prescribed carvedilol (Coreg) 6.25 mg bid. The pills are available in 3.125 mg tablets. How many pills will the pharmacy provide the client with to fill her prescription over a 2-week period?

42. A doctor orders furosemide 40 mg IV push. The bottle label reads Furosemide (Lasix) 20 mg/2 mL. How many millilitres will the nurse give?

CASE STUDY APPLICATIONS

43. Mr. L has just been diagnosed with early heart failure, and his physician has prescribed hydrochlorothiazide, atorvastatin (Lipitor), and lisinopril (Prinivil). His blood pressure is slightly elevated, his blood cholesterol is marginally high, and he has stenosis of the mitral valve that seems to be worsening. Although he is not an athletic person, Mr. L likes to take long walks after dinner. He confides that at his age of 60 he has no intention of taking any of the medications, but intends to try Chinese herbal therapy.

    a.   You are developing a teaching plan for Mr. L. You want to explain the rationale for each of his medications. What information will you include in the teaching plan?

    b.   How do you assess Mr. L's need for alternative therapy, and what is your best response to his concern about prescription drugs?

    c.   Knowing that health promotion is an essential nursing action, what lifestyle changes would you suggest to Mr. L to improve his cardiac health?

44. Mrs. C, an elderly client, is transferred from a rehabilitation centre to an acute care setting with a diagnosis of heart failure and the following vital signs: BP 120/90, pulse 108/min, and laboured respirations 32/min. Assessment of breath sounds reveals coarse rhonchi and wheezing on inspiration and expiration. A 4.5 kg weight gain has been observed over a 3-day period. The care plan includes digoxin (Lanoxin) 0.5 mg IV STAT to be repeated in 4 hours and then an oral dose of 0.25 mg/day.

    a.   What assessment data support the diagnosis of heart failure?

    b.   Why would the care plan include a STAT dose of digoxin with a dose repeating in 4 hours and then a lower daily dose?

    c.   What other bodily system must the nurse pay close attention to in the assessment of this client with heart failure?

CHAPTER 25

DRUGS FOR DYSRHYTHMIAS

FILL IN THE BLANK

From the textbook, find the correct word(s) to complete the statement(s).

1. After the action potential has passed and the myocardial cell is in a depolarized state, repolarization depends on removal of _____ from the cell.

2. Calcium channel blockers are only effective against _____ dysrhythmias.

3. Severe dysrhythmias may result in _____.

4. The most common type of dysrhythmia is _____.

5. The adverse vascular effect related to the use of quinidine is _____.

6. Beta-blockers are contraindicated for clients with three types of heart abnormalities:_____, _____, and _____.

7. Label the parts of the conduction pathway and the events of the ECG in Figure 25.1.
    a. _____   d. _____   g. _____
    b. _____   e. _____   h. _____
    c. _____   f. _____

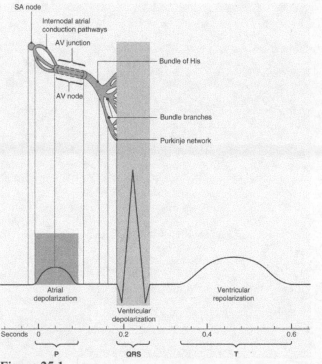

Figure 25.1

Source: Core Concepts in Pharmacology, Workbook by Holland/Adams © 2003. Reprinted by permission of Pearson Education, Inc., Upper Saddle River, NJ.

MATCHING

For questions 8 through 16, match the drug in column I with the classification in column II.

Column I

8. _____ Quinidine gluconate (Apo-Quin-G)

9. _____ Amiodarone (Cordarone)

10. _____ Diltiazem (Cardizem)

11. _____ Verapamil (Isoptin)

12. _____ Phenytoin (Dilantin)

13. _____ Propranolol (Inderal)

14. _____ Lidocaine (Xylocaine)

15. _____ Procainamide (Apo-Procainamide, Pronestyl)

16. _____ Adenosine (Adenocard, Adenoscan)

Column II

a. Sodium channel blocker

b. Potassium channel blocker

c. Beta-adrenergic blocker

d. Calcium channel blocker

e. Miscellaneous (none of the above)

MULTIPLE CHOICE

17. Which of the following best describes dysrhythmias?
    a. Abnormalities of electrical conduction in the heart
    b. Diminished cardiac output
    c. Narrowing of the coronary arteries
    d. High blood pressure

18. Which of the following is *not* a type of dysrhythmia?
    a. Atrial tachycardia
    b. Ventricular flutter
    c. Sinus bradycardia
    d. Premature subventricular contractions

19. Where does cardiac conduction in the heart begin?
    a. Atrioventricular bundle
    b. Atrioventricular (AV) node
    c. Sinoatrial (SA) node
    d. Purkinje fibres

20. Under resting conditions, a new action potential crosses the myocardium approximately how many times every minute?
    a. 60
    b. 75
    c. 85
    d. 110

21. In most myocardial cells and in neurons, an action potential begins when channels located in the plasma membrane open and _____ rushes into the cell, producing a rapid depolarization..

    a. Calcium

    b. Phosphate

    c. Potassium

    d. Sodium

22. Which of the following is *not* a class of antidysrhythmic drugs?

    a. Sodium channel blockers

    b. Alpha-adrenergic blockers

    c. Potassium channel blockers

    d. Calcium channel blockers

23. Which of the following is the basic pharmacological mechanism by which nearly all antidysrhythmic drugs terminate or prevent abnormal rhythms?

    a. Increase heart rate until rhythm returns to normal

    b. Dilate coronary arteries so that more blood gets to the myocardium

    c. Slow the impulse conduction velocity until rhythm returns to normal

    d. Lower the blood pressure so the heart has less workload

24. A blockade of sodium channels in myocardial cells will do which of the following?

    a. Slow the spread of impulse conduction

    b. Speed the spread of impulse conduction

    c. Stop the spread of impulse conduction

    d. Worsen a dysrhythmia

25. The physician orders 50 mg lidocaine (Xylocaine) for a client with a dysrhythmia. The nurse will administer this drug by the _____ route to terminate _____ dysrhythmias.

    a. PO, ventricular

    b. PO, atrial

    c. IV, atrial

    d. IV, ventricular

26. Which antidysrhythmic drug acts by blocking beta-adrenergic receptors in the heart?

    a. Verapamil (Isoptin)

    b. Digoxin (Lanoxin)

    c. Amiodarone (Cordarone)

    d. Propranolol (Inderal)

27. Clients taking sodium channel blockers should be advised to avoid all of the following *except*

    a. Alcohol

    b. Caffeine

   c.   Moderate exercise

   d.   Tobacco

28. The nurse is administering quinidine for acute tachycardia. The nurse will assess for the most common side effects, which are related to which body system?

   a.   CNS

   b.   Gastrointestinal

   c.   Cardiovascular

   d.   Pulmonary

29. Beta-adrenergic blockers are used to treat a large number of cardiovascular diseases. Which of the following is *not* one of the uses of beta-blockers?

   a.   Anticoagulant

   b.   Hypertension

   c.   Heart failure

   d.   Dysrhythmias

30. How do beta-adrenergic blockers prevent dysrhythmias?

   a.   Speed impulse conduction across the myocardium

   b.   Slow impulse conduction across the myocardium

   c.   Blockade calcium channels

   d.   Blockade sodium channels

31. Propranolol (Inderal) is classified as which of the following?

   a.   Sodium channel blocker

   b.   Beta-blocker

   c.   Potassium channel blocker

   d.   Calcium channel blocker

32. Which of the following is *not* an expected adverse effect in a client taking propranolol (Inderal)?

   a.   Diminished sex drive

   b.   Hypotension

   c.   Bradycardia

   d.   Tachycardia

33. How do potassium channel blockers prevent dysrhythmias?

   a.   Block beta-adrenergic receptors in the myocardium

   b.   Reduce blood pressure

   c.   Interfere with calcium ion channels

   d.   Prolong the refractory period of the heart

34. Why are potassium channel blockers *not* generally considered first-line therapy for dysrhythmias?

   a.   They are expensive.

   b.   They are not approved for use in Canada.

    c. They have potentially serious side effects.

    d. They are difficult to administer.

35. The most serious adverse effects from amiodarone (Cordarone) are related to which body system?

    a. CNS

    b. Pulmonary

    c. Cardiovascular

    d. Gastrointestinal

36. Blocking calcium ion channels has a number of effects on the heart and vascular system. These effects are most similar to which of the following?

    a. Sodium channel blockers

    b. Potassium channel blockers

    c. Beta-adrenergic blockers

    d. Cardiac glycosides

37. The nurse would administer which of the following antidysrhythmics IV to rapidly terminate serious atrial dysrhythmias?

    a. Adenosine (Adenocard)

    b. Amiodarone (Cordarone)

    c. Propranolol (Inderal)

    d. Verapamil (Isoptin)

MAKING CONNECTIONS

38. The main benefit of phosphodiesterase inhibitors (such as milrinone) is in the treatment of which of the following?

    a. Hypertension

    b. Coagulation disorders

    c. Heart failure

    d. Shock

39. Which of the following is the most widely used class of agents for the treatment of clinical depression?

    a. Barbiturates

    b. Na^+, K^+-ATPase inhibitors

    c. Benzodiazepines

    d. Selective serotonin reuptake inhibitors

40. A client taking sumatriptan (Imitrex) likely suffers from which of the following?

    a. Sleep disorders

    b. Seizures

    c. Migraines

    d. Schizophrenia

41. What is GABA?
    a. Surgical procedure used to help clients who are psychotic
    b. Neurotransmitter
    c. Drug used to treat bipolar disorder
    d. Widely abused hallucinogen

CALCULATIONS

42. A solution of diltiazem (Cardizem) 125 mg/100 mL D5W is to infuse at a rate of 20 mg/hr.
    What is the mL/hr flow rate?

43. A client with atrial fibrillation has amiodarone (Cordarone) ordered at 0.5 mg/min. The concentration is amiodarone 900 mg in 250 mL D5W.
    How many mL/hr should the IV pump be programmed to deliver?

CASE STUDY APPLICATIONS

44. Ms. D, age 67, is brought to the hospital by paramedics after collapsing on the street. She has a history of heart failure and has been taking digoxin and furosemide. The ER physician determines that she is experiencing a myocardial infarction accompanied by severe tachycardia.
    a. The ER nurse should collect what assessment data before propranolol is started?
    b. The client is also given quinidine. Why would this drug be used? What position should Ms. D be in during IV administration of this drug, and why?
    c. The nurse should anticipate what adverse effects from the use of quinidine and propranolol?

45. You are working in an ICU. On admission to the unit, you are told that a client admitted for chest pain is demonstrating paroxysmal supraventricular tachycardia. You know the client has a PRN order for verapamil (Isoptin) if supraventricular tachycardia occurs.
    a. What nursing assessment must you make before administering Isoptin?
    b. If the client will remain on Isoptin, what client teaching must be done?
    c. What nursing diagnoses may be identified for this client?

CHAPTER 26

DRUGS FOR COAGULATION DISORDERS

FILL IN THE BLANK

From the textbook, find the correct word(s) to complete the statement(s).

1. Identify steps in the coagulation cascade shown in Figure 26.1.

    A. _____

    B. _____

    C. _____

2. Identify steps in fibrinolysis shown in Figure 26.2.

    A. _____

    B. _____

    C. _____

3. The most commonly prescribed coagulation modifiers are the _____.

4. The _____ are a class of drugs that dissolve life-threatening clots.

5. _____ are drugs that inhibit the normal removal of fibrin.

6. Two laboratory tests used to determine the anticoagulation effects of warfarin (Coumadin) are _____ and _____.

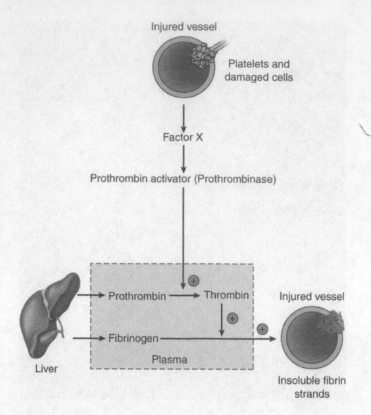

Figure 26.1
*Source: Core Concepts in Pharmacology, Workbook by Holland/Adams, © 2003. Reprinted by permission
of Pearson Education, Inc., Upper Saddle River, NJ.*

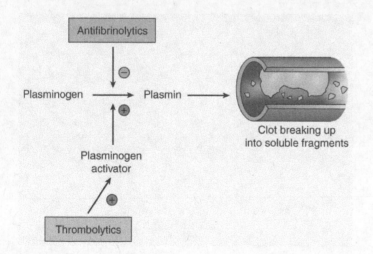

Figure 26.2
*Source: Core Concepts in Pharmacology, Workbook by Holland/Adams, © 2003. Reprinted by permission
of Pearson Education, Inc., Upper Saddle River, NJ.*

MATCHING

For questions 7 through 14, match the drug in column I with the classification in column II.

Column I	Column II
7. _____ Warfarin (Coumadin, Warfilone)	a. Anticoagulant: general type
8. _____ Abciximab (ReoPro)	b. Anticoagulant: antiplatelet type
9. _____ ASA (Aspirin)	c. Anticoagulant: LMWH type
10. _____ Enoxaparin (Lovenox)	d. ADP receptor blocker
11. _____ Reteplase (Retavase)	e. Glycoprotein IIb/IIIa receptor blocker
12. _____ Tirofiban (Aggrastat)	f. Thrombolytic
13. _____ Aminocaproic acid (Amicar)	g. Antifibrinolytic
14. _____ Ticlopidine (Apo-Ticlopidine)	

MULTIPLE CHOICE

15. Which of the following clump and adhere to the wall of an injured blood vessel to begin the process of hemostasis?
    a. Platelets
    b. Red blood cells
    c. White blood cells
    d. Antibodies

16. What is the solid, insoluble part of a blood clot called?
    a. Fibrin
    b. Thrombin
    c. Prothrombin
    d. Plasmin

17. Hemophilia A is caused by a lack of which of the following?
    a. Platelets
    b. Red blood cells
    c. Clotting factor VIII
    d. Clotting factor II

18. Which organ is responsible for making many of the factors necessary for blood clotting?
    a. Kidney
    b. Liver
    c. Brain
    d. Skin

19. What is the process of clot removal called?

    a.   Embolysis

    b.   Thrombolysis

    c.   Plasminolysis

    d.   Fibrinolysis

20. What is the specific class of drugs that promotes the formation of clots?

    a.   Antifibrinolytics

    b.   Thrombolytics

    c.   Fibrinolytics

    d.   Plasminogen activators

21. The nurse is administering heparin. Which lab test should the nurse use to monitor pharmacotherapy with heparin?

    a.   Bleeding time

    b.   PT

    c.   INR

    d.   aPTT

22. Anticoagulants are drugs that do which of the following?

    a.   Dissolve thrombi that have been recently formed

    b.   Shorten PT time

    c.   Prevent thrombi from forming or growing larger

    d.   Cause platelets to become less sticky

23. What is the primary advantage of using low molecular weight heparins (LMWHs) rather than heparin?

    a.   LMWHs possess greater anticoagulant activity.

    b.   LMWHs may be given by the oral route.

    c.   LMWHs produce a more stable effect on coagulation; therefore fewer lab tests are needed.

    d.   LMWHs have a prolonged duration of action.

24. The nurse must monitor for the most serious adverse effect of anticoagulant therapy. Which of the following is the most serious?

    a.   Hemorrhage

    b.   Severe headaches

    c.   Electrolyte depletion

    d.   Cardiac arrhythmias

25. The nurse must administer which of the following antagonists if serious hemorrhage occurs during heparin therapy?

    a.   Protamine sulfate

    b.   Vitamin K

    c.   Adenosine diphosphate (ADP)

    d.   Desmopressin (DDAVP)

26. When teaching a client about using warfarin, the nurse should tell the client that the anticoagulant activity can take how long to reach its maximum effect?

    a.   Several minutes

    b.   Several hours

    c.   Several days

    d.   Several weeks

27. The nurse must ensure that vitamin K is available as an antidote to treat an overdose with which of the following?

    a.   ASA

    b.   Heparin and LMWH

    c.   Aminocaproic acid (Amicar)

    d.   Warfarin (Coumadin)

28. A client calls the nurse and says that he has stopped taking warfarin because his prescription expired. The nurse should know that the pharmacological activity of warfarin will take how long to diminish?

    a.   10 minutes

    b.   10 hours

    c.   24 hours

    d.   3 days

29. ASA causes its anticoagulant effect by inhibiting which of the following?

    a.   Plasminogen

    b.   Prothrombin

    c.   Thromboxane A_2

    d.   Glycoprotein IIb/IIIa

30. Glycoprotein IIb/IIIa inhibitors act by blocking the final step in which of the following?

    a.   Hemostasis

    b.   Platelet aggregation

    c.   Activation of plasminogen

    d.   Formation of vitamin K

31. The primary action of streptokinase is to convert plasminogen to which of the following?

    a.   Plasminogen activator

    b.   Plasmin

    c.   Fibrin

    d.   Fibrinogen

32. The nurse understands that the primary action of antifibrinolytics is to do which of the following?
    a.   Dissolve thrombi
    b.   Prevent thrombi
    c.   Reverse the effects of anticoagulants
    d.   Prevent excessive bleeding following surgery

33. Which of the following is *not* an indication for thrombolytic therapy?
    a.   Acute myocardial infarction
    b.   Postoperative bleeding
    c.   Pulmonary embolism
    d.   Deep vein thrombosis (DVT)

MAKING CONNECTIONS

34. A client is receiving warfarin, which is 98% bound to plasma proteins. The antidepressant paroxetine (Paxil), which is 95% bound, is added to the client's daily medications. If the paroxetine displaces warfarin from its binding sites, which of the following will most likely occur?
    a.   Toxicity from warfarin
    b.   Toxicity from paroxetine
    c.   Diminished effect from warfarin
    d.   Diminished effect from paroxetine

35. The antidepressant imipramine (Tofranil) is metabolized to its active form, desipramine, in the liver. How should the dose of imipramine for clients with liver cirrhosis be modified?
    a.   Increased above average
    b.   Decreased below average
    c.   Remain the same as average
    d.   This client should not receive imipramine.

36. Which of the following is a widely used class of antipsychotic medications?
    a.   Phenothiazines
    b.   Benzodiazepines
    c.   MAO inhibitors
    d.   Anticholinergics

37. What is the primary goal of the nurse for clients who have been prescribed PRN pain medications?
    a.   Administer the least amount of pain medication possible
    b.   Administer analgesics only when pain becomes intolerable
    c.   Ensure that dependence does not develop
    d.   Alleviate the pain

38. Of the following four drugs, which is *not* related to the other three?

    a.   Phenytoin (Dilantin)

    b.   Phenobarbital (PMS-Phenobarbital)

    c.   Sumatriptan (Imitrex)

    d.   Ethosuximide (Zarontin)

CALCULATIONS

39. A client with deep vein thrombosis has an order for heparin 2500 U per hour. The solution strength is 50,000 U in 1000 mL D5W.

    What is the mL/hr flow rate?

40. A client is receiving 20,000 U heparin in 500 mL D5W. The rate is set at 30 mL/hr.

    How many units is the client receiving per hour?

    How many units will the client receive in a day?

CASE STUDY APPLICATIONS

41. Ms. S is being discharged from the hospital following surgery for replacement of a heart valve. She will be placed on long-term warfarin (Coumadin) therapy. You are developing this client's discharge teaching plan.

    a.   List the activities that you will teach Ms. S to avoid.

    b.   Describe the signs and symptoms that would alert Ms. S to adverse effects of warfarin therapy.

    c.   What medications and herbal supplements should be avoided while Ms. S is being treated with warfarin?

42. Mr. P, age 50, is being admitted to the hospital for the third time this year. He has a history of alcohol abuse, diabetes, and heart failure. He was brought to the hospital with a complaint of abdominal pain and vomiting of bright red blood. His diagnosis is perforated ulcer. The client states that he has been taking warfarin for an irregular heartbeat and Glucophage for diabetes.

    a.   With this limited admission history, what factors might have contributed to Mr. P's acute bleeding episode?

    b.   What nursing diagnoses and client outcomes would be essential in this situation?

    c.   What medications might be ordered for Mr. P?

CHAPTER 27

DRUGS FOR SHOCK

FILL IN THE BLANK

From the textbook, find the correct word(s) to complete the statement(s).

1. In the early stages of shock, the body compensates for the fall in blood pressure by increasing the activity of the _____ nervous system.

2. Norepinephrine (Levophed, Norepinephrine Bitartrate) acts directly on _____ -adrenergic receptors to raise blood pressure.

3. Dopamine selectively stimulates _____-receptors, whereas at higher doses it stimulates _____-receptors.

4. Dopamine is used to increase the force of the myocardial contraction by stimulating _____-receptors.

5. The first goal in the treatment of shock is to provide _____.

6. _____ is indicated for the treatment of acute, massive blood loss.

7. The major adverse outcome when using a colloid to treat shock is _____.

8. When given in large doses, hetastarch (Hespan) can increase _____, _____, and _____.

MATCHING

For questions 9 through 15, match the drug in column I with the primary class in column II.

Column I

9. _____ Norepinephrine (Levophed, Norepinephrine Bitartrate)

10. _____ Digoxin (Lanoxin, Apo-, PMS-Digoxin)

11. _____ Phenylephrine (Neo-Synephrine)

12. _____ Hetastarch (Hespan)

13. _____ Dopamine hydrochloride (Dopastat, others)

14. _____ Dextran 70 (Macrodex)

15. _____ Methoxamine (Vasoxyl)

Column II

a. Vasoconstrictor

b. Cardiotonic

c. Colloid

MULTIPLE CHOICE

16. The nurse is administering epinephrine 0.25 mL of 1:1000, every 10 minutes. Which of the following should the nurse monitor to prevent overdose from the drug?

    a. Hypoglycemia

    b. Hypertension

    c. Bronchospasm

    d. Diarrhea

17. Shock is a condition characterized by which of the following?

    a. Extremely high blood pressure

    b. Abnormal cardiac rhythm

    c. Vital tissues not receiving enough blood to function properly

    d. The heart not pumping with sufficient contractility

18. Which of the following is *not* a common sign or symptom of shock?

    a. Feeling weak, with no specific symptoms

    b. Restlessness, anxiety, confusion, lack of interest

    c. Thirst

    d. Hypertension

19. A weak or unresponsive client with obvious trauma or bleeding to a limb might be experiencing what type of shock?

    a. Hypovolemic

    b. Neurogenic

    c. Cardiogenic

    d. Anaphylactic

20. In many types of shock, what is the most serious medical challenge facing the client?

    a. Heart failure

    b. Brain damage

    c. Hypotension

    d. MI

21. What is the purpose of administering vasoconstrictors to a client with shock?

    a. To prevent dysrhythmias

    b. To stabilize blood pressure

    c. To prevent post-shock mortality

    d. To prevent blood pressure from rising to harmful levels

22. Which of the following applies to most of the agents used to raise blood pressure in clients with shock?
    a.   CNS stimulants
    b.   CNS depressants
    c.   Activate the parasympathetic nervous system
    d.   Activate the sympathetic nervous system

23. Norepinephrine activates which adrenergic receptors?
    a.   Alpha
    b. $Beta_1$
    c.   Both alpha and $beta_1$
    d.   Neither alpha nor $beta_1$

24. In addition to its use in shock, norepinephrine is also of value in treating which of the following?
    a.   Cardiac arrest
    b.   Hypertension
    c.   Dysrhythmias
    d.   Strokes

25. The primary use of cardiotonic drugs in the treatment of shock is to increase which of the following?
    a.   Blood pressure
    b.   Force of myocardial contraction
    c.   Heart rate
    d.   Conduction velocity across the myocardium

26. The nurse is ready to administer dobutamine (Dobutrex) 2.5 µg/kg for 5 min. The nurse should know that this drug belongs to which of the following?
    a.   Vasoconstrictors
    b.   Crystalloids
    c.   Colloids
    d.   Cardiotonic agents

27. A widespread inflammatory response to bacterial, fungal, or parasitic infection can result in which type of shock?
    a.   Cardiogenic
    b.   Hypovolemic
    c.   Neurogenic
    d.   Septic

MAKING CONNECTIONS

28. Which of the following is an expected effect of beta-adrenergic blockers?
    a. Increased heart rate
    b. Lowered blood pressure
    c. Dilation of bronchial smooth muscle
    d. Increased myocardial contractility

29. Which of the following is a cholinergic blocker?
    a. Metoprolol
    b. Succinylcholine
    c. Neostigmine
    d. Atropine

30. Which of the following is *not* classified as an NSAID?
    a. Acetaminophen
    b. ASA
    c. Celecoxib
    d. Ibuprofen

31. Antiplatelet agents are primarily prescribed to do which of the following?
    a. Lower blood cholesterol
    b. Dissolve thrombi
    c. Prevent thromboembolic disease
    d. Prevent migraines

32. Most barbiturate use in children is limited to which of the following conditions?
    a. Sleep disorders
    b. Seizure disorders
    c. Depression
    d. Anxiety

CALCULATIONS

33. Dopamine hydrochloride has been ordered at 4 μg/kg/min using a 400 mg/250 mL D5W solution. The client weighs 92.4 kg.

    What are the dosage per minute and mL/hr flow rate?

34. Dobutamine (Dobutrex) 5 μg/kg/min has been ordered using a 500 mg/250 mL D5W solution. The client weighs 99.4 kg.

    What is the mL/hr flow rate?

CASE STUDY APPLICATIONS

35. Paramedics arrive at the scene of an automobile crash and discover a 35-year-old victim who is wandering around the scene confused. The client has several superficial wounds that are bleeding, although the amount of blood does not appear to be great. Initial vital signs show slightly elevated blood pressure and weak pulse. The paramedics treat the wounds, administer oxygen, and keep the client warm and lying on a stretcher while they treat other injured people at the scene. Twenty minutes later, the client is unresponsive with a blood pressure of 70/40 and no identifiable pulse. ECG reveals a ventricular dysrhythmia that appears to be quickly worsening. The paramedics immediately administer the following drugs: dextran 70 (Macrodex), norepinephrine (Levophed), dobutamine (Dobutrex), lidocaine (Xylocaine).

    a.   What assessment data support a diagnosis of hypovolemic shock?

    b.   What nursing diagnosis would be most appropriate at the scene of this accident?

    c.   What is the rationale for each drug, and how will you evaluate effectiveness?

36. At the same auto crash described in the previous question, paramedics find an elderly client who has a closed head injury. The client is unconscious and has no bleeding evident. Vital signs show slow respirations, very low pulse rate, and a blood pressure of 94/52. Pupils are unresponsive to light.

    a.   What type of shock is this client most likely experiencing? List all assessment data that lead you to this conclusion.

    b.   What drugs would you expect to implement in order to reverse the symptoms of shock?

    c.   What data would lead you to evaluate this case as being a successfully treated case of neurogenic shock?

CHAPTER 28

DRUGS FOR HEMATOPOIETIC DISORDERS

FILL IN THE BLANK

From the textbook, find the correct word(s) to complete the statement(s).

1. Red blood cell formation, also known as _____, is regulated by the hormone _____.

2. Human erythropoietin is marketed as the drug _____.

3. Free _____ is toxic. Therefore, the body binds the mineral to protein complexes.

4. Classification of anemia is generally based on the _____ and _____ of the erythrocyte.

5. _____ and _____ maintain iron stores inside cells.

6. After erythrocytes die, most of the iron in their hemoglobin is _____ for later use.

MATCHING

For questions 7 through 14, match the indication in column I with the drug in column II.

Column I

7. _____ Pernicious anemia

8. _____ Anemic HIV-infected client

9. _____ AIDS-related immunosuppression

10. _____ Anemia caused by chemotherapy

11. _____ Neutropenia caused by chemotherapy

12. _____ Chronic renal failure

13. _____ Megaloblastic anemia

14. _____ Anemia from peptic ulcer disease

Column II

a. Epoetin alfa

b. Filgrastim

c. Cyanocobalamin

d. Ferrous sulfate

MULTIPLE CHOICE

15. Nursing interventions for clients receiving hematopoietic growth factor therapy include which of the following?
    a.   Assess for a history of uncontrolled hypertension
    b.   Assess for food or drug allergies
    c.   Monitor client for early signs of CVA or MI
    d.   All of the above

16. Actions of colony-stimulating factors that improve the function of cells include all of the following *except*
    a.   Increased migration of leukocytes to antigens
    b.   Increased antibody toxicity
    c.   Rapid platelet production
    d.   Increased phagocytosis

17. Clients who are neutropenic secondary to chemotherapy treatments can be expected to receive which of the following?
    a.   Erythropoietin
    b.   Filgrastim
    c.   Oprelvekin
    d.   Sargramostim

18. Sargramostim (Leukine) is used to treat which of the following?
    a.   Non-Hodgkin's lymphoma and acute lymphoblastic leukemia
    b.   AIDS-related immunosuppression
    c.   Neither a nor b
    d.   Both a and b

19. Client teaching for filgrastim (Neupogen) includes all of the following *except*
    a.   Take medication with a full glass of water to decrease the risk of kidney damage.
    b.   Wash hands frequently and avoid people with infections.
    c.   Report chest pain, palpitations, respiratory problems, fever, chills, and malaise to the doctor immediately.
    d.   Keep all laboratory and doctor appointments.

20. What is the only suitable route when administering oprelvekin (Neumega)?
    a.   PO
    b.   IV
    c.   SC
    d.   IM

21. Which of the following statements about vitamin B_{12} is *false*?
    a. It can be synthesized by certain plants.

    b. It can be synthesized by bacteria.

    c. Very small amounts of B_{12} are required daily.

    d. The most common cause of B_{12} deficiency is lack of intrinsic factor.

22. Which of the following statements about pernicious anemia is *false*?
    a. It affects more than one body system.

    b. The stem cells produce abnormally large leukocytes that do not fully mature.

    c. Permanent nervous system damage may result if the disease remains untreated.

    d. Intrinsic factor is required to prevent the disease.

23. Which of the following is *not* a common cause of iron deficiency?
    a. Blood loss

    b. Pregnancy

    c. Intensive athletic training

    d. Kidney disease

24. Which of these statements regarding iron preparations is *false*?
    a. Prior to administering an IV dose, the client must receive a test dose.

    b. Iron should be taken with food to increase absorption.

    c. Iron may cause nausea, vomiting, and constipation.

    d. Iron may turn stools dark green or black.

25. Which of the following drugs must be given using the Z-track method?
    a. Ferrous sulfate

    b. Cyanocobalamin

    c. Filgrastim

    d. Epoetin alfa

26. Which of the following statements regarding folic acid is *false*?
    a. It does not require intrinsic factor for intestinal absorption.

    b. The most common cause of deficiency is insufficient dietary intake.

    c. Deficiency is commonly seen in chronic alcoholics.

    d. It is unsafe to take this preparation during pregnancy.

MAKING CONNECTIONS

27. An anticholinergic drug is one that blocks the effects of which of the following?
    a. Epinephrine
    b. Norepinephrine
    c. Acetylcholine
    d. Serotonin

28. Which major depolarizing neuromuscular blocker is used during surgery?
    a. Succinylcholine (Quelicin)
    b. Acetylcholine
    c. Prazosin (Minipress)
    d. Bethanechol (PMS-Bethanechol)

29. Which of the following would be used to treat mild to moderate pain due to inflammation?
    a. Oxycodone (OxyContin)
    b. Meperidine (Demerol)
    c. Ibuprofen (Advil)
    d. Acetaminophen (Tylenol)

30. What antagonist may be administered if serious hemorrhage occurs during heparin therapy?
    a. Protamine sulfate
    b. Vitamin K
    c. Adenosine diphosphate (ADP)
    d. Desmopressin (DDAVP)

31. Which of the following would be used to lower extremely high blood pressure within minutes?
    a. Hydralazine (Apo-Hydralazine)
    b. Nitroprusside (Nitropress)
    c. Doxazosin (Cardura)
    d. Prazosin (Minipress)

CALCULATIONS

32. A client who weighs 57 kg is to receive filgrastim (Neupogen) at the minimum dose of 5 µg/kg/day subcutaneously.

    How much filgrastim would the nurse give the client?

33. A pediatric client weighs 30 kg. The physician has ordered a subcutaneous daily dose of filgrastim 750 µg. The maximum recommended subcutaneous dose is 20 µg/kg/day.

    Is this dose within the recommended limits?

CASE STUDY APPLICATIONS

34. Mr. B is a 58-year-old client who is coming to the dialysis clinic three times a week. He is receiving Epogen injections after each treatment.

    a. What information can you give this client regarding the reason he needs to receive erythropoietin?

    b. What side effects of erythropoietin should be assessed during each clinic visit?

    c. One of your goals for this client is "to promote client independence regarding self-care." What client education is necessary for Mr. B?

35. Mr. J, age 63, has been admitted to your unit with a diagnosis of megaloblastic anemia. He complains of feeling tired and weak. He states, "I just can't make myself do anything." Mr. J has a history of gout and chronic gastritis. He wants to know why he is not on an iron preparation, since that is how a friend's anemia was treated. Further assessment reveals that Mr. J has virtually no knowledge of his disease or treatment. Your nursing care plan includes teaching interventions to address this knowledge deficit.

    a. You are evaluating Mr. J's understanding of why he feels tired and weak. What should he tell you?

    b. What information would you give Mr. J regarding self-care?

    c. How would you explain to Mr. J that an iron preparation is probably not the answer to his problem?

36. Mrs. Z has been receiving chemotherapy for her cancer. She is admitted to your unit with a diagnosis of neutropenia. She has been started on filgrastim injections and placed on neutropenic precautions.

    a. What assessments must you make prior to giving Mrs. Z her first injection of filgrastim?

    b. What information would you give this client regarding side effects of her medication?

    c. While evaluating Mrs. Z's understanding of your teaching, you ask her to tell you how she can decrease her risk of getting an infection. What should she be able to tell you?

CHAPTER 29
DRUGS FOR PULMONARY DISORDERS

FILL IN THE BLANK

From the textbook, find the correct word(s) to complete the statement(s).

1. The process of moving air in and out of the lungs is called _____.

2. A machine that vaporizes a liquid drug into a fine mist that can be inhaled is called a _____.

3. The two primary disorders classified as COPD are _____ and _____.

4. The most commonly used non-narcotic antitussive is _____.

5. _____ uses a propellant to deliver a measured dose of drug to the lung during each breath.

6. Even under optimal conditions, only 10% to 50% of drugs administered using aerosol therapy reach the _____ tree.

7. After using an inhaler, a client should wait for _____ before using a second one.

8. Clients using methylxanthines may report a _____ taste.

9. The common cold is a _____ infection of the _____.

MATCHING

For questions 10 through 18, match the drug in column I with the primary class in column II.

Column I

10. _____ Triamcinolone (Nasacort, Nasacort AQ)

11. _____ Codeine

12. _____ Dextromethorphan (PMS-Dextromethorphan)

13. _____ Hydrocodone bitartrate (Hycodan)

14. _____ Budesonide (GEN-Budesonide AQ)

15. _____ Beclomethasone (Beclovent, Apo-Beclomethasone)

16. _____ Acetylcysteine (Mucomyst, others)

17. _____ Guaifenesin (Robitussin)

18. _____ Fluticasone (Flovent)

Column II

a. Antitussive: non-opioid

b. Antitussive: opioid

c. Expectorant

d. Mucolytic

e. Glucocorticoid

MULTIPLE CHOICE

19. During inspiration, air leaving the trachea enters which area of the body next?

    a. Pharynx

    b. Bronchioles

    c. Alveoli

    d. Bronchi

20. Exchange of gases occurs in which pulmonary structure?

    a. Pharynx

    b. Bronchioles

    c. Alveoli

    d. Bronchi

21. When assessing a client, the nurse must know that which of the following is *not* characteristic of asthma?

    a. Inflammation

    b. Infection

    c. Bronchoconstriction

    d. Dyspnea

22. Which of the following drug classes would *least* likely be prescribed for asthma?

    a. Beta$_2$-agonists

    b. Methylxanthines

    c. Glucocorticoids

    d. Beta-blockers

23. The most effective antitussives are from which drug class?

    a. Opioids

    b. Glucocorticoids

    c. Beta$_2$-agonists

    d. NSAIDs

24. Which of the following is *not* true of glucocorticoids?

    a. They are hormones.

    b. They are effective at terminating episodes of asthma in progress.

    c. If taken for longer than 10 days, they can produce significant adverse effects.

    d. They are the preferred, evidence-based therapy for asthma.

25. Glucocorticoids improve asthma symptoms by which of the following mechanisms?

    a. Causing bronchodilation

    b. Suppressing inflammation

c. Blocking histamine release

d. Drying bronchial secretions

26. The nurse should know that candidiasis of the throat is a common complication during therapy with which class of medications?
    a. Inhaled glucocorticoids
    b. Mast cell stabilizers
    c. Beta$_2$-agonists
    d. Mucolytics

27. The nurse should teach clients that the primary use of mast cell inhibitors in the treatment of asthma is which of the following?
    a. To terminate acute asthma attacks
    b. To prevent asthma attacks
    c. To reduce secretions
    d. To reduce infections

28. Cromolyn (Apo-Cromolyn, others) acts by which of the following mechanisms?
    a. Causing bronchodilation
    b. Suppressing the cough reflex
    c. Blocking histamine release
    d. Drying bronchial secretions

29. What is the most common reason for school absenteeism?
    a. Asthma
    b. Ear infections
    c. Colds
    d. Heart disease

30. What is the primary action of an antitussive?
    a. Suppress the cough reflex
    b. Dry bronchial secretions
    c. Block histamine release
    d. Reduce the viscosity of bronchial secretions

31. What is the primary action of an expectorant?
    a. Suppress the cough reflex
    b. Dry bronchial secretions
    c. Reduce inflammation
    d. Reduce the viscosity of bronchial secretions

MAKING CONNECTIONS

32. The nurse would administer which of the following for opioid overdose?
    a. Methadone
    b. Epinephrine
    c. Naloxone
    d. Dobutamine

33. Epoetin alfa is administered for which of the following reasons?
    a. Boost the immune system
    b. Increase the number of erythrocytes
    c. Reduce neurotoxicity of antineoplastic medications
    d. Promote passive immunity

34. Quinapril lowers blood pressure by which mechanism?
    a. Direct dilation of arterioles
    b. Decreasing sympathetic output from the CNS
    c. Blocking the conversion of angiotensin I to angiotensin II
    d. Blocking the flow of calcium into arterioles

35. Drugs such as epinephrine that increase the force of myocardial contraction are said to have what kind of effect?
    a. Positive inotropic
    b. Positive chronotropic
    c. Negative inotropic
    d. Negative chronotropic

36. Which of the following drugs has analgesic, anti-inflammatory, and antipyretic activity?
    a. Morphine sulfate
    b. ASA
    c. Acetaminophen
    d. Vicodin (hydrocodone with acetaminophen)

CALCULATIONS

37. A client has aminophylline ordered at 0.25 mg/kg/hr. The client weighs 50 kg.
    How many milligrams should be administered over a 6-hour period?

38. A client has albuterol 4 mg ordered tid. A concentrate of 2 mg in 5 mL is available.
    How many millilitres would be given per each dose?

CASE STUDY APPLICATIONS

39. Mr. H has been admitted to a respiratory unit after being treated in the ER for an exacerbation of asthma. The client states that he has been on a beclomethasone inhaler and an oral theophylline preparation for about 2 months. His last exacerbation of asthma was about 2 months ago, and he claims that he adheres to his medication regimen. About a week ago, Mr. H started having a persistent cough, productive of thick green sputum. He has been short of breath and has been wheezing in the ER. The physician prescribes lorazepam and metaproterenol while Mr. H is in the ER. The nurse has chosen a nursing diagnosis of "ineffective airway clearance due to infective process causing increased mucus production."

    a. Which assessment would indicate a possible infection and ineffective airway clearance?

    b. Which nursing interventions would need to be completed for the diagnosis of ineffective airway clearance?

    c. Give the therapeutic rationale for the two drugs taken by Mr. H prior to the ER visit.

    d. Give the therapeutic rationale for the two drugs prescribed to Mr. H during his ER visit.

40. Ms. D comes to a clinic with history of a cold. She has been self-medicating with acetaminophen (Tylenol), diphenhydramine (Benadryl), and pseudoephedrine (Sudafed). The client now presents with an earache and a non-productive cough and wheezing. The physician provides the client with a prescription for Robitussin AC and a salbutamol inhaler. He tells Ms. D to continue to take pseudoephedrine and acetaminophen. He also prescribes an antibiotic for her ear infection. The client asks you why she can't take diphenhydramine and why the doctor's choice of medications would be better than hers.

    a. What nursing diagnosis would you choose for the client?

    b. Which interventions would you need to complete for the client?

    c. What will you teach the client about the medications she is taking?

CHAPTER 30

DRUGS FOR IMMUNE SYSTEM MODULATION

FILL IN THE BLANK

From the textbook, find the correct word(s) to complete the statement(s).

1. B cells initiate _____ immunity and secrete _____ that neutralize or mark the antigen for destruction by other cells in the immune system.

2. When the client's immune system is stimulated to produce antibodies due to exposure to a specific antigen, it is referred to as _____ immunity.

3. The administration of gamma globulin after exposure to hepatitis is referred to as _____ immunity.

4. Activated T cells recognize specific antigens and produce hormone-like proteins called _____ that regulate the intensity and duration of the immune response.

5. Immunostimulants, referred to as _____, have been approved to boost certain functions of the immune system.

6. Immunosuppressants are effective at inhibiting a client's immune system but must be monitored carefully as loss of immune function can lead to _____.

7. Four drug classes used to dampen the immune response are _____, _____, _____, and _____.

MATCHING

For questions 8 through 13, match the drug in column I with the primary class in column II.

Column I

8. _____ Interferon alfa-2 (Intron A)

9. _____ Cyclosporine (Neoral, Sandimmune)

10. _____ DTaP-IVP

11. _____ Infliximab (Remicade)

12. _____ Azathioprine (Imuran)

13. _____ Cytomegalovirus immune globulin (CytoGam)

Column II

a. Calcineurin inhibitor

b. Immune globulin preparation

c. Immunostimulant

d. Vaccine

e. Antibody

f. Antimetabolite / cytotoxic agent

MULTIPLE CHOICE

14. Foreign agents that elicit a specific immune response are referred to as which of the following?
    a. Immunoglobulins
    b. Cytokines
    c. Antigens
    d. Antibodies

15. The primary function of plasma cells is to secrete which of the following?
    a. Complement
    b. Histamine
    c. Antibodies
    d. Cytokines

16. Memory B cells are programmed to remember the initial antigen interaction. If the body is exposed to the same antigen in the future, high levels of antibodies are manufactured in what time frame?
    a. 2 to 3 hours
    b. 2 to 3 days
    c. 2 to 3 weeks
    d. 2 to 3 months

17. Which drugs must be administered to avoid the body's rejection of an organ transplant?
    a. COX-2 inhibitors
    b. H_2-receptor antagonists
    c. Immunosuppressants
    d. Systemic glucocorticoids

18. Which drug produces its therapeutic effects by inhibiting T cells?
    a. Cyclosporine (Sandimmune)
    b. Prednisone
    c. ASA
    d. Celecoxib (Celebrex)

19. The nurse is administering the client 18 mg/kg of cyclosporine. The nurse should monitor the client for primary adverse effects relating to which system/organ?
    a. Immune system
    b. Lung
    c. GI tract
    d. Kidney

20. Which is *not* currently a type of vaccine suspension?
    a. Live microbes
    b. Killed microbes

c. Microbes that are alive but attenuated

d. Bacterial toxins

21. For effective client education, the nurse must know that the purpose of a vaccine is which of the following?

a. To treat active infections

b. To prevent inflammation, should an infection occur

c. To prevent infections from occurring

d. To suppress the immune system so that hypersensitivity to antigens does not occur

22. The nurse needs to understand that a toxoid is classified as which of the following?

a. Vaccine

b. Immunosuppressant

c. Anti-inflammatory agent

d. Antigen

23. Which biological response modifier would be prescribed for the treatment of Kaposi's sarcoma?

a. Interleukin-2

b. Interleukin-11

c. Interferon alfa

d. Interferon beta

24. Which biological response modifier would be prescribed for the treatment of metastatic renal carcinoma?

a. Interleukin-2

b. Interleukin-11

c. Interferon alfa

d. Interferon beta

25. Which biological response modifier is reserved for the treatment of severe multiple sclerosis?

a. Interleukin-2

b. Interleukin-11

c. Interferon alfa

d. Interferon beta

MAKING CONNECTIONS

26. Which drug administration method has the highest potential for severe adverse effects?
    a. PO
    b. IM
    c. IV
    d. SC

27. Which GABA channel is opened by benzodiazepines such as diazepam?
    a. Na^+
    b. K^+
    c. Cl^-
    d. Ca^{2+}

28. For which disorder are neuroleptic drugs used for treatment?
    a. Clinical depression
    b. Bipolar disorder
    c. Psychosis
    d. ADHD

29. Which is a potential early adverse effect from nitrous oxide?
    a. Restlessness or anxiety
    b. Dysrhythmia
    c. Hypertension
    d. Mania

30. Which primary action of digoxin (Lanoxin) is effective in the treatment of heart failure?
    a. It dilates the coronary arteries.
    b. It increases cardiac conduction.
    c. It decreases blood pressure.
    d. It increases cardiac contractility/output.

CALCULATIONS

31. Mr. K is to receive cytomegalovirus immune globulin (CytoGam). The order reads as follows: to be given IV 150 mg/kg within 72 hours of transplantation, then 100 mg/kg 2, 4, 6, and 8 wk post transplant, then 50 mg/kg 12 and 16 wk post transplant. Mr. K weighs 81.6 kg.
    How many milligrams will he receive in 72 hours and in 2, 4, 6, 8, 12, and 16 weeks?

32. Ms. B is to receive tacrolimus (Prograf) 0.15 mg/kg/day q12h. She weighs 45.3 kg.
    How many milligrams will she receive in 12 hours and in 24 hours?

CASE STUDY APPLICATIONS

33. Mrs. L has been diagnosed with hairy cell leukemia, and it has been recommended that she begin receiving immunostimulant therapy. During the initial physical assessment, it was determined that she is 6 weeks pregnant. Because the physician has determined that interferon beta-1b is the appropriate drug for this condition, the nurse must carefully monitor the client for signs of complications related to the drug therapy and the status of the pregnancy.

    a. What possible adverse reaction can this drug have on pregnancy?

    b. What complications and/or adverse reactions do immunostimulants cause?

    c. What side effects should clients taking immunostimulants be instructed to report to their primary nurse?

34. Ms. H recently received a kidney transplant and is being released home. The nurse discharging her determines that extensive client education regarding the purpose, action, and possible adverse reactions to immunosuppressants is necessary for the future well-being of this client.

    a. What is the purpose of immunosuppressants, and for how long will it be necessary for Ms. H to receive this drug therapy?

    b. Explain the action of this class of drugs.

    c. What are the possible adverse reactions to this drug therapy?

35. AJ is 1 year old and has just received his measles, mumps, and rubella (MMR) vaccine. His mother is not sure why her son needs to have "all of these shots." The nurse explains to AJ's mother the rationale for her son receiving the vaccinations. The nurse also presents information on the possible adverse reactions and explains that severe reactions to vaccinations are rare.

    a. What rationale would you give the mother for the vaccinations?

    b. What adverse reactions would you teach the mother to monitor?

CHAPTER 31

DRUGS FOR INFLAMMATION, FEVER, AND ALLERGIES

FILL IN THE BLANK

From the textbook, find the correct word(s) to complete the statement(s).

1. The central purpose of inflammation is _____.

2. _____ cells detect foreign agents or injury and respond by releasing histamine.

3. Large amounts of hydrochloric acid are secreted in the stomach in response to the presence of _____.

4. First-line drugs for the treatment of mild to moderate inflammation are the _____.

5. _____ are natural hormones released by the adrenal cortex that have powerful effects on nearly every cell in the body.

6. During long-term therapy with glucocorticoids, the nurse must be alert for signs of a condition referred to as _____ syndrome.

7. ASA is avoided in pediatric clients younger than 18 years who present with fever because of the possibility of _____ syndrome.

MATCHING

For questions 8 through 14, match the primary class in column I with the drug in column II.

Column I

8. _____ Dexamethasone (Decadron, Apo-Dexamethasone)

9. _____ Etodolac (Apo-, Gen-Etodolac)

10. _____ Oxaprozin (Daypro, Apo-Oxaprozin)

11. _____ Prednisolone (PMS-Prednisolone, Prednisolone)

12. _____ Celecoxib (Celebrex)

13. _____ ASA (Aspirin)

14. _____ Triamcinolone (Kenalog, Triamcinolone Acetonide)

Column II

a. Ibuprofen-like agent

b. Selective COX-2 inhibitor

c. Glucocorticoid

d. None of the above

MULTIPLE CHOICE

15. The nurse would determine that the use of hydrocortisone would be contraindicated in a client experiencing which of the following?

    a.   An active infection associated with inflammation

    b.   Pain associated with inflammation

    c.   Nasal congestion

    d.   Hypertension

16. What is the primary action of histamine?

    a.   Vasodilator

    b.   Vasoconstrictor

    c.   Sympathomimetic

    d.   Cardiotonic agent

17. Rapid release of histamine on a massive scale throughout the body is responsible for which of the following?

    a.   Irreversible inhibition of cyclooxygenase

    b.   Allergic rhinitis

    c.   Immunosuppression

    d.   Anaphylaxis

18. Which drug does *not* exert an anti-inflammatory effect?

    a.   ASA

    b.   Ibuprofen

    c.   Acetaminophen

    d.   COX-2 inhibitors

19. The nurse administering high doses of ASA should look for adverse effects related to which body system?

    a.   GI

    b.   Cardiovascular

    c.   Endocrine

    d.   Nervous

20. What is the primary advantage of using the selective COX-2 inhibitors over ASA?

    a.   They are less expensive.

    b.   They are more efficacious.

    c.   They have fewer adverse effects on the digestive system.

    d.   They have greater anticoagulant ability.

21. If administered over a long period, which class of drugs has the potential to suppress the normal functions of the adrenal gland?

    a. NSAIDs

    b. H_2-receptor antagonists

    c. Immunosuppressants

    d. Glucocorticoids

22. Which drug class is most effective at relieving severe inflammation?

    a. NSAIDs

    b. Systemic glucocorticoids

    c. H_2-receptor antagonists

    d. COX-2 inhibitors

23. A client is discharged with a prescription for naproxen 500 mg bid. The nurse should teach that the most common side effect of this drug is which of the following?

    a. Rash

    b. Nausea/vomiting

    c. Headache

    d. Possible infections

24. Glucocorticoids have many indications. Which of the following is *not* an indication for drugs in this class?

    a. Neoplasia

    b. Arthritis

    c. Asthma

    d. Pain

MAKING CONNECTIONS

25. Which route would potentially result in the most severe adverse effects?

    a. PO

    b. IV

    c. IM

    d. SC

26. For which condition is phenytoin (Dilantin) most frequently used?

    a. Bipolar disorder

    b. Migraines

    c. Schizophrenia

    d. Seizures

27. Which organ is responsible for the first-pass effect?

    a. Liver

    b. Brain

    c. Kidneys

    d. Small intestine

28. Which of the following is an opioid?

    a. Hydralazine

    b. Hydrocortisone

    c. Hydrocodone

    d. Hydrochlorothiazide

29. Which of the following is the most common adverse effect of cholestyramine?

    a. Hypotension

    b. Drowsiness

    c. Bloating, nausea, or constipation

    d. Increased LDL levels

CALCULATIONS

30. A mother is to give her son Tylenol 30 gtts PO every 4 hours for elevated temperature.

    How many millilitres would she give her son in one dose?
    What would be the total gtts and millilitres given in 24 hours?

31. A physician has prescribed naproxen for stiff and painful joints. The order reads "Naprosyn 500 mg PO qid." The pharmacy sends 250 mg tablets.

    How many tablets would the client receive in one dose?
    How many milligrams will the client receive in a 24-hour period, and would the amount be within the recommended dosage for a 24-hour period?

CASE STUDY APPLICATIONS

32. Mr. E is an 18-year-old client who presents to the ER on a Sunday complaining of a severe toothache. During examination, the nurse practitioner notes an abscess surrounding a molar that is red, swollen, and inflamed. The client also presents with a temperature of 39°C. Based on the presenting symptoms, the nurse practitioner suspects a systemic bacterial infection and prescribes the following medications: ampicillin, A.C. & C tablets (acetylsalicylic acid plus codeine), and ketoprofen. The responsibility for client education related to drug therapy falls to you, the student nurse. What are your goals for this client in regard to education?

    a. Explain the therapeutic rationale for A.C. & C tablets and ketoprofen.

    b. Explain why the nurse practitioner did not prescribe a corticosteroid to reduce the inflammation.

    c. Explain the most common adverse reactions to A.C. & C tablets and ketoprofen.

33. BB is a 64-year-old woman who has been complaining of stiff and painful joints in both hands. The doctor has prescribed Celebrex. The client education for this condition should include potential adverse reactions to the class of medications and when to notify the physician in relationship to these adverse reactions. The client should also receive information on non-pharmacological methods to reduce symptoms.

    a.   Determine the drug classification.

    b.   Why are the medications in this drug class the drugs of choice for treatment of inflammation?

    c.   What conditions should the nurse assess the client for prior to the client receiving any drug from this classification?

34. Ms. C has brought her 6-month-old son into the ER with a temperature of 38.5°C. The physician orders Tylenol infant drops to reduce the temperature. Ms. C is a 17-year-old, first-time mother without a support system at home. She looks to the nurse for information on the proper method for administering the medication to her son.

    a.   Why did the physician order Tylenol and not Aspirin?

    b.   Why did the physician order infant drops?

    c.   What disorder can be acquired with Aspirin therapy in young children?

CHAPTER 32

DRUGS FOR BACTERIAL INFECTIONS

FILL IN THE BLANK

From the textbook, find the correct word(s) to complete the statement(s).

1. Technically, _____ refers to natural substances produced by microorganisms that can kill other microorganisms. Drugs responsible for killing infectious microorganisms are called _____.

2. Genetic errors referred to as _____ commonly occur in bacterial cells and result in drug resistance.

3. When anti-infectives are used against a wide variety of microorganisms, they are classified as _____.

4. _____ occurs secondary to anti-infective therapy.

5. An enzyme secreted by bacteria that limits the therapeutic usefulness of penicillins is _____.

6. _____ are a widely prescribed class of antibiotics, similar in structure and function to the penicillins.

7. _____ antibiotics are safer alternatives to penicillin because they can generally be administered over a shorter time.

8. Narrow-spectrum antibiotics classified as _____ are useful for the treatment of serious gram-negative infections, but they also have the potential for producing ear and kidney toxicity.

MATCHING

For questions 9 through 18, match the type of medication in column I with the pharmacological category in column II.

Column I

9. _____ Amoxicillin (Apo-Amoxi, Novomoxin)

10. _____ Ciprofloxacin (Cipro)

11. _____ Cefepime (Maxipime)

12. _____ Gentamicin (Garamycin)

13. _____ Neomycin (Cicatrin)

14. _____ Erythromycin (Apo-Erythro, Erybid, Erythromid)

15. _____ Doxycycline (Apo-Doxycycline, Vibramycin)

16. _____ Cephalexin (Apo-, Nu-Cephalex, Keflex)

17. _____ Rifampin (Rifadin, Rofact)

18. _____ Vancomycin (PMS-Vancomycin, Vancocin)

Column II

a. Penicillin

b. Cephalosporin

c. Tetracycline

d. Macrolide

e. Aminoglycoside

f. Fluoroquinolone or miscellaneous

g. Antitubercular agent

For questions 19 through 25, match the organism in column I with the condition(s) in column II.

Column I

19. _____ *Vibrio*

20. _____ *Streptococcus*

21. _____ *Rickettsia*

22. _____ *Klebsiella*

23. _____ *Borrelia*

24. _____ *Escherichia*

25. _____ *Chlamydia*

Column II

a. Venereal disease, endometriosis

b. Cholera

c. Traveller's diarrhea, UTI, bacteremia, endometriosis

d. Pharyngitis, pneumonia, skin infections, septicemia, endocarditis

e. Lyme disease

f. Rocky Mountain spotted fever

g. Pneumonia, UTI

MULTIPLE CHOICE

26. What is the value of using an antibiotic that is classified as a broad-spectrum antibiotic?
    a. It produces a large number of side effects.
    b. It is effective against a small number of organisms.
    c. It is effective against a large number of organisms.
    d. It has a high potency.

27. What is the action of bactericidal drugs?
    a. They have a high potency.
    b. They have high efficacy.
    c. They kill the infectious agent.
    d. They slow the growth of the infectious agent.

28. What is the advantage of using amoxicillin (Apo-Amoxi, Novomoxin) over penicillin G?
    a. Less expensive
    b. Greater absorption
    c. Fewer side effects
    d. Penicillinase resistance

29. Which class of antibiotics is usually reserved for urinary tract infections and has serious adverse effects on hearing and kidney function?
    a. Macrolides
    b. Aminoglycosides
    c. Tetracyclines
    d. Sulfonamides

30. Which antibiotic is known as the "last chance" drug for treatment of resistant infections?
    a. Clarithromycin
    b. Dicloxacillin
    c. Vancomycin
    d. Trimethoprim-sulfamethoxazole

31. Which antibiotic would most likely be used for the dental client who is allergic to penicillin?
    a. Clindamycin
    b. Amoxicillin
    c. Sulfisoxazole
    d. Erythromycin

32. Which of the following terms describes a drug that is effective against a large number of different species of bacteria?
    a. Bactericidal
    b. Bacteriostatic
    c. Broad spectrum

d.   Narrow spectrum

33. Photosensitivity and teeth discoloration are potential adverse effects of which of the following?

a.   Aminoglycosides

b.   Metronidazole

c.   Cephalosporins

d.   Tetracyclines

34. Which of the following is a drug of choice for the treatment of *Mycobacterium tuberculosis*?

a.   Erythromycin

b.   Gentamicin

c.   Vancomycin

d.   Isoniazid

35. Which of the following is an antibiotic responsible for causing the red-man syndrome side effect?

a.   Cefotaxime

b.   Tetracycline HCl

c.   Erythromycin

d.   Vancomycin

36. How does drug therapy of tuberculosis differ from that of most other infections?

a.   Clients with tuberculosis have no symptoms.

b.   Mycobacteria have a cell wall that is resistant to penetration by anti-infective drugs.

c.   Clients usually require therapy for a shorter time.

d.   Antitubercular drugs are used extensively for treating the disease, not preventing it.

37. What is the purpose of culture and sensitivity testing?

a.   To prevent an infection, a practice called chemoprophylaxis

b.   To determine which antibiotic is most effective against the infecting microorganism

c.   To identify bacteria that have acquired resistance

d.   To promote the development of drug-resistant bacterial strains by killing the bacteria sensitive to a drug

38. Which of the following types of antibiotics are more likely to cause superinfections?

a.   Narrow-spectrum antibiotics

b.   Broad-spectrum antibiotics

c.   Original penicillin

d.   Bacteriostatic drugs

39. Which antibiotic class is most widely used because of its higher margin of safety and effectiveness?

a.   Penicillins

b.   Tetracyclines

c.   Macrolides

d.   Aminoglycosides

40. Which of the following factors contribute to acquired resistance?

a.   Errors during replication of bacterial DNA

b.   Overuse of antibiotics

c.   Not taking antibiotic therapy for the prescribed length of time

d.   All of the above

MAKING CONNECTIONS

41. Which local anesthetic drug might interfere with the antibacterial activity of some sulfonamide drugs?

a.   Benzocaine

b.   Tetracaine

c.   Bupivacaine

d.   Lidocaine

42. Which action might influence antibiotic absorption within the stomach?

a.   Taking an antacid along with the antibiotic

b.   Drinking a glass of water with the antibiotic

c.   Taking an antibiotic suspension without shaking up the medicine vial

d.   Taking the antibiotic just before going to bed

43. If convulsive seizures were to develop with antibiotic therapy, which symptoms would most likely *not* be observed?

a.   Jerking muscular movements

b.   Difficulty breathing and biting of the tongue

c.   Blank stare with psychotic symptoms

d.   Loss of bladder control

44. Following oral administration, chlorpromazine is rapidly inactivated by the liver. What is this inactivation called?

a.   Enterohepatic recirculation

b.   First-pass effect

c.   Gastric-hepatic barrier

d.   Enzyme induction

45. Which term is *not* associated with the drug levodopa?

a.   Anticholinergic

b.   Anti-Parkinson agent

c.   Dopamine

d.   Sympathomimetic

CALCULATIONS

46. A client is to receive amoxicillin 500 mg PO every 6 hours for 7 days. The pharmacy sends to the floor amoxicillin 1 g in scored tablets.
    How many tablets will the client receive each dose?
    How many tablets will the client receive in a 12-hour period?

47. A client is receiving Cipro for a urinary tract infection. The order reads as follows: Cipro 500 mg PO qid for 5 days. The pharmacy sends Cipro 250 mg.
    How many tablets will the client receive in a 24-hour period?

CASE STUDY APPLICATIONS

48. For several years, Ms. P has taken antibiotics on a frequent basis for kidney infections. She has been informed that she is likely to develop a drug-resistant infection. Determine possible reasons why she has reoccurring kidney infections and suggest interventions to reduce the reoccurrence of the problem.

    a.   What are the potential results of the widespread use of antibiotics?

    b.   What is the relationship between the long-term use of antibiotics and resistant strains of bacteria?

    c.   What is the potential problem that Ms. P may develop?

    d.   What will happen to the therapeutic effect of the antibiotic?

49. Mr. N has been diagnosed with bacterial pneumonia and has been treated with a broad-spectrum antibiotic until the bacteria can be isolated and the appropriate drug administered. The client asks the RN the rationale for starting him on one antibiotic when the drug therapy may be changed after lab results have isolated the bacteria.

    a.   Why are broad-spectrum antibiotics sometimes prescribed?

    b.   What tests must be done to identify the microbe?

    c.   What changes in treatment will be recommended after the microbe is identified?

50. Mr. K is an 88-year-old client with impaired renal function who has been diagnosed with a UTI. He has been receiving a sulfonamide. His primary healthcare provider has determined that this is not an appropriate course of treatment for Mr. K. Examine the factors that support this decision and the potential adverse effects that might be expected if the treatment continues.

    a.   What are the potential adverse effects of sulfonamides?

    b.   What is the nurse's role in sulfonamide therapy?

    c.   How does sulfonamide therapy affect the client's intake of fluids?

CHAPTER 33

DRUGS FOR FUNGAL, PROTOZOAN, AND HELMINTHIC INFECTIONS

FILL IN THE BLANK

From the textbook, find the correct word(s) to complete the statement(s).

1. _____ are single-celled or multicellular organisms that are more complex than bacteria.

2. _____ is the drug of choice for fungal infections of the skin, vagina, and mouth.

3. The _____ was established to provide 24-hour access to _____ for persons with severe malaria.

4. Fungal diseases are referred to as _____.

5. Superficial fungal infections are sometimes referred to as _____.

6. Systemic mycoses typically affect the _____, _____, and _____.

7. Some of the newer antifungal agents may be used for either _____ or _____ infections.

8. The largest class of antifungals, _____, inhibits _____ synthesis, causing the fungal plasma membrane to become porous, or leaky.

9. _____ was the drug of choice for many years in the treatment of systemic fungal infections.

10. The major advantage of the azoles is that they may be administered _____.

MATCHING

For questions 11 through 16, match the fungus in column I with whether it usually causes a systemic or topical infection in column II.

Column I

11. _____ Aspergillus fumigatus

12. _____ Epidermophyton floccosum

13. _____ Coccidioides immitis

14. _____ Histoplasma capsulatum

15. _____ Sporothrix schenckii

16. _____ Mucorales

Column II

a. Systemic infection

b. Topical infection

For questions 17 through 22, match the antifungal drug in column I with the indication in column II.

Column I

17. _____ Butoconazole (Gynazole)

18. _____ Econazole (Ecostatin)

19. _____ Flucytosine (Ancotil)

20. _____ Griseofulvin (Fulvicin)

21. _____ Nystatin (Nadostine, PMS-Nystatin)

22. _____ Undecylenic acid (Desenex, Fungicure)

Column II

a. Skin mycoses

b. Ringworm, skin, and nail infections

c. Vaginal mycoses

d. Severe systemic infections

e. Candidiasis

f. Athlete's foot, diaper rash

MULTIPLE CHOICE

23. Systemic mycoses are frequently quite severe and affect more than one body system. These mycoses often require which treatment?

    a. Topical agents only

    b. Oral medications only

    c. Parenteral medications only

    d. Oral and parenteral medications

24. Some systemic antifungal drugs are included in the treatment regimen of disorders not related to a fungal infection. Which disorder applies to this situation?

    a. Extensive burns

    b. Cancer

    c. Organ transplants

    d. Influenza

25. Which drug is not in widespread use for systemic fungal infections?

    a. Fluconazole (Apo-Fluconazole, Diflucan)

    b. Itraconazole (Sporanox)

    c. Ketoconazole (Apo-Ketoconazole, Nizoral)

    d. Amphotericin B (Abelcet, AmBisome, Fungizone, Amphotec)

26. Candidiasis affects the skin, vagina, and mouth. Which drug is used to treat this condition and is available in a wide variety of formulations, including cream, ointment, powder, tablets, and lozenges?

    a. Naftifine (Naftin)

    b. Ciclopirox olamine (Loprox)

    c. Nystatin (Nadostine, PMS-Nystatin)

    d. Atovaquone/proguanil (Malarone)

27. The nurse is administering an IV of amphotericin B for a severe fungal infection of the bowel. The nurse should monitor for which most common side effect of systemic amphotericin B therapy?

    a. Phlebitis

    b. Neurotoxicity

    c. Gastric reflux

    d. Dryness of the mouth

28. Superficial antifungal drugs are ineffective in which disorder?

    a. Nail infection

    b. Infections of the mucous membranes

    c. Suppressed immune system

    d. Infection of the scalp and hair

29. Which medication would more likely be used in the treatment of travellers' diarrhea, a condition caused by protozoans that thrive in Africa, South America, and Asia?

    a. Praziquantel (Biltricide)

    b. Mebendazole (Vermox)

    c. Primaquine

    d. Metronidazole (Apo-Metronidazole, Flagyl)

30. How many days does it take for merozoites to be released into the blood, resulting in fever and chills?

    a. 7 to 14 days

    b. 14 to 25 days

    c. 21 to 28 days

    d. 28 to 35 days

31. Which organ(s) does amebiasis affect, frequently causing severe ulcers and/or abscesses?

    a. Large intestine and liver

    b. Small intestine

    c. Heart

    d. Kidney and heart

32. What is the drug of choice for the treatment of most forms of amebiasis?

    a. Mebendazole (Vermox)

    b. Amphotericin B (Fungizone)

    c. Metronidazole (Apo-Metronidazole, Flagyl)

    d. Primaquine

33. The nurse is preparing to treat a client for a helminthic infection. What is the drug of choice for the treatment of most helminthic infections?

    a. Mebendazole (Vermox)

    b. Amphotericin B (Fungizone)

    c. Metronidazole (Apo-Metronidazole, Flagyl)

    d. Primaquine

34. Client education for the treatment of helminths should include which of the following?
    a. Instruct the client to stop the drug therapy as soon as he or she feels better.

    b. Instruct the client that all family members need to be treated at the same time to prevent re-
        infection.

    c. Instruct the client to wear tight underwear.

    d. Instruct the client not to wash bedding until the drug regimen is completed.

35. What preventive measures can be taken to avoid helminthic infections in children?
    a. Washing hands

    b. Avoiding biting the nails

    c. Keeping diapers and undergarments clean and dry

    d. All of the above

MAKING CONNECTIONS

36. The nurse should teach clients receiving thiazide diuretics for hypertension to do which of the
    following?
    a. Change positions slowly

    b. Limit consumption of potassium-rich foods

    c. Increase consumption of sodium-rich foods

    d. Discontinue taking the medication if adverse effects occur

37. The nurse administering ferrous sulfate should monitor for the most common side effects of the drug
    that affect which of the following?
    a. Heart

    b. Gastrointestinal tract

    c. Blood

    d. Liver

38. Calcium channel blockers are used for their effects on which of the following?
    a. Myocardium

    b. Skeletal muscle

    c. Autonomic nervous system

    d. Renal tubule

39. A client who is allergic to penicillin G has the potential for a cross allergy to which of the following?
    a. Ampicillin

    b. Tetracycline

    c. Ciprofloxacin

    d. Vancomycin

40. To which of the following drug classifications does ibuprofen belong?

    a. Salicylates

    b. Opioids

    c. Selective COX-2 inhibitors

    d. NSAIDs

CALCULATIONS

41. The physician has ordered amphotericin B 0.25 mg/kg daily for a client weighing 150 lbs.
    What is the client's weight in kilograms?
    How many milligrams of medication will the client receive a day?

42. Fluconazole (Diflucan) has been ordered to treat a client's yeast infection. The order reads 200 mg PO
    on day 1 to be followed by 100 mg PO daily for a total drug regimen of 2 weeks.
    What is the total number of milligrams the client will receive daily after day 1?

CASE STUDY APPLICATIONS

43. Mrs. B is 38 weeks pregnant and displays the symptoms of vaginal candidiasis. The apparent infection
    is not serious, but it is a concern to the nurse. Client education regarding treatment is a priority for this
    client in relation to the pregnancy.

    a. What approach should Mrs. B take to have this infection treated?

    b. What precautions should be considered during the treatment?

44. Mr. J returned last night from a week-long business trip to India. This was his first trip out of the
    country. He arrives at your clinic with the following symptoms: fatigue, headache, and thirst. He is
    concerned that he may be experiencing these symptoms due to malaria.

    a. Why can you be confident that these symptoms are not a result of malaria?

    b. What might be causing these symptoms?

    c. If Mr. J was to return to a malaria zone, what precautions should he take to avoid infection?

45. Mrs. G has returned from an extended vacation in Latin America and displays the symptoms of
    amebiasis. The RN must understand the progression of this disease to carefully monitor this client's
    condition. He must also be sure that the client receives education in relationship to her drug regimen.

    a. What drug regimen will the client receive for this condition?

    b. What are the most common adverse reactions to this drug regimen?

    c. Primarily, this is a disease of what organ of the body?

CHAPTER 34
DRUGS FOR VIRAL INFECTIONS

FILL IN THE BLANK

From the textbook, find the correct word(s) to complete the statement(s).

1. The basic structure of a virus includes the outer protein coat, or the _____, and the inner genetic material in the form of _____ or _____.

2. Viruses are considered _____; therefore, they require a host to replicate.

3. During the _____ stage, the client is asymptomatic and may not be aware of the HIV infection.

4. The classification of medications used to block components of the replication cycle of HIV is _____.

5. The standard aggressive treatment for HIV-AIDS, using as many as four drugs concurrently, is called _____.

6. Oseltamivir (Tamiflu) and zanamivir (Relenza) are examples of a newer classification of drugs called the _____ and are used to treat active influenza infection.

7. Saquinavir (Inverase) is the prototype drug for antiretrovirals known as _____.

8. Hepatitis B (HBV) is caused by a _____ virus and is transmitted primarily through exposure to _____ and _____.

9. _____ is the drug most often used for the treatment of herpes viruses.

10. Rebetron is currently used for the treatment of chronic _____ infection.

MATCHING

For questions 11 through 15, match the description in column I with the term in column II.

Column I

11. _____ Nucleoside reverse transcriptase inhibitors

12. _____ Non-nucleoside reverse transcriptase inhibitors

13. _____ Protein coat

14. _____ Mature infective particle

15. _____ Highly active antiretroviral therapy

Column II

a. HAART

b. Capsid

c. NRTI

d. NNRTI

e. Virion

MULTIPLE CHOICE

16. Which drug used to treat HIV-AIDS is a non-nucleoside reverse transcriptase inhibitor?
    a. Zidovudine (Retrovir, Novo-AZT)
    b. Nevirapine (Viramune)
    c. Lamivudine (3TC)
    d. Indinavir (Crixivan)

17. Acyclovir (Zovirax) is *not* an effective treatment for which virus?
    a. Herpes simplex virus types 1 and 2
    b. Cytomegalovirus
    c. Varicella-zoster virus
    d. Epstein-Barr virus

18. The nurse should teach adult clients that the best approach to influenza treatment is which of the following?
    a. Prevention through annual vaccinations
    b. Amantadine (Symmetrel)
    c. Oseltamivir (Tamiflu)
    d. Zanamivir (Relenza)

19. The nurse is treating a client who recently acquired an HIV infection. Which of the following is true regarding HIV pharmacotherapy?
    a. Clients with HIV are able to live symptom-free much longer.
    b. The FDA has approved more than 16 new antiviral drugs for the cure of HIV.
    c. Drugs have been developed that treat only slowly mutating and less-resistant HIV strains.
    d. Drugs have become available that treat the HIV-infected mother but without much success with the newborn.

20. What is the purpose of highly active antiretroviral therapy (HAART)?
    a. To eliminate the virus from the blood
    b. To isolate HIV to the lymph nodes
    c. To reduce the plasma level of HIV to its lowest possible value
    d. All of the above

21. Which class of antivirals has most recently been discovered?
    a. Non-nucleoside reverse transcriptase inhibitors (NNRTIs)
    b. Nucleoside reverse transcriptase inhibitors (NRTIs)
    c. Fusion inhibitors
    d. DNA synthesis inhibitors

22. The nurse treating a client who is taking zidovudine (Novo-AZT, Retrovir) should monitor for which major adverse effect?
    a.   Reduced number of red and white blood cells
    b.   Painful inflammation of blood vessels at the site of infusion
    c.   Nephrotoxicity
    d.   Both b and c

23. The nurse should instruct the client receiving NRTIs to report which adverse effects?
    a.   Rash, abdominal pain, nausea, vomiting, numbness, burning of the feet or hands
    b.   Fever, chills, blistering of the skin, reddening of the skin, muscle or joint pain
    c.   Headache, insomnia, fever, constipation, cough, fainting, visual changes
    d.   None of the above

24. The nurse should instruct the client receiving NNRTIs to report which adverse effects?
    a.   Rash, abdominal pain, nausea, vomiting, numbness, burning of the feet or hands
    b.   Fever, chills, blistering of the skin, reddening of the skin, muscle or joint pain
    c.   Headache, insomnia, fever, constipation, cough, fainting, visual changes
    d.   None of the above

25. The nurse should instruct the client receiving protease inhibitors to report which adverse effects?
    a.   Rash, abdominal pain, nausea, vomiting, numbness, burning of the feet or hands
    b.   Fever, chills, blistering of the skin, reddening of the skin, muscle or joint pain
    c.   Headache, insomnia, fever, constipation, cough, fainting, visual changes
    d.   None of the above

26. When a virus mutates, which molecules are altered?
    a.   RNA or DNA
    b.   Beta-lactam rings
    c.   Enzymes
    d.   Proteins

MAKING CONNECTIONS

27. Which drug or drug class induces hepatic microsomal enzymes, resulting in drug-drug interactions?
    a.   ASA
    b.   Phenobarbital
    c.   Phenothiazines
    d.   Opioids

28. A drug that increases the renal reabsorption of antiviral medication would have what affect?
    a.   Increase the half-life of the antiviral
    b.   Decrease the half-life of the antiviral

    c.   No effect on the half-life of the antiviral

    d.   Increase excretion as well

29. Drugs from which class can mask the signs and symptoms of a serious viral infection?

    a.   Beta-adrenergic blockers

    b.   Benzodiazepines

    c.   Glucocorticoids

    d.   Phenothiazines

30. Naproxen (Naprosyn) is classified as which of the following?

    a.   Salicylate

    b.   Selective COX-2 inhibitor

    c.   Opioid

    d.   NSAID

31. The nurse would administer which drug to stimulate the production of platelets?

    a.   Epoetin alfa

    b.   Filgrastim

    c.   Cyanocobalamin

    d.   Oprelvekin

CALCULATIONS

32. Mrs. V is to receive amantadine (Symmetrel) 100 mg PO bid for 5 days for an episode of influenza. The pharmacy has only 50 mg tablets on hand.
How many tablets would Mrs. V receive per dose?
How many tablets would she receive per day?

33. Mr. X was ordered acyclovir PO 400 mg bid to treat a herpes virus infection. He had a 1-week supply on hand for this dose of acyclovir, in 400 mg tablets. The physician subsequently increased the frequency of the order. It now reads 400 mg tid.
How many more tablets will Mr. X require for the new order, for 1 week?

CASE STUDY APPLICATIONS

34. Mr. R is HIV-positive and was told that combination drug therapy would be more effective than a single drug. The nurse should include in the client education the rationale behind this type of drug therapy, the class of the drugs, and their individual actions. The nurse must remember that client education must be explained in terms that the client can understand.

    a.   Why is combination drug therapy more effective against HIV?

    b.   What are the drugs classes used in the combination therapy?

    c.   What is the action of each drug?

35. Mrs. B is pregnant with her first child and is in her third trimester. Her delivery date is late fall. Her physician has recommended that she receive the influenza vaccination. Assess the rationale for this recommendation based on the information known at this time.

    a.   What is the rationale for her physician recommending the influenza vaccination?

    b.   How long is the vaccination effective?

    c.   Which antiviral drug has been used for many years to prevent and treat influenza?

36. Mr. C, a nurse, has been diagnosed with hepatitis B. His physician has informed him that this disease causes inflammation and necrosis of the liver. The RN in charge of client education for Mr. C has determined that he should be aware of symptoms displayed with his condition and also how it can be transmitted to others.

    a.   How is this disease transmitted?

    b.   What are the symptoms displayed with acute hepatitis B?

    c.   What are the symptoms displayed with chronic hepatitis B?

37. Ms. M has been diagnosed with genital herpes. She is also 3 months pregnant. The nurse responsible for this client's care should be aware of the potential adverse reactions of most medications in relationship to pregnancy.

    a.   Should the physician prescribe an antiviral medication for the client at this time?

    b.   What antiviral would mostly likely be recommended for genital herpes if the answer to question a is *yes*?

CHAPTER 35

DRUGS FOR NEOPLASIA

FILL IN THE BLANK

From the textbook, find the correct word(s) to complete the statement(s).

1. Treatment approaches found to increase the effectiveness of anticancer drugs include
    _____, _____, and _____.

2. Bone marrow suppression is a major adverse effect of a class of drugs called _____.

3. By blocking the synthesis of _____, methotrexate (Apo-Methotrexate) inhibits replication
    in rapidly dividing cancer cells.

4. Most antitumor antibiotics are administered _____ or through direct instillation into a
    body cavity using a catheter.

5. Vinca alkaloids, taxoids, and topoisomerase inhibitors are classified as _____.

6. A natural class of antineoplastic medications referred to as _____ and _____
    antagonists have fewer cytotoxic effects than seen with other antitumour medications.

7. _____ modifiers assist in limiting the severe immunosuppressive effects of other
    anticancer drugs by stimulating the body's immune system.

MATCHING

For questions 8 through 13, match the type of tumour in column I with the part of the body in column II.

Column I

8. _____ Adenoma

9. _____ Lipoma

10. _____ Leukemia

11. _____ Lymphoma

12. _____ Glioma

13. _____ Sarcoma

Column II

a. Lymphatic tissue

b. Central nervous system

c. Bone, muscle, and cartilage

d. Glandular tissue

e. Adipose tissue

f. Skin

g. Blood-forming cells in bone marrow

For questions 14 through 22, match the medication in column I with the pharmacological category in column II.

Column I

14. _____ Cyclophosphamide (Cytoxan)

15. _____ Fluorouracil (Fluoroplex)

16. _____ Vincristine sulfate (Oncovin)

17. _____ Methotrexate (Apo-Methotrexate)

18. _____ Bleomycin (Blenoxane)

19. _____ Etoposide (VePesid)

20. _____ Tamoxifen citrate (Apo-Tamox, Tamofen)

21. _____ Levamisole (Ergamisol)

22. _____ Streptozocin (Zanosar)

Column II

a. Alkylating agents

b. Antimetabolites

c. Antitumor antibiotics

d. Hormones and hormone antagonists

e. Plant-derived agents

f. Biological response modifiers and miscellaneous antineoplastics

MULTIPLE CHOICE

23. What is the mechanism of action of antimetabolites in the treatment of neoplasia?
    a. Changing the structure of DNA in cancer cells
    b. Disrupting critical cell pathways in cancer cells
    c. Preventing cell division
    d. Activating the body's immune system

24. The nurse should instruct the client to implement which changes in lifestyle to reduce the probability of developing cancer?
    a. Examining the skin for abnormal lesions or changes to moles
    b. Exercising regularly and keeping body weight within normal guidelines
    c. Examining the body monthly for abnormal lumps
    d. All of the above

25. When should women have an annual Pap test and pelvic examination?
    a. Upon turning 18 years old
    b. When they become sexually active
    c. At puberty
    d. Both a and b

26. Which approach has a goal of eliminating 100% of cancer cells and reducing toxicity?
    a. Using multiple drugs in lower doses from different antineoplastic classes
    b. Increasing the concentration of different antineoplastic drugs
    c. Increasing the dose of one type of antineoplastic drug
    d. Combining radiation therapy with chemotherapy

27. Which problem is *not* an expected adverse effect of chemotherapy?

    a. Alopecia

    b. Nausea

    c. Hypercholesterolemia

    d. Leukopenia

28. Which drug changes the shape of DNA and prevents it from functioning normally?

    a. Cyclophosphamide (Cytoxan)

    b. Methotrexate (Apo-Methotrexate)

    c. Doxorubicin (Adriamycin)

    d. Vincristine (Oncovin)

29. Which is the primary drug for AIDS-related Kaposi's sarcoma?

    a. Mechlorethamine (Mustargen)

    b. Vincristine (Oncovin)

    c. Doxorubicin (Adriamycin)

    d. Teniposide (Vumon)

30. Which chemotherapeutic agent is a natural product from the Pacific yew?

    a. Mechlorethamine (Mustargen)

    b. Paclitaxel (Taxol)

    c. Vinblastine sulfate (Velbe)

    d. Teniposide (Vumon)

31. The nurse administering vincristine (Oncovin) should monitor for which serious adverse effect?

    a. Flu-like symptoms

    b. Hepatotoxicity

    c. Neurotoxicity

    d. Immunosuppression

32. Which is the drug of choice for treating breast cancer?

    a. Vincristine sulfate (Oncovin)

    b. Streptozocin (Zanosar)

    c. Teniposide (Vumon)

    d. Tamoxifen citrate (Apo-Tamox, Tamofen)

33. Which anticancer drug has a similar chemical structure to the insecticide DDT?

    a. Interferon alfa-2 (Intron A)

    b. Mitotane (Lysodren)

    c. Paclitaxel (Taxol)

    d. Vincristine sulfate (Oncovin)

34. Which drug inhibits the enzyme tyrosine kinase?
    a. Rituximab (Rituxan)

    b. Vincristine sulfate (Oncovin)

    c. Imatinib (Gleevec)

    d. Asparaginase (Kidrolase)

35. Which drug would *not* be used in the treatment of prostate cancer?
    a. Vinorelbine tartrate (Navelbine)

    b. Megestrol (Megace)

    c. Bicalutamide (Casodex)

    d. Leuprolide (Eligard, Lupron)

36. Which drug most likely would be used for palliative treatment of malignant melanoma?
    a. Teniposide (Vumon)

    b. Idarubicin (Idamycin)

    c. Dactinomycin (Cosmegen)

    d. Hydroxyurea (Apo-Hydroxyurea, Hydrea)

37. Which drug class would most likely displace an antineoplastic drug from protein-binding sites in the plasma, increasing its effect?
    a. NSAIDs

    b. Sedative-hypnotics

    c. Antidepressants

    d. Calcium channel blockers

MAKING CONNECTIONS

38. Heart failure is sometimes observed in clients using antineoplastic drugs. Which symptoms would be observed in such a client?
    a. Hypokalemia

    b. Peripheral edema

    c. Dehydration

    d. Dysrhythmias

39. What are glycoprotein IIb/IIIa inhibitors used to treat?
    a. Blood coagulation disorders

    b. Depression

    c. Tuberculosis

    d. HIV-AIDS

40. Valproic acid is used in the pharmacotherapy of migraines, bipolar disorder, and which of the following?

    a. Schizophrenia

    b. Angina

    c. Dysrhythmias

    d. Seizures

41. Indomethacin is a medication that prevents prostaglandin synthesis. It is most commonly used in the treatment of which of the following?

    a. Fungal infections

    b. Pain and inflammation

    c. Hypotension

    d. Alzheimer's disease

42. What is the purpose of administering filgrastim to clients with a sarcoma?

    a. Boost platelet production

    b. Prevent anemia

    c. Suppress a hyperresponse of the immune system

    d. Boost neutrophil production

CALCULATIONS

43. A client is to receive tamoxifen 20 mg qd for the treatment of metastatic breast cancer. The medication is only available in 10 mg form.
    How many tablets would the client receive per dose?

44. A client has begun to experience periods of nausea and vomiting as an adverse reaction to tamoxifen therapy. The order reads Compazine 25 mg IM q6h PRN for nausea and/or vomiting. The pharmacy has only Compazine 50 mg/2 mL available.
    How many total millilitres should the client receive per day?

CASE STUDY APPLICATIONS

45. Mr. U is a 40-year-old factory worker with a grade 10 education. With his early cancer of the prostate, he has been told that a drug killing 99% of tumour cells would be considered a very effective drug, but the remaining cells could cause his tumour to return. Mr. U displays lack of understanding about his condition. As the nurse responsible for providing health education, assess the situation and determine what information you would include in the following areas.

    a. Explain the treatment to prevent recurrence of the tumour in relationship to the stage of the tumour when the treatment began.

    b. Explain why some classes of antineoplastics might be more effective than others in relationship to the cancer's stage.

    c. Explain the rationale for specific dosing schedules.

46. Ms. H has been receiving chemotherapy for 3 weeks and has experienced a number of side effects, including nausea, vomiting, infections, and anorexia. She is an independent 67-year-old who chooses to remain at home alone during her treatment. As the home healthcare nurse assigned to this case, examine possible interventions to put into place.

    a. What medications may be used to treat nausea and vomiting related to chemotherapy?

    b. What interventions may be used to lower the risk of infections?

    c. Describe the interventions for maintaining nutritional balance during chemotherapy.

47. Mrs. Y, a 32-year-old schoolteacher who recently began taking tamoxifen for metastatic breast cancer, and has experienced a "tumour flare." She is concerned with the outcome of this development in regard to her recovery. As the RN assigned to her, examine your client education goals and interventions.

    a. Explain this condition with respect to the medication.

    b. Explain the classification of this drug.

    c. Explain the type of tumours this medication is effective against.

    d. Explain the unique feature of this medication.

    e. Should this medication be given during pregnancy?

CHAPTER 36

DRUGS FOR PEPTIC ULCER DISEASE

FILL IN THE BLANK

From the textbook, find the correct word(s) to complete the statement(s).

1. The digestive system consists of two basic anatomical divisions: the _____ canal and the _____ organs.

2. The primary functions of the GI tract are to physically _____ ingested food and to provide the necessary _____ and surface area for chemical _____ and _____ of nutrients into the bloodstream.

3. The small intestine is lined with tiny projections called _____ and _____ that provide a huge surface area for the absorption of _____.

4. Substances are propelled along the GI tract by the process of _____, the rhythmic contraction of layers of _____ muscle.

5. The _____ prevents the stomach contents from moving backwards into the esophagus, a condition known as _____.

6. The _____ cells secrete pepsinogen and the _____ cells secrete hydrochloric acid and _____, which is essential for the absorption of vitamin B_{12}.

7. Gastric juice is the most _____ in the body and has a pH of _____.

8. An ulcer is an _____ of the _____ layer of the GI tract; the _____ is the most common site.

9. External risk factors associated with _____ (PUD) include drugs, particularly _____, _____, and _____.

10. The primary cause of PUD is infection by the gram-negative bacterium _____.

MATCHING

For questions 11 through 17, match the correct term in column I with the definition in column II.

Column I	Column II
11. _____ GERD	a. Ulcerations in the lower small intestine
12. _____ PUD	b. Hypersecretion of gastric acid
13. _____ Crohn's disease	c. Lesion in the stomach or small intestine
14. _____ Ulcerative colitis	d. Increased acid secretion in the stomach
15. _____ NSAIDs	e. Backward movement of stomach contents
16. _____ H_2-receptors	f. Non-steroidal anti-inflammatory drugs
17. _____ Zollinger-Ellison syndrome	g. Erosions in the large intestine

MULTIPLE CHOICE

18. In caring for a client with peptic ulcer disease, the healthcare provider must understand that digestive enzymes are secreted by all of the following *except*

    a. Salivary glands

    b. Stomach

    c. Pancreas

    d. Microvilli

19. The nurse is developing education materials for the client. Which of the following is *not* a risk factor associated with PUD?

    a. Family history

    b. Blood type AB

    c. Psychological stress

    d. *Helicobacter pylori*

20. During an assessment, the nurse should recognize which characteristic symptom as most indicative of a duodenal ulcer?

    a. Gnawing or burning in the upper abdomen

    b. Nighttime pain, nausea, and vomiting

    c. Bright red blood in the stool

    d. Bright red blood in the vomit

21. The client has a prior history of gastric ulcers. Which of the following would be increased in the presence of a recurrence?

    a. Hunger, even after meals

    b. Blood pressure

    c. Urinary frequency in the 30- to 50-year age group

    d. Pain, briefly relieved by food

22. Inflammatory bowel disease (IBD) includes which of the following?

    a. Both gastric and duodenal ulcers

    b. Zollinger-Ellison syndrome

    c. Crohn's disease and ulcerative colitis

    d. PUD and GERD

23. The client is overweight and complaining of an intense burning (heartburn) in the chest, which is indicative of which of the following conditions?

    a. PUD

    b. GERD

    c. IBD

    d. Crohn's disease

24. In developing a plan of care for the client with peptic ulcer disease, the nurse needs to include all of the following *except*
    a. Smoking cessation
    b. Abstinence from alcohol
    c. Avoidance of caffeine
    d. Severe dietary restrictions

25. Which class of drugs reduces acid secretion in the stomach by binding irreversibly to an enzyme in the parietal cells?
    a. H_2-receptor antagonists
    b. Serotonin receptor antagonists
    c. Proton pump inhibitors
    d. Antacids

26. Which class of peptic ulcer medications consists of alkaline combinations of aluminium hydroxide and magnesium hydroxide?
    a. Phenothiazines
    b. Serotonin receptor antagonists
    c. Proton pump inhibitors
    d. Antacids

27. Which of the following best describes the mechanism of action of sucralfate?
    a. Kills H. pylori
    b. Adds a gel-like protective mucus over the ulcer
    c. Reduces secretion of acid
    d. Increases the secretion of bicarbonate

MAKING CONNECTIONS

28. Why is tetracycline not used in children under 12 years of age?
    a. It causes penicillin-like reactions.
    b. It stains forming deciduous teeth.
    c. It is primarily used to treat acne.
    d. It is only used to treat Lyme disease.

29. Why is clarithromycin (Biaxin) an effective treatment for *H. pylori*?
    a. It is effective against gram-positive and gram-negative organisms.
    b. It is a macrolide that can be given to people with penicillin allergies.
    c. It is considered to be a broad-spectrum antibiotic.
    d. All of the above

30. Which of the following statements regarding metronidazole (Flagyl) is *false*?

    a.   It is considered an antibacterial agent.

    b.   It is effective in the treatment of STIs.

    c.   It is classified as an aminoglycoside.

    d.   It is used in the treatment of protozoan infections.

31. Trizivir is a combination drug that contains abacavir, lamivudine, and zidovudine. This drug is most likely used to treat which infection?

    a.   Bacterial

    b.   Fungal

    c.   Herpes

    d.   HIV-AIDS

32. Mr. D is receiving an HMG-CoA reductase inhibitor. He is most likely being treated for which of the following?

    a.   High lipid levels in the blood

    b.   Stroke

    c.   Schizophrenia

    d.   Hypertension

CALCULATIONS

33. A client is to receive the following medication: Ranitidine (Zantac) 50 mg IV in 100 mL to infuse in 30 minutes by microdrip.
How many gtt/hr is this?
How many mL/hr will the nurse set the infusion pump to deliver?

34. Your client has an order for aluminum hydroxide (Amphojel) qid PO. Each dose requires 30 mL of liquid.
What times would the nurse give this medication?
How much medication, in millilitres, is required for a 24-hour period?
How much medication, in millilitres, is required for a week?

CASE STUDY APPLICATIONS

35. Mr. G is an elderly client who is admitted with a recurrence of gastric ulcers. His wife tells you that he has been taking cimetidine (Tagamet) as an OTC preparation. She tells you that he no longer complains of a gnawing pain in his stomach but has become increasingly confused within the past 3 days. During your initial assessment you note that the client is oriented to person and time but not place.

    a.   Name at least two appropriate nursing diagnoses for this client.

    b.   Prioritize your diagnoses and give your rationales.

36. You continue to care for Mr. G, and you note that cimetidine has been discontinued by doctor's order. Your client is now on ranitidine (Zantac).

    a.   What would be your short-term goal for this client?

    b.   During implementation of your plan of care, what laboratory values would you assess for this client, and why?

37. You are preparing Mr. G for discharge. You note that he has been placed on omeprazole and antacids. You are preparing your client education for both Mr. G and his wife related to these medications.

    a.   What would be an appropriate nursing diagnosis for this couple?

    b.   What basic instruction is necessary in relation to OTC medications?

    c.   What does this client need to know about the timing of his medications?

CHAPTER 37

DRUGS FOR GASTROINTESTINAL DISORDERS

FILL IN THE BLANK

From the textbook, find the correct word(s) to complete the statement(s).

1. Psychological factors related to nausea occur during periods of extreme _____ or when confronted with unpleasant _____, _____, and _____.

2. The two major drug classes used to effectively treat nausea due to motion sickness are _____ and _____.

3. Vomiting may cause a change in the _____ of the blood, resulting in metabolic _____.

4. _____ are used for the treatment of obesity, although they produce only _____ effects.

5. Constipation is identified by a decrease in the _____ of _____.

6. The etiology of constipation may be related to insufficient _____, especially insoluble _____.

7. Severe constipation can lead to a fecal _____ and a complete _____ of the bowel.

8. Prophylactic pharmacotherapy with _____ is appropriate to preclude straining or bearing down during _____.

9. The role of the nurse in pharmacotherapy involves careful _____ of a client's condition and providing _____.

10. Laxatives are contraindicated in _____, _____, and _____ because of the risk of causing _____ perforation.

MATCHING

For questions 11 through 17, match the term in column I with the definition in column II.

Column I

11. _____ Laxative

12. _____ Cathartic

13. _____ Bulk-forming agent

14. _____ Stool softener

15. _____ Stimulant

16. _____ OTC

17. _____ Mineral oil

Column II

a. Causes water and fat to be absorbed into stools

b. Promotes defecation

c. Lubricates the stool and colon

d. Irritates the bowel, causing peristalsis

e. Absorbs water, increasing size of fecal mass

f. Medications available without a prescription

g. Implies a strong and complete bowel emptying

MULTIPLE CHOICE

18. Acting on which of the following client complaints would the nurse discontinue laxative therapy?

    a. Nausea with dry skin

    b. Mild abdominal discomfort

    c. Diarrhea and cramping

    d. A soft-formed stool

19. Which of the following describing stimulant laxatives is *false*?

    a. Peristalsis is increased by irritating the colon.

    b. Results are both rapid and effective.

    c. They are never used in combination with other types.

    d. They are frequently used as an aid to a bowel prep.

20. Clients receiving prochlorperazine (PMS-Prochlorperazine, Stemetil) for nausea must be monitored for which of the following?

    a. Extrapyramidal symptoms

    b. Cholinergic side effects

    c. Early Parkinson's disease

    d. Hyperemesis gravidarum

21. Client education should include which of the following?

    a. Goals of therapy

    b. Reason for treatment

    c. Possible side effects

    d. All of the above

22. A nursing assessment of a client on laxative therapy should include all of the following *except*
    a. Vital signs
    b. Abdominal assessment
    c. Level of consciousness
    d. Character of stool

23. Which of the following is a bulk-forming laxative?
    a. Psyllium mucilloid (Metamucil, Psyllium)
    b. Docusate (Colace, Soflax, others)
    c. Senna root
    d. *Cascara sagrada*

24. Dimenhydrinate is an antiemetic that belongs to which of the following drug classifications?
    a. Antihistamines
    b. Serotonin receptor blockers
    c. Glucocorticoids
    d. Phenothiazines

25. The nurse should recognize which of the following as a complication secondary to the administration of bulk-forming laxatives?
    a. Bowel perforation
    b. Severe hypotension
    c. Stimulation of defecation
    d. Obstruction of the esophagus

26. Which of the following categories of laxatives is known for its high sodium content?
    a. Bulk-forming laxatives
    b. Stimulant laxatives
    c. Osmotic laxatives
    d. Herbal laxative preparations

27. Which of the following drugs for weight loss was removed from the market for causing heart valve defects?
    a. Dextroamphetamine (Dexedrine)
    b. Fenfluramine and phentermine (Fen-Phen)
    c. Orlistat (Xenical)
    d. Dimenhydrinate (Dramamine)

28. When should drugs used to stimulate emesis be administered?
    a. Whenever poisoning is suspected
    b. When a bowel obstruction has been confirmed
    c. Only in emergency situations, under the direction of a healthcare provider
    d. None of the above

29. Scopolamine (Buscopan, Hyoscine, Transderm-V) is an effective antiemetic for motion sickness that is classified as which of the following?

   a.   Adrenergic agonist

   b.   Cholinergic agonist

   c.   Anticholinergic

   d.   Ganglionic blocker

MAKING CONNECTIONS

30. Theophylline is a bronchodilator chemically related to caffeine. What is its primary indication?

   a.   Shock

   b.   Asthma

   c.   Parkinson's disease

   d.   Migraines

31. Diphenhydramine (Benadryl) is an antihistamine. Which of the following is a common side effect?

   a.   Headache

   b.   Nasal stuffiness

   c.   Drowsiness

   d.   Salivation

32. Indapamide is a thiazide-like diuretic that is chemically related to sulfonamides. What are many sulfonamides used to treat?

   a.   Peptic ulcers

   b.   Viral infections

   c.   Bacterial infections

   d.   Anxiety

33. Naldecon Senior DX is a combination drug consisting of dextromethorphan 10 mg and guaifenesin 200 mg. Naldecon is most likely prescribed for which of the following?

   a.   Cold and flu symptoms

   b.   Mild to moderate pain

   c.   Asthma

   d.   Hypertension

34. Alkylating agents such as cyclophosphamide (Cytoxan) are primarily used to treat which of the following?

   a.   Immune disorders

   b.   Severe inflammation

   c.   Cancer

   d.   HIV-AIDS

CALCULATIONS

35. Your client is to receive prochlorperazine (PMS-Prochlorperazine, Stemetil) 10 mg, q4–6h, IM, PRN for relief of nausea and vomiting. The medication on hand is 25 mg per 2 mL ampule.
    How much of this medication will be used for each dose?
    What type of syringe should be used?
    What length and gauge of needle is appropriate for this medication?

36. To control loose stools, your client has been prescribed diphenoxylate with atropine (Lomotil). A dose of 2.5 mg PO qid has been ordered.
    How many milligrams will this client receive in 24 hours?

CASE STUDY APPLICATIONS

37. Mr. D is admitted to hospital complaining of an inability to move his bowels for the past 5 days. You observe that his abdomen is distended; he is somewhat anxious; his vital signs are slightly elevated in comparison to those you received in a report from the ER nurse. The doctor has ordered an osmotic laxative.

    a. Identify two high-priority nursing diagnoses for this client.

    b. What are the goals related to each of these diagnoses?

    c. List at least two nursing actions that will be implemented to assist in achieving these goals.

    d. What criteria would you use to determine the effectiveness of your plan of care based on client outcomes?

38. Mrs. W, age 82, complains of diarrhea for the past 3 days. She states that she has had five or more liquefied stools a day during this time. She has not noted any bleeding, however. Antidiarrheal therapy has begun.

    a. As the nurse assigned to this client, what will you include in your initial assessment?

    b. What objective data will be important for you to observe?

    c. What safety issues would need to be considered?

39. Ms. C, age 24, is admitted with severe nausea and vomiting. She tells you that she has experienced this discomfort every morning for a week. Her pregnancy test comes back positive. This condition is known as hyperemesis gravidarum. Intravenous fluids are ordered along with an antiemetic.

    a. What assessment will you make to ensure the safety of mother and fetus?

    b. What is the primary therapeutic goal for Ms. C?

    c. Prochlorperazine (Stemetil) is the prototype drug for antiemetics. Would it be appropriate for this client? If not, why?

    d. What outcome criteria will alert you to the fact that this client's goals have been accomplished?

40. You assist with the admission of Mrs. G, 158 kg, 173 cm. She is complaining of hunger, stating, "I have not eaten since yesterday." It is now noon and lunch trays are being served. The client tells you that she is not only "hungry" but has a "large appetite" and requests two cheeseburgers for lunch instead of the usual one that appears on her tray. You note on her admission assessment that she has been on the anorexiant orlistat (Xenical).

   a. What dietary restrictions should be part of this client's education?

   b. What supplemental medications may be needed because of the decreased absorption of other substances?

   c. What non-pharmacological support will supplement the care plan of this client in relation to her "hunger," "appetite," and "weight reduction program"?

CHAPTER 38

DRUGS FOR NUTRITIONAL DISORDERS

FILL IN THE BLANK

From the textbook, find the correct word(s) to complete the statement(s).

1. Vitamins are essential substances needed in very small _____ to maintain _____.

2. An important characteristic of vitamins is that, with the exception of vitamin _____, human cells cannot _____ them.

3. Without vitamin K, abnormal _____ is produced and _____ is affected.

4. Vitamins that dissolve in lipids are called _____ and include vitamins _____, _____, _____, and _____.

5. _____ vitamins cannot be absorbed in the small _____ but can be stored in large quantities in the _____ and adipose tissue.

6. _____ (DRI) represents the _____ amount of vitamin or other nutrient needed daily to prevent a _____ in a healthy adult.

7. _____, or toxic levels of vitamins, has been reported for vitamins _____, _____, _____, _____, _____, _____, and _____.

8. _____ is the most common cause of _____ deficiency.

9. Vitamin D_2, also known as _____, is obtained from fortified milk, margarine, and other dairy products.

10. _____ is considered a primary antioxidant, preventing the formation of _____ that damage cell _____ and other cellular structures.

MATCHING

For questions 11 through 17, match the vitamin in column I with the description in column II.

Column I		Column II	
11. _____	Vitamin K	a.	Problems with night vision
12. _____	Vitamins A, D, E, and K	b.	Skeletal abnormalities
13. _____	Vitamin A deficiency	c.	Synthesis of heme
14. _____	Vitamin D	d.	Fat-soluble vitamins
15. _____	Vitamin B complex	e.	Antidote for warfarin (Coumadin)
16. _____	Vitamin B_6	f.	Folic acid
17. _____	Vitamin B_9	g.	Twelve different vitamins

MULTIPLE CHOICE

18. Which of the following statements does *not* refer to vitamin B_{12} (cyanocobalamin)?

    a. Important in cell replication

    b. Lacks results in pernicious anemia

    c. Important in myelin synthesis

    d. Deficiency results in uremia

19. Client education related to vitamins must include which of the following?

    a. The specific reason for the prescribed vitamin therapy

    b. Monitoring of the specific brands being taken

    c. RDIs as stated on the label

    d. That only low-income groups suffer from deficiencies

20. Which of the following vitamins would the nurse recommend for tissue healing?

    a. Vitamin D (Calcijex, Rocaltrol)

    b. Vitamin E (Aquisol E, Pro E, others)

    c. Vitamin A (Arovit A)

    d. Vitamin C (Activa C, others)

21. Enteral nutrition includes all of the following routes *except* which one?

    a. Intravenous tube feeding

    b. Nasogastric tube feeding

    c. Gastrostomy tube feeding

    d. Oral feeding

22. A client is likely to receive total parenteral nutrition (TPN) for which of the following conditions?

    a. Major surgery

    b. Bowel obstruction

    c. Inadequate oral intake

    d. Difficulty swallowing

23. Macrominerals and microminerals require educating the client on which of the following?

    a. They should be taken at less than the RDI.

    b. They are organic substances necessary to maintain homeostasis.

    c. All minerals can reach toxic levels unless taken as prescribed.

    d. Minerals are necessary for lipid lowering to occur.

24. Client education for TPN must include which of the following?

    a. Clean technique when changing dressings and tubing

    b. Signs and symptoms of hyperglycemia

    c. Need to report increased feelings of hunger

    d. Stabilization of nutritional status

25. When the client is on loop diuretics, the nurse will need to assess which of the following?

    a.   Potassium level

    b.   Sodium level

    c.   Magnesium level

    d.   All of the above

26. Hypomagnesemia will produce which of the following symptoms?

    a.   Nausea, vomiting, and constipation

    b.   Weakness, anorexia, and bleeding abnormalities

    c.   Muscular twitches, cramps, and spasms

    d.   General weakness, hypertension, and respiratory depression

27. Why must clients receiving TPN be monitored for fluid volume excess/overload?

    a.   TPN is a hypertonic solution that can cause a fluid shift.

    b.   Endogenous insulin is insufficient for glucose metabolism.

    c.   Strict aseptic technique will prevent infections.

    d.   Weighing will assist with monitoring intake and output.

MAKING CONNECTIONS

28. The client complains of gnawing pain in the epigastric area that is temporarily relieved by food, but then recurs within 30 minutes after eating. With a history of PUD, which diagnosis should be suspected by the nurse?

    a.   Gastric ulcer

    b.   Duodenal ulcer

    c.   Crohn's disease

    d.   IBS

29. When should drugs used to stimulate emesis be used?

    a.   Only in emergency situations

    b.   Whenever poisoning is suspected

    c.   Whenever overdose is suspected

    d.   Only by a physician

30. What is ulceration in the distal portion of the small intestine called?

    a.   Cohn's disease

    b.   Ulcerative colitis

    c.   Irritable bowel syndrome

    d.   All of the above

31. Scopolamine (Transderm-V) is an effective antiemetic that is usually prescribed as which of the following?

    a. Liquid suspension

    b. Subcutaneous injection

    c. Dermal patch

    d. Intramuscular injection

32. Herbal remedies for diarrhea include which of the following preparations?

    a. Senna root

    b. Cascara leaves

    c. Acidophilus

    d. Sibutramine

CALCULATIONS

33. The client has pernicious anemia. The order reads as follows: Administer cyanocobalamin 200 μg/month IM. The vial reads 100 μg/mL in a 30 mL vial.
How much will the nurse give per monthly dose?

34. The client has hypomagnesemia. He is about to receive magnesium sulfate 250 mg in 250 mL over 4 hours.
How many millilitres per hour will he receive?

CASE STUDY APPLICATIONS

35. Mr. W, age 78, has developed aspiration pneumonia due to an impaired swallowing reflex. The physician has decided to place a gastrostomy tube for enteral feedings. He is to be placed on a specialized feeding.

    a. Because of his respiratory condition, the client will require a custom food supplement. Which would you

    recommend? Why?

    b. Laboratory tests will determine his ability to heal. What laboratory results will you need to monitor?

    c. Name the four types of enteral feedings that are available.

    d. What is your overall goal for this client?

    e. What nursing interventions will you employ to aid in achieving this goal?

    f. What evaluative criteria will you use to determine if the goal was met?

36. Mrs. G has had a stroke, so the nurse believes that TPN is in order. Your client goes to the OR for the insertion of a central line. During your post-op assessment you notice the solution infusing at the site of insertion.

    a. What type of solution will this client receive?

    b. Why is this form of feeding necessary?

  c. What is the short-term goal for this client?

  d. What is the long-term goal for this client?

  e. What nursing interventions are required in this client's care?

  f. How will you evaluate the effectiveness of the plan of care?

37. Mr. S is admitted with malabsorption syndrome secondary to chemotherapy. The doctor discusses with him the need for central line placement.

  a. Why is a central line necessary?

  b. Will this type of feeding be short term?

  c. What is your goal for this client?

  d. Can the client return home with this type of feeding?

CHAPTER 39

DRUGS FOR PITUITARY, THYROID, AND ADRENAL DISORDERS

FILL IN THE BLANK

From the textbook, find the correct word(s) to complete the statements(s).

1. _____ are chemical messengers released in response to a change in the body's internal environment.

2. When administering antidiuretic hormones, the nurse should carefully assess fluid and _____ balance.

3. Vasopressin injection (Pressyn AR) should never be administered by the _____ route.

4. Prior to administration of levothyroxine (Synthroid), the nurse should thoroughly assess the client's _____ system.

5. Graves' disease may cause tachycardia, weight loss, elevated body temperature, and _____.

6. Propylthiouracil (Propyl-Thyracil) may cause GI distress and should be administered _____ meals.

7. The nurse must be aware that glucocorticoids increase the client's susceptibility to _____.

MATCHING

For questions 8 through 12, match the disease in column I with the related concept in column II.

Column I	Column II
8. _____ Cushing's syndrome	a. Thyroid hormone (Synthroid)
9. _____ Adrenal cortex hyposecretion	b. Vasopressin (Pressyn AR)
10. _____ Graves' disease	c. Linked to glucocorticoid use
11. _____ Myxedema (adults) and cretinism (children)	d. Glucocorticoids
12. _____ Diabetes insipidus	e. Propylthiouracil (Propyl-Thyracil)

For questions 13 through 15, match the drug in column I with the class in column II.

Column I	Column II
13. _____ Prednisone (Apo-Prednisone)	a. Thyroid medication
14. _____ Propylthiouracil (Propyl-Thyracil)	b. Antithyroid medication
15. _____ Levothyroxine (Synthroid)	c. Glucocorticoid

MULTIPLE CHOICE

16. The nurse is monitoring a client's lab tests and notices a rise in parathyroid hormone (PTH). Which of the following lab values may also occur in this client?
    a. Increased blood glucose
    b. Decreased blood glucose
    c. Decreased serum calcium
    d. Increased serum calcium

17. The nurse understands that negative feedback ensures endocrine homeostasis by doing which of the following?
    a. Stimulating the release of a secondary hormone
    b. Stimulating the release of a primary hormone
    c. Inhibiting the action of a secondary hormone
    d. Inhibiting the action of a primary hormone

18. The nurse is caring for a client who is receiving hormone replacement therapy (HRT). Which of the following is *not* an example of HRT?
    a. Thyroid hormone after thyroidectomy
    b. Supplying insulin to a client whose pancreas is not functioning
    c. Testosterone for hypogonadism
    d. Adrenal cortex dysfunction

19. Which of the following hormones is *not* released from the anterior pituitary gland?
    a. Thyroid-stimulating hormone (TSH)
    b. Antidiuretic hormone
    c. Growth hormone
    d. Adrenocorticotropic hormone (ACTH)

20. A client receiving levothyroxine (Synthroid) may experience which of the following adverse effects?
    a. Loss of weight
    b. Lack of energy
    c. Reduced pulse rate
    d. Reduced body temperature

21. It is important that the nurse teach female clients that long-term use of levothyroxine (Synthroid) may be associated with which of the following symptoms?
    a. Osteoporosis
    b. Decreased white blood cell count
    c. Weight gain
    d. Decreased incidence of insomnia

22. The nurse would most likely administer antithyroid medications to clients with which of the following symptoms?

    a. Dysrhythmia

    b. Weight loss

    c. Reduced activity

    d. Anemia

23. Which of the following will ultimately result in release of glucocorticoids from the adrenal glands?

    a. Corticotropin-releasing factor (CRF)

    b. Adrenocorticotropic hormone (ACTH)

    c. Falling levels of cortisol

    d. All of the above

24. Which of the following drugs is often administered by alternate-day dosing and requires the nurse to provide specific client teaching?

    a. Thyroid hormone

    b. Antithyroid drug

    c. Corticosteroid

    d. Insulin

25. In caring for a client with Cushing's syndrome, the nurse understands that this disorder is associated with which of the following hormones?

    a. Mineralocorticoids

    b. Glucocorticoids

    c. Androgens

    d. ADH

26. The nurse should observe for which of the following adverse effects of hydrocortisone therapy?

    a. Asthma

    b. Rhinitis

    c. Nausea

    d. Mood and personality changes

27. Which of the following corticosteroids has mineralocorticoid activity?

    a. Hydrocortisone (Hydrocortisone)

    b. Methylprednisolone (Medrol)

    c. Prednisolone (Dioptimyd)

    d. Prednisone (Apo-Prednisone)

28. A deficiency of growth hormone will result in which of the following?

    a. Dwarfism

    b. Diabetes insipidus

    c.   Urinary retention

    d.   Mental impairment

29. Vasopressin (Pressyn AR) is prescribed for which of the following primary symptoms?

    a.   Altered metabolism

    b.   Polyuria

    c.   Inflammation

    d.   Altered blood glucose levels

MAKING CONNECTIONS

30. Which of the following will change during thyroid therapy if only the heart rate increases?

    a.   Dysrhythmia

    b.   Peripheral vascular resistance

    c.   Cardiac output

    d.   Stroke volume

31. Cholestyramine will decrease the absorption of levothyroxine if given at the same time. Clients take cholestyramine for what type of disorder?

    a.   Hypertension

    b.   High blood cholesterol levels

    c.   Peptic ulcers

    d.   Weight gain

32. Fluconazole and other azole drugs are indicated for which of the following?

    a.   Fungal infections

    b.   Malaria

    c.   Diarrhea

    d.   Constipation

33. Which vitamin is considered to be an antidote for overdoses of warfarin (Coumadin)?

    a.   A

    b. B_2

    c. B_{12}

    d.   K

34. A drug's trade name is assigned by which of the following?

    a.   Physician

    b.   Pharmacist

    c.   Drug manufacturer

    d.   FDA

CALCULATIONS

35. The physician ordered vasopressin 10 U SC bid for a client. The pharmacy has vasopressin 20 U/mL. How many millilitres will the nurse administer?

36. The physician ordered propylthiouracil 200 mg PO for a client. The pharmacy has propylthiouracil in 50 mg tablets.
    How many tablets will the nurse administer?

CASE STUDY APPLICATIONS

37. Ms. Z has diabetes. She is also a candidate for thyroid therapy resulting from a pre-existing hypothyroid disorder. Examples of the medications she might take include levothyroxine sodium (Synthroid) and liothyronine (Cytomel).

    a. In planning proper care, what complications of using these drugs simultaneously would the nurse consider?

    b. What nursing interventions would be appropriate?

38. Mr. D, age 35, receives a diagnosis of Graves' disease. He wants to know how his new medication propylthiouracil (Propyl-Thyracil) will affect his life.

    a. List the important client teaching related to propylthiouracil.

    b. Describe nursing interventions that will assist this client in adjusting to his medication regimen.

CHAPTER **40**

DRUGS FOR DIABETES MELLITUS

FILL IN THE BLANK

From the textbook, find the correct word(s) to complete the statements(s).

1. Juvenile-onset diabetes is called _____; maturity-onset diabetes is referred to as _____.

2. A class of drugs prescribed after diet and exercise have failed to bring blood glucose levels to within normal limits is the _____.

3. In type 2 diabetes mellitus, insulin receptors in the target tissues have become _____ to the hormone.

4. The treatment goal with insulin therapy is to maintain _____ levels within strict, normal limits.

MATCHING

For questions 5 through 7, match the drug in column I with the type of diabetes in column II.

Column I		Column II	
5.	_____ Regular insulin (Humulin-R)	a.	Type 1 diabetes mellitus
6.	_____ Glipizide (Glucotrol)	b.	Type 2 diabetes mellitus
7.	_____ Tolbutamide (Apo-Tolbutamide)		

For questions 8 through 12, match the drug in column I with the classification in column II.

Column I		Column II	
8.	_____ Glyburide (Apo-Glyburide)	a.	Alpha-glucosidase inhibitor
9.	_____ Nateglinide (Starlix)	b.	Biguanide
10.	_____ Metformin HCl (Glucophage)	c.	Meglitinide
11.	_____ Acarbose (Glucobay)	d.	Sulfonylurea
12.	_____ Rosiglitazone (Avandia)	e.	Thiazolidinedione

MULTIPLE CHOICE

13. Which of the following stimulates the pancreas to secrete insulin?
    a. Hyperglycemia
    b. Hypoglycemia
    c. Glucagon
    d. Keto acids

14. While taking a health history, the nurse should recognize that which of the following is *not* a short-term sign of type 1 DM?
    a. Polyuria
    b. Polyphagia
    c. Acidosis
    d. Polydipsia

15. When giving insulin, the nurse knows the most common route of administration is which of the following?
    a. Oral
    b. Intradermal
    c. Subcutaneous
    d. Intramuscular

16. When planning follow-up care, the nurse should know that which of the following is a longer-acting form of insulin?
    a. Humalog
    b. Humulin-N
    c. Humulin-L
    d. Humulin-U

17. Which of the following adverse effects occurs when too much insulin has been administered?
    a. Hypoglycemia
    b. Tachycardia
    c. Convulsions
    d. All of the above

18. When giving oral antihyperglycemics, the nurse expects which of the following actions to occur?
    a. The pancreas is stimulated to secrete more insulin.
    b. Insulin receptors in target tissues become more sensitive.
    c. The liver is inhibited from releasing glucose.
    d. Both a and b

19. Which of the following administration techniques applies to Lantus (insulin glargine)?
    a. Insulin injection sites do not have to be rotated.
    b. It must not be mixed in the syringe with any other insulin.

c.   It is given 4 to 6 hours before meals.

d.   It may be given IM.

20. During oral antihyperglycemic therapy, the nurse should assess for which symptoms related to abnormalities in liver function?

a.   Yellowed skin, pale stools, dark urine

b.   Pink skin, light-brown stools, yellow urine

c.   Pale skin, red-tinged stools, amber urine

d.   Red skin, dark stools, clear urine

21. If injection sites are not rotated regularly, the diabetic client may suffer from which of the following?

a.   Petechiae

b.   Lipodystrophy

c.   Hematoma

d.   Pustules

22. Which of the following nursing diagnoses is *not* appropriate for the client receiving insulin therapy?

a.   Risk for injury

b.   Risk for imbalanced nutrition

c.   Risk for role confusion

d.   Risk for infection

23. When considering glucose regulation in the body, which of the following components of homeostasis would be restored following insulin therapy?

a.   Sensor (senses glucose in the bloodstream)

b.   Control centre (determines the set point for glucose levels in the bloodstream)

c.   Effector (responds to the increased levels of glucose in the bloodstream)

d.   Receptor (produces a response at the site of glucose action)

MAKING CONNECTIONS

24. If a client is prescribed regular insulin (Humulin-R) and is also prescribed an antihypertensive drug, which of the following would likely mask symptoms of hypoglycemic reaction due to insulin therapy?

a.   Hydrochlorothiazide

b.   Timolol

c.   Nifedipine

d.   Enalapril

25. Which of the following antihypertensives would reverse the hypoglycemic effect of antidiabetic pharmacotherapy?

a.   Hydrochlorothiazide

b.   Timolol

c.   Nifedipine

d.   Enalapril

26. Why must the nurse instruct a client receiving glipizide (Glucotrol) to avoid crushing or chewing the tablets?

a.   The client may choke.

b.   The effectiveness of the medication would be hindered.

c.   It would cause blood glucose levels to rise too rapidly.

d.   Irritation of the oral mucosa may occur.

27. MAO inhibitors used for the treatment of _____ may potentiate hypoglycemic effects when used with _____.

a.   Mood disorders, insulin

b.   Depression, dextrothyroxine

c.   Cushing's syndrome, corticosteroids

d.   Attention deficit–hyperactivity disorder, epinephrine

CALCULATIONS

28. The physician ordered Humulin-L U100 35 U SC, regular Humulin-R U100 20 U. A U100 insulin syringe is available.
What is the total amount of insulin to be given?

29. The physician ordered glipizide 10 mg PO daily. The pharmacy has glipizide 5 mg.
How many tablets will the nurse administer?

CASE STUDY APPLICATIONS

30. Mr. D is 70 years old and has type 2 DM. You are performing an initial assessment.

a.   In planning Mr. D's nursing care, which kind of diabetic therapy would he likely require?

b.   What would the nurse teach Mr. D about the optimal blood glucose level for people with type 2 diabetes mellitus?

31. Mr. Y is a 35-year-old firefighter who smokes and is somewhat overweight. Over the past 5 years, he has begun to develop slightly elevated blood pressure as determined by annual exams. He feels as if he should lose weight and is concerned about his energy level. At his last clinic visit, lab results revealed a fasting blood glucose level of 9.0 mmol/L. His blood pressure was 150/90 mm Hg. Mr. Y was not taking medications for any reported disorder.

a.   What would be expected signs of hyperglycemia in this client?

b.   In planning Mr. Y's nursing treatment, what preliminary assessments would be needed?

c.   If this client were to require oral antihyperglycemic therapy, which important teaching areas should the nurse focus on?

CHAPTER 41

DRUGS FOR DISORDERS OF THE FEMALE REPRODUCTIVE SYSTEM

FILL IN THE BLANK

From the textbook, find the correct word(s) to complete the statements(s).

1. _____ is the hormone that regulates sperm or egg production; _____ in the female triggers the release of an egg, a process known as ovulation.

2. The permanent cessation of menses, caused by lack of estrogen secretion by the ovaries, is _____.

3. The absence of menstruation is called _____.

4. A class of drugs called _____ is often prescribed for dysfunctional uterine bleeding.

5. The anterior pituitary hormone _____ increases the synthesis of milk within the mammary glands; the posterior pituitary hormone _____ causes milk to be ejected.

MATCHING

For questions 6 through 9, match the drug in column I with the classification in column II.

Column I

6. _____ Norethindrone (Micronor, Nor-Q.D.)

7. _____ Magnesium sulfate

8. _____ Misoprostol (Cytotec)

9. _____ Estradiol valerate (Delestrogen, Duragen-10, Valergen)

Column II

a. Estrogen

b. Uterine stimulant

c. Tocolytic

d. Progestin

For questions 10 through 14, match the drug classification in column I with the indication in column II.

Column I

10. _____ Progestins

11. _____ Estrogens

12. _____ Oral contraceptives

13. _____ Oxytocics

14. _____ Tocolytics

Column II

a. Prevention of conception

b. Dysfunctional uterine bleeding

c. Replacement therapy in women and prostate cancer treatment in men

d. Premature labour

e. Induction of labour

MULTIPLE CHOICE

15. The nurse is to administer a triphasic type of oral contraceptive. Which of the following is classified as triphasic?
    a. Alesse
    b. Lo/Ovral
    c. Ortho-Novum 10/11
    d. Ortho-Novum 7/7/7

16. Which of the following potential consequences of estrogen loss related to postmenopausal conditions should be included in a teaching plan for the postmenopausal client?
    a. Insomnia
    b. Sexual disinterest
    c. Mood disturbances
    d. Osteoporosis

17. Which of the following drugs used to treat endometriosis is a GnRH agonist?
    a. Estropipate (Ogen)
    b. Ethinyl estradiol (Estinyl, Fcminone)
    c. Estradiol (Estraderm, Estrace)
    d. Leuprolide acetate (Lupron)

18. The nurse understands that which of the following uterine stimulants may also be used for short-term treatment of gastric ulcers?
    a. Oxytocin (Syntocinon)
    b. Misoprostol (Cytotec)
    c. Dinoprostone (Cervidil, Prepidil, Prostin E_2)
    d. Methylergonovine maleate (Methergine)

19. The following medications may be prescribed for the client with preeclampsia. The nurse understands that which of these may also be used as an anticonvulsant?
    a. Oxytocin (Syntocinon)
    b. Magnesium sulfate
    c. Ritodrine hydrochloride (Yutopar)
    d. All of the above

20. In developing a teaching plan for the client taking oral contraceptives, the nurse teaches the client that which of the following may decrease the effectiveness of her chosen method of contraception?
    a. Antibiotics
    b. Antineoplastics
    c. Calcium channel blockers
    d. Antihypertensives

21. Which endocrine gland(s) releases steroid hormones such as estrogen and androgens?

    a. Pituitary gland

    b. Pancreas

    c. Adrenal glands

    d. Hypothalamus

22. A nurse teaches a client that the oral contraceptive she is taking is effective because it produces a thick cervical mucus. Which of the following medications has this action?

    a. Progesterone micronized (Prometrium)

    b. Estradiol (Estraderm, Estrace)

    c. Estropipate (Ogen)

    d. Ethinyl estradiol (Estinyl, Feminone)

23. Which of the following drugs is used for termination of early pregnancy?

    a. Estropipate (Ogen)

    b. Ethinyl estradiol (Estinyl, Feminone)

    c. Mifepristone (Mifeprix)

    d. Ritodrine hydrochloride (Yutopar)

24. Which of the following would not be included in the teaching plan as a benefit of conjugated estrogen and progestin therapy?

    a. Lowered risk of colon cancer

    b. Reduction in LDL cholesterol

    c. Weight loss

    d. Increase in bone mass

25. The school nurse teaches a group of 9-year-old girls that the function of natural progesterone is which of the following?

    a. To build up the lining of the uterus

    b. To prevent ovulation

    c. To prepare the uterus for implantation of the embryo

    d. To begin the onset of menstrual bleeding

26. The nurse is screening a client for the appropriateness of oral contraceptive use. He understands that oral contraceptives are contraindicated in clients with which of the following disorders?

    a. Hypertension

    b. Hyperglycemia

    c. Potential for blood clots and stroke

    d. Depression

MAKING CONNECTIONS

27. In relation to women's healthcare, where would the barbiturate thiopental sodium (Pentothal) most likely be used?

    a. Coronary care unit

    b. Sleep disorder clinic

    c. Cancer clinic

    d. Operating room

28. What is the classification of interferon alpha-2a?

    a. Alkylating agent

    b. Biological response modifier

    c. Hormone

    d. Coagulation modifier

29. Which of the following drugs, if given in high doses, could induce hypothyroidism?

    a. Amiodarone

    b. Finasteride

    c. Repaglinide

    d. Rosiglitazone

30. A client with diabetes is also diagnosed with hypothyroidism. Which of the following reactions to treatment with levothyroxine (Synthroid) would be most expected?

    a. Immediate improvement of symptoms

    b. Initial worsening of symptoms

    c. No change in symptoms

    d. Decreased need for insulin

31. A client with diabetes asks about using stevia as a sugar substitute. Which of the following is *not* true about stevia?

    a. It is an herb found in Paraguay.

    b. It sweetens foods better than sugar.

    c. It is approved by the FDA.

    d. It does not appear to have a negative effect on blood glucose.

CALCULATIONS

32. The physician ordered gonadorelin acetate (Lutrepulse) 100 µg IV added to 100 cc D5W to be infused over 2 hours. The drop factor is 15 gtt/cc.
    How many gtt/min should be given to infuse the total amount in 2 hours?

33. The physician ordered Depo-Provera 100 mg IM. The pharmacy has 400 mg/mL.
    How many millilitres will the nurse administer?

CASE STUDY APPLICATIONS

34. Ms. M, at age 50, is concerned about the unpleasant effects accompanying menopause. Her last menstrual period was several months ago, and she is beginning to experience hot flashes, night sweats, nervousness, and insomnia. The nurse suggests hormone replacement therapy (HRT). Ms. M states she knows nothing about HRT.

    a. What nursing diagnosis is appropriate for Ms. M? State the expected outcome for this nursing diagnosis.

    b. State the client teaching necessary to assist Ms. M in achieving the expected outcome.

35. Mrs. E, a primigravida who is 30 weeks pregnant, is in labour. Following rupture of the membranes, she is receiving oxytocin IV.

    a. What assessment data are necessary for the nurse to gather to monitor for adverse effects?

    b. List nursing actions related to this medication.

CHAPTER 42

DRUGS FOR DISORDERS OF THE MALE REPRODUCTIVE SYSTEM

FILL IN THE BLANK

From the textbook, find the correct word(s) to complete the statements(s).

1. _____ are testosterone-like compounds with hormonal activity.

2. A side effect of testosterone therapy in female clients is the appearance of masculine characteristics, or _____.

3. The first oral medication approved for erectile dysfunction was _____.

4. _____ is an enlargement of the prostate gland that occurs mostly in men of advanced age.

5. _____ are sex hormones found in male and female clients.

6. _____ is teratogenic to the male fetus.

MATCHING

For questions 7 through 11, match the drug in column I with the classification in column II.

Column I

7. _____ Testosterone (Andro 100, Histerone, Testoderm)

8. _____ Prazosin (Minipress)

9. _____ Finasteride (Proscar)

10. _____ Danazol (Danocrine)

11. _____ Terazosin (Apo-Terazosin)

Column II

a. Androgen

b. Alpha-adrenergic blocker

c. Alpha-reductase inhibitor

MULTIPLE CHOICE

12. The client is concerned about erectile dysfunction. The nurse understands that this condition may be successfully treated with which of the following?

    a. Testosterone (Andro 100, others)

    b. Sildenafil (Viagra)

    c. Finasteride (Proscar)

    d. Doxazosin (Cardura)

13. When screening for risk factors for erectile dysfunction, the nurse should ask the client about which of the following diseases?

    a. Diabetes

    b. Hypertension

    c. Benign prostatic hyperplasia (BPH)

    d. Both a and b

14. The nurse must include which of the following adverse effects when providing teaching to a client receiving anabolic steroids?

    a. Liver damage

    b. Appearance of masculine characteristics

    c. Muscle weakness

    d. Cardiovascular disease

15. The nurse recognizes that the client is taking a natural therapy for BPH when the client states that he is taking which of the following?

    a. Saw palmetto

    b. Ginkgo biloba

    c. St. John's wort

    d. Black cohosh

16. Androgens may be abused by which of the following?

    a. Older adults to improve sexual function

    b. Athletes to improve athletic performance

    c. College students to increase mental acuity

    d. Middle-aged men to arrest hair loss

17. The nurse recognizes which of the following as a symptom of male hypogonadism?

    a. Abundant axillary hair

    b. Decrease in subcutaneous fat

    c. Reduced libido

    d. Hyperactivity

18. The wife of a client taking anabolic steroids reports to the nurse that her husband has become aggressive. What is the most appropriate response?

    a. "Try speaking to your husband in a low, calm voice."

    b. "Tell me about your behaviour prior to his aggressive acts."

    c. "Have you contacted the domestic abuse hotline?"

    d. "This is a common behavioural change related to anabolic steroid use."

19. A nurse gives instructions on how to apply testosterone transdermal patches. How frequently would the sites need to be rotated?

    a. Every 72 hours within an anatomical region, and to a different anatomical region every 3 days

    b. Every 2 hours within an anatomical region, and to a different anatomical region every 14 days

    c.   Every 24 hours within an anatomical region, and to a different anatomical region every 7 days

    d.   Every 4 hours within an anatomical region, and to a different anatomical region every 10 days

20. The nurse must routinely monitor which of the following lab values for a client receiving androgen therapy?

    a.   Serum cholesterol

    b.   Hematocrit

    c.   Prothrombin time

    d.   Alpha fetoprotein

21. The nurse understands which of the following drugs to be contraindicated when used concurrently with sildenafil (Viagra)?

    a.   Nitroglycerin

    b.   Sulfonamides

    c.   Sodium bicarbonate

    d.   Metoclopromide

22. Which of the following nurses should *not* be assigned to administer medication to the client receiving finasteride (Proscar)?

    a.   Mike, age 29, LPN with male pattern baldness

    b.   Lydia, age 35, registered nurse with a cold

    c.   Jack, age 40, recently licensed practical nurse

    d.   Susan, age 25, pregnant registered nurse

MAKING CONNECTIONS

23. Stress often has an effect on the release of hormones. Which of the following nervous system components would activate hormonal release at the level of the hypothalamus and adrenal glands?

    a.   Somatic nervous system

    b.   Sympathetic nervous system

    c.   Central nervous system

    d.   Sensory nervous system

24. Glucocorticoids would produce an effect at which of the following target receptor locations?

    a.   Plasma membrane of the target cell

    b.   Cytoplasm of the target cell

    c.   Nucleus of the target cell

    d.   Cellular component other than the nucleus

25. Cimetidine (Tagamet) is sometimes given to clients who are taking glucocorticoids in order to prevent which disorder?

    a.   Hypertension

    b.   Constipation

    c.   Thromboembolic disease

    d.   Peptic ulcer disease

26. The nurse understands that the therapeutic regimen of an adolescent with diabetes is compromised when he states which of the following?

    a.   "I'll eat ice cream at the party and take more insulin."

    b.   "Taking my blood sugar at the party will be uncomfortable."

    c.   "I'll bring my insulin and syringes to the party."

    d.   "I can eat party foods that contain protein."

27. In teaching an adult client with diabetes how to control his blood glucose, the nurse should encourage him to keep the fasting blood glucose at which level?

    a.   Below 6.0 mmol/L

    b.   Between 4.0 and 6.0 mmol/L

    c.   Above 6.0 mmol/L

    d.   Between 5.0 and 8.0 mmol/L

CALCULATIONS

28. The physician ordered danazol (Danocrine) 150 mg PO. The pharmacy has 100 mg tablets. How many tablets will the nurse administer?

29. The physician ordered terazosin (Apo-Terazosin) 4 mg PO. The pharmacy has 2 mg capsules. How many capsules will the nurse administer?

CASE STUDY APPLICATIONS

30. Mr. E, a 62-year-old client, is receiving finasteride (Proscar) because of an enlarged prostate. He asks the nurse how he will know if the medication is working and when he can stop taking it.

    a.   List the nursing interventions and client teaching appropriate for Mr. E.

    b.   State specifically how the nurse will evaluate medication effectiveness.

31. Mr. S, a 38-year-old married man, has been diagnosed with low testosterone levels. Mr. S has type 1 diabetes and prides himself on his knowledge of herb use related to health.

    a.   What assessment data are important for the nurse to obtain before Mr. S begins androgen therapy?

    b.   What nursing interventions and client education are appropriate for Mr. S related to his diabetes?

CHAPTER 43

DRUGS FOR RENAL DISORDERS AND DIURETIC THERAPY

FILL IN THE BLANK

From the textbook, find the correct word(s) to complete the statements(s).

1. Thiazide diuretics act on the _____ tubule of the nephron.

2. Sodium and potassium are exchanged in the _____ tubule, where Na^+ is _____ back into the body and K^+ is _____ into the tubule.

3. Identify the parts of the nephron shown in Figure 43.1.

    a. _____

    b. _____

    c. _____

    d. _____

    e. _____

    f. _____

    g. _____

    h. _____

    i. _____

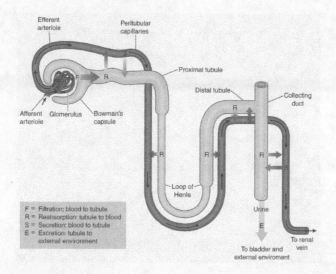

Figure 43.1

Source: Core Concepts in Pharmacology, Workbook by Holland/Adams, © 2003. Reprinted by permission of Pearson Education, Inc., Upper Saddle River, NJ.

MATCHING

For questions 4 through 13, match the drug in column I with the classification in column II.

Column I

4. _____ Bumetanide (Burinex)

5. _____ Quinethazone (Hydromox)

6. _____ Triamterene (Apo-Triazide)

7. _____ Metolazone (Zaroxolyn, Mykrox)

8. _____ Mannitol (Osmitrol)

9. _____ Spironolactone (Aldactone)

10. _____ Acetazolamide (Diamox)

11. _____ Furosemide (Lasix)

12. _____ Methazolamide (Neptazane)

13. _____ Hydrochlorothiazide (HCTZ, Urozide)

Column II

a. Loop diuretic

b. Thiazide or thiazide-like diuretic

c. Potassium-sparing diuretic

d. Carbonic anhydrase inhibitor diuretic

e. Osmotic diuretic

MULTIPLE CHOICE

14. The nurse administering diuretics understands that reabsorption and secretion are critical to pharmacokinetics. The composition of the filtrate that passes through Bowman's capsule is similar to which of the following?

    a. Plasma

    b. Plasma minus large proteins

    c. Urine

    d. Blood

15. Medications in the filtrate that pass across the walls of the nephron to re-enter the blood use what process?

    a. Reabsorption

    b. Urination

    c. Secretion

    d. Absorption

16. Drugs, such as penicillin G, that are too large to pass through Bowman's capsule enter the urine by crossing from the blood to the filtrate using what process?

    a. Excretion

    b. Reabsorption

    c. Metabolism

    d. Secretion

17. The nurse explains to the client that the main function of a diuretic is to increase which of the following?

    a. Reabsorption of water in the nephron

    b. Blood flow through Bowman's capsule

    c. Urine output

    d. Secretion of water in the nephron

18. The nurse understands that most diuretics act by blocking the reabsorption of which of the following in the nephron?

    a. Large proteins

    b. Potassium

    c. Electrolytes

    d. Sodium

19. Which of the following classes of diuretics can cause large amounts of fluid to be excreted by the kidney in a short time when administered IV?

    a. Loop

    b. Thiazide

    c. Osmotic

    d. Potassium-sparing

20. Medications that block reabsorption of sodium also affect the amount of water in the filtrate. What effect (if any) does this have on urine flow?

    a. No effect

    b. Increased flow

    c. Decreased flow

    d. Increased or decreased flow depending on lifestyle factors

21. The nurse is administering a thiazide diuretic. The nurse should monitor for which relatively common and serious side effect of diuretic therapy?

    a. Edema

    b. Hyperkalemia

    c. Dehydration

    d. Hypertension

22. The nurse is administering a loop diuretic. The nurse must monitor for which of the following adverse effects specific to the loop class of diuretics?

    a. Hepatotoxicity

    b. Ototoxicity

    c. Dehydration

    d. Acidosis

23. Which of the following is the most widely prescribed class of diuretics?
    a. Loop (high-ceiling) diuretics
    b. Potassium-sparing diuretics
    c. Carbonic anhydrase inhibitors
    d. Thiazides

24. The nurse should know that which of the following clients would most likely be administered a thiazide diuretic?
    a. 50-year-old male with mild to moderate hypertension
    b. 34-year-old female with pyelonephritis
    c. 80-year-old with dehydration
    d. 60-year-old with lung cancer

25. The nurse teaches the client that intake of potassium-rich foods should not be increased during therapy with which of the following medications?
    a. Furosemide (Lasix)
    b. Chlorothiazide (Diuril)
    c. Spironolactone (Aldactone)
    d. Acetazolamide (Diamox)

26. The nurse is administering 50 mg/day of spironolactone (Aldactone) to a client with edema. The nurse should know that spironolactone acts by inhibiting which of the following?
    a. Aldosterone
    b. Carbonic anhydrase
    c. Potassium reabsorption in the distal tubule
    d. Sodium reabsorption in the loop of Henle

27. Which diuretic is prescribed specifically to decrease intraocular fluid pressure in clients with open-angle glaucoma?
    a. Hydrochlorothiazide (HCTZ, Urozide)
    b. Triamterene (Apo-Triazide)
    c. Chlorthalidone (Apo-Chlorthalidone)
    d. Acetazolamide (Diamox)

MAKING CONNECTIONS

28. Phenothiazines can cause extrapyramidal symptoms. Which of the following medications would be given to reverse this syndrome?
    a. Benztropine
    b. Atropine sulfate
    c. Midazolam
    d. Naloxone

29. Scopolamine (Transderm-V) is an anticholinergic drug primarily used for which of the following?

    a. Dysrhythmias

    b. Hypertension

    c. Inflammation

    d. Motion sickness

30. An adrenergic crisis is evidenced by which of the following?

    a. Decreased heart rate

    b. Decreased respiratory rate

    c. Increased peristalsis

    d. Dilated pupils

31. An opioid antagonist will likely be administered if the respirations of a patient receiving an opioid drug fall below how many breaths per minute?

    a. 20

    b. 18

    c. 15

    d. 10

32. All of the following affect circadian rhythm and therefore the medication regimen *except* which one?

    a. Temperature

    b. Hour of sleep

    c. Blood pressure

    d. Age at menarche

CALCULATIONS

33. The physician ordered metolazone (Zaroxolyn, Mykrox) 1 mg PO. The pharmacy has 0.5 mg tablets. How many tablets will the nurse administer?

34. The physician ordered furosemide (Lasix) 20 mg PO to be given as needed. The patient takes no more than one 20 mg pill every 3 days.
    About how many pills should the client have on hand for the month of April?

CASE STUDY APPLICATIONS

35. Mr. S is an active 56-year-old who was diagnosed with hypertension 12 months ago. At that time, he was placed on verapamil (Isoptin), hydrochlorothiazide (HCTZ), and oral potassium chloride. He has not returned to your office since the initial diagnosis. During the past 12 months, he has reduced his weight from 127 kg to 90 kg using a rigorous exercise and diet program. Although he is proud of his lifestyle changes, he is complaining of fatigue, dizziness, heart palpitations, and muscle weakness.

    a. List two or three nursing diagnoses appropriate for Mr. S.

    b. What further assessment data should be obtained?

36. Ms. F, a 49-year-old international business person, works 70 hours per week and was recently diagnosed with hypertension. Ms. F reports smoking one pack per day for the past 15 years. She is concerned about the new medication prescribed for her, spironolactone (Aldactone). She appears distressed yet in a hurry to return to work.

   a.   What immediate goals are appropriate for Ms. F?

   b.   What client teaching is appropriate for Ms. F? Include teaching methods.

CHAPTER 44

DRUGS FOR FLUID, ELECTROLYTE, AND ACID-BASE DISORDERS

FILL IN THE BLANK

From the textbook, find the correct word(s) to complete the statements(s).

1. _____ are used to replace fluids that have been lost and to promote urine output.

2. When the body's pH drops below _____, acidosis occurs and symptoms of CNS depression are observed.

3. The normal pH of most body fluids is approximately _____.

4. Increasing the renal excretion of bicarbonate ion will increase the _____ of the blood.

5. _____ IV fluids cause water to move from the interstitial fluid to the plasma.

6. _____ IV fluids cause water to move from the plasma to the interstitial fluid.

7. _____ IV fluids produce no net fluid shift.

MATCHING

For questions 8 through 12, match the drug in column I with the classification in column II.

Column I	Column II
8. _____ Dextran 70 in normal saline	a. Colloid
9. _____ 5% dextrose in water (D5W)	b. Crystalloid
10. _____ Plasma-Lyte 148	
11. _____ Hetastarch 6% in normal saline	
12. _____ Lactated Ringer's	

MULTIPLE CHOICE

13. The nurse is administering sodium bicarbonate PO 1 g/day. The nurse will begin to recognize symptoms of alkalosis at a pH above which of the following?

    a. 6.5

    b. 7.0

    c. 7.35

    d. 7.45

14. The nurse is assessing for metabolic acidosis. The nurse should first assess for abnormalities in which body system?

    a. GI

    b. CNS

    c. Renal

    d. Cardiovascular

15. The nurse would expect to administer which of the following to a client with alkalosis?

    a. Sodium bicarbonate

    b. Sodium chloride combined with potassium chloride

    c. Lithium carbonate

    d. Aluminium hydroxide

16. When treating acidosis, the nurse should know that which of the following is a drug of choice?

    a. Sodium bicarbonate

    b. Sodium chloride

    c. Ammonium chloride

    d. Potassium chloride

17. When treating hypokalemia, the nurse should know that which of the following is a drug of choice?

    a. Sodium bicarbonate

    b. Sodium chloride

    c. Ammonium chloride

    d. Potassium chloride

18. The nurse should monitor for which common side effect of oral potassium chloride when treating a client for hypokalemia?

    a. Drowsiness

    b. Nausea and vomiting

    c. Hypoglycemia

    d. Muscle weakness and fatigue

19. In severe cases, serum potassium levels may be quickly lowered by administration of which of the following?

    a. Glucose and insulin

    b. Furosemide

    c. Acetazolamide

    d. Sodium bicarbonate

20. Colloids cause water molecules to move from the tissues into the blood vessels through their ability to increase which of the following?

    a. Potassium levels

    b. Sodium levels

    c.   Sodium excretion

    d.   Osmotic pressure

21. Clients who need sodium replacement may be prescribed an IV solution containing which of the following?

    a.   Large proteins

    b.   Glucose

    c.   Electrolytes

    d.   Dextran

22. The nurse should know that which of the following clients is most likely to suffer from acidosis?

    a.   70-year-old with kidney failure

    b.   34-year-old who has ingested excess sodium bicarbonate

    c.   15-year-old with hyperventilation due to anxiety

    d.   57-year-old taking diuretics

23. Which of the following situations may lead to alkalosis?

    a.   Hypoventilation, or shallow breathing

    b.   Severe vomiting

    c.   Severe diarrhea

    d.   Diabetes mellitus

24. The nurse correctly identifies hyponatremia when reviewing which of the following lab values?

    a.   Sodium 133 mEq/L

    b.   Sodium 148 mEq/L

    c.   Potassium 3.5 mEq/L

    d.   Potassium 5.5 mEq/L

25. The nurse should teach clients taking potassium supplements to take the drug according to which method?

    a.   With no other medications

    b.   An hour before or 2 hours after a meal

    c.   With a meal

    d.   In the morning, on awakening

MAKING CONNECTIONS

26. Which of the following antihypertensive drug classes inhibits aldosterone secretion?

    a.   ACE inhibitors

    b.   Calcium channel blockers

    c.   Adrenergic agents

    d.   Direct-acting vasodilators

27. An altered physical condition caused by the nervous system adapting to repeated drug use is known as which of the following?

    a. Psychological dependence

    b. Physical dependence

    c. Tolerance

    d. Withdrawal

28. Which of the following is *least* likely to be caused by use of diuretics in the elderly client?

    a. Incontinence

    b. Social isolation

    c. Depression

    d. Improved mental acuity

29. The nurse encourages intake of cranberry juice for a client with frequent urinary tract infections because cranberries may do which of the following?

    a. Increase the urine acidity

    b. Decrease the urine acidity

    c. Increase hematocrit levels

    d. Decrease hematocrit levels

30. Which of the following is considered to be an intermediate-acting thiazide diuretic?

    a. Furosemide (Lasix)

    b. Metolazone (Zaroxolyn)

    c. Chlorothiazide (Diuril)

    d. Spironolactone (Aldactone)

CALCULATIONS

31. The physician ordered crystalloid solution 1000 cc 0.9% NaCl to infuse by pump over 8 hours.
    The nurse will set the pump at what rate?

32. The physician ordered ammonium chloride 8 g/day in divided doses q6h. The pharmacy sends 500 mg tablets.
    How many tablets will the nurse administer at each dose?

CASE STUDY APPLICATIONS

33. Ms. L decided to lose weight and chose a plan that eliminated almost all dietary carbohydrates. She has been taking hydrochlorothiazide, ASA for her arthritis, and potassium chloride. After 2 weeks, she can no longer endure the stomach pain, nausea, and cramping. Her husband reports that his wife has shown considerable fatigue and sleepiness.

    a. Analyze the assessment data to develop a nursing plan of care for Ms. L.

    b. What client teaching is appropriate for Ms. L?

34. Mr. W, a 60-year-old utility worker, was admitted to the ER with symptoms of hyponatremia following an 8-hour workday. The environmental temperature averaged 30°C.

   a.   What additional assessment data are important for the nurse to gather?

   b.   What nursing interventions would be appropriate to assist Mr. W in avoiding hyponatremia in the future?

CHAPTER 45

DRUGS FOR MUSCLE SPASMS AND SPASTICITY

FILL IN THE BLANK

From the textbook, find the correct word(s) to complete the statement(s).

1. Disorders associated with _____ are some of the most difficult conditions to treat because of the mechanisms underlying them.

2. Movement disorders span the _____, _____, _____, and _____ body systems.

3. Involuntary contractions of a muscle or group of muscles are called _____.

4. Pharmacotherapy used for muscle spasm usually includes _____, _____, and _____ drugs.

5. A muscle condition that results from damage to the CNS is _____.

6. A chronic neurological disorder in which involuntary muscle contraction forces body parts into abnormal postures is _____.

7. Botulinum therapy lasts for _____ months.

MATCHING

For questions 8 through 15, match the drug in column I with the drug classification in column II.

Column I

8. _____ Cyclobenzaprine hydrochloride (Cycloflex, Flexeril)

9. _____ Dantrolene sodium (Dantrium)

10. _____ Quinine (Apo-, Novo-Quinine)

11. _____ Diazepam (Valium, Apo-, PMS-Diazepam)

12. _____ Chlorzoxazone (Paraflex, Parafon Forte)

13. _____ Botulinum toxin A (Botox, Cosmetic, Botox PWS)

14. _____ Orphenadrine (Disipal)

15. _____ Methocarbamol (Robaxin, PMS-Methocarbamol)

Column II

a. Centrally acting skeletal muscle relaxants

b. Direct-acting antispasmodics

MULTIPLE CHOICE

16. Causes of muscle spasms include all *except* which one?
    a. Over-medication with antipsychotic drugs
    b. Overdose of calcium
    c. Hypocalcemia
    d. Epilepsy

17. Non-pharmacological measures that may be used to treat muscle spasms include all *except* which one?
    a. Encouraging the use of the affected muscle
    b. Thermotherapy
    c. Hydrotherapy
    d. Ultrasound

18. Which of the following statements about cyclobenzaprine hydrochloride (Cycloflex, Flexeril) is *false*?
    a. Its mechanism of action is similar to that of tricyclic antidepressants.
    b. It is effective in cerebral palsy.
    c. It is meant for short-term use.
    d. It is not recommended for use in children.

19. All of the following drugs are effective in the treatment of spasticity *except* which one?
    a. Baclofen
    b. Diazepam
    c. Dantrolene
    d. Cyclobenzaprine

20. How does the botulinum toxin produce its effects?
    a. It blocks the release of norepinephrine from nerve tissue.
    b. It blocks the release of acetylcholine from cholinergic nerve terminals.
    c. It increases the release of acetylcholine from cholinergic nerve terminals.
    d. It increases the rate at which GABA is broken down in the body.

21. When teaching a client receiving a centrally acting antispasmodic drug, which statement is *not* correct?
    a. "You should avoid hazardous activities such as driving if the drug makes you drowsy."
    b. "You should avoid alcohol and antihistamines."
    c. "If you have severe side effects, stop taking the drug at once."
    d. "You should not take this drug if you have liver disease."

22. All of the following statements regarding dantrolene sodium (Dantrium) are correct *except* which one?
    a. Its use is contraindicated in clients with malignant hyperthermia.
    b. It is useful in spasms of head and neck muscles.
    c. It is useful in cases of spinal cord injury or CVA.
    d. It does not affect cardiac or smooth muscle.

23. Side effects of botulinum therapy includes all of the following *except* which one?
    a.   Increased muscle strength
    b.   Headache and nausea
    c.   Eyelid drooping
    d.   Erythema

24. Which of these drugs is produced by bacteria and is responsible for food poisoning in high levels?
    a.   Dantrolene
    b.   Botulinum toxin
    c.   Quinine sulfate
    d.   Diazepam

25. Which of the following drug classes increases the risk of unfavourable reactions to antispasmodics?
    a.   MAO inhibitors
    b.   Pain medications
    c.   Antibiotics
    d.   Anticonvulsants

26. Clients who abruptly discontinue baclofen (Lioresal, Apo-, PMS-Baclofen) may experience which of the following?
    a.   Palpitations, chest pain, dyspnea
    b.   Urinary retention
    c.   Hallucinations, paranoia, seizures
    d.   Dry mouth and photosensitivity

27. Your client reports to you that in addition to the drug therapy provided by his nurse, he is using cayenne *(Capsicum annum)* for his muscle spasms. Which precaution should this client take?
    a.   Wear sun block and long sleeves
    b.   Never apply to broken skin
    c.   Do not use if drinking alcohol
    d.   Discontinue use at once with any urinary hesitancy

MAKING CONNECTIONS

28. What is the neurotransmitter for skeletal muscle contraction?
    a.   Acetylcholine
    b.   Serotonin
    c.   Norepinephrine
    d.   Epinephrine

29. Which physiological action other than sympathomimetic activation depends on norepinephrine?
    a. Appropriate learning and memory
    b. Normal firing of neurons
    c. Proper muscle movements
    d. Stable mood and emotional functioning

30. Dopamine is synthesized naturally from which of the following precursors?
    a. Choline
    b. Tyrosine
    c. Tryptophan
    d. Pyruvate

31. Which of the following neurotransmitters is also known as 5-hydroxytryptamine?
    a. Dopamine
    b. Serotonin
    c. *N*-Methyl-D-aspartate
    d. Norepinephrine

32. Which of the following statements about NSAIDs is *false*?
    a. They are used to decrease inflammation after injuries.
    b. They include ASA, ibuprofen, naproxen, and acetaminophen.
    c. One of their main side effects is GI upset.
    d. They are used to treat fever.

CALCULATIONS

33. The client has an order for dantrolene (Dantrium) 75 mg bid. On hand are tablets labelled "dantrolene 25 mg."
    How many tablets should the nurse give for each dose?
    How many milligrams will the nurse give per day?

34. The client has an order for cyclobenzaprine (Flexeril) 20 mg tid. On hand are tablets labelled "cyclobenzaprine 10 mg."
    How many tablets should the nurse give for each dose?
    Is this a safe dose?

CASE STUDY APPLICATIONS

35. Ms. H has been experiencing lower back pain for 2 months due to muscle spasms. So far, no other disorders have been identified that could explain this pain. Her doctor has prescribed cyclobenzaprine (Flexeril).

    a. Describe other non-drug therapies that might help in this case.

    b. When teaching Ms. H about adverse reactions to cyclobenzaprine, what information should be included?

    c. How will the nurse determine whether this drug is effective?

    d. Prior to discharge, your goal is to have the client state ways to prevent recurrence of her symptoms. What preventive teaching should be done for this client?

36. Your client, Ms. B, has a career as a model and fashion designer. She expresses concern over the "crow's feet and frown lines" she's beginning to develop. She asks for information on the new Botox injections she has heard about. She expresses concern over the fact that she's heard they use a "poison" to remove facial wrinkles but says, "It would be great to look 16 again!" Your nursing diagnosis is knowledge deficit related to use of cosmetic procedures, and teaching is a planned intervention.

    a. What misinformation do you need to correct when talking with this client?

    b. What side effects does Ms. B need to be aware of before having the Botox injections?

37. Mr. P is a 21-year-old client with cerebral palsy who is cared for at home by his parents. His mother expresses concern over his spasticity and wants "better drugs" to control it. He is currently using baclofen (Lioresal).

    a. What assessments will the nurse carry out?

    b. What non-drug therapy might be useful for Mr. P?

    c. What client/family teaching should be done regarding Mr. P's use of antispasmodic drugs at home?

    d. What client/family teaching should be done regarding non-drug and safety interventions for Mr. P?

CHAPTER 46

DRUGS FOR BONE AND JOINT DISORDERS

FILL IN THE BLANK

From the textbook, find the correct word(s) to complete the statement(s).

1. One of the most important minerals in the body responsible for bone formation is _____.

2. Calcium levels in the bloodstream are controlled by two endocrine glands, the _____ glands and the _____ gland.

3. Calcium disorders are often related to _____ disorders.

4. Osteomalacia, referred to as _____ in children, is a disorder characterized by the softening of bones without alteration of basic bone structure.

5. Two important disorders characterized by weak and fragile bones are _____ and _____.

6. The hormone responsible for bone resorption is _____; the hormone responsible for bone deposition is _____.

7. Cholecalciferol is converted to an intermediate vitamin form called _____; this intermediate form is transported to the kidneys where enzymes transform it into _____, an active form of vitamin D.

8. The two major forms of calcium used in pharmacotherapy are _____ and _____.

9. The drugs of choice for Paget's disease are _____.

10. _____ treat rheumatoid arthritis by suppressing autoimmunity.

11. Drugs preventing the accumulation of uric acid in the bloodstream or joint cavities are called _____.

MATCHING

For questions 12 through 18, match the drug in column I with the classification in column II.

Column I

12. _____ Calcitriol (Calcijex, Rocaltrol)

13. _____ Calcium carbonate (Calsan, Caltrate, others)

14. _____ Allopurinol (Apo-Allopurinol)

15. _____ Etidronate disodium (Didronel)

16. _____ Gold sodium thiomalate (Myochrysine)

17. _____ Colchicine

18. _____ Alendronate sodium (Fosamax)

Column II

a. Calcium supplement

b. Vitamin D therapy

c. Bone resorption inhibiting drug

d. Disease-modifying drug

e. Uric acid inhibitor

For questions 19 through 23 match the indication in column I with the drug in column II.

Column I

19. _____ Osteomalacia, rickets, and hypocalcemia

20. _____ Osteoporosis, Paget's disease

21. _____ Gouty arthritis

22. _____ Rheumatoid arthritis

23. _____ Osteoarthritis

Column II

a. Alendronate sodium (Fosamax)

b. Probenecid (Benemid, Probalan)

c. Ergocalciferol (Vitamin D_2)

d. Hydroxychloroquine sulfate (Gen-Hydroxychloroquine)

e. Sodium hyaluronate

MULTIPLE CHOICE

24. Which of the following statements regarding calcium in the body is *false*?

a. When concentrations are too high, sodium permeability decreases across cell membranes.

b. When concentrations are too low, cell membranes become hyperexcitable.

c. Calcium must be present for the body to form vitamin D.

d. Calcium is important for body processes such as blood coagulation and muscle contraction.

25. Diseases and conditions of calcium and vitamin D metabolism include all *except* which one?

a. Osteomalacia

b. Rheumatoid arthritis

c. Osteoporosis

d. Paget's disease

26. Possible etiologies of hypocalcemia include all *except* which one?

a. Hyposecretion of parathyroid hormone

b. Digestive-related malabsorption disorders

    c.   Lack of adequate intake of calcium-containing foods

    d.   Paget's disease

27. You are helping your elderly client who has osteoporosis choose her weekly menu. Which of the following choices would be *least* useful in helping her maintain adequate calcium intake?

    a.   Carton of milk for breakfast

    b.   Salmon croquette for dinner

    c.   Turnip greens for dinner

    d.   Baked potato for lunch

28. Calcium gluconate is contraindicated in clients with all of the following conditions *except* which one?

    a.   Osteomalacia

    b.   Digitalis toxicity

    c.   Kidney stones

    d.   Cardiac dysrhythmia

29. Client teaching regarding vitamin D therapy includes all *except* which one?

    a.   Take exactly as directed; it can become toxic if taken in excess quantities.

    b.   Avoid alcohol and other hepatotoxic drugs.

    c.   Avoid sunlight exposure due to susceptibility to sunburn.

    d.   Do not start a low-fat diet unless first discussed with the nurse.

30. All of the following are risk for factors for osteoporosis *except* which one?

    a.   Anorexia nervosa

    b.   Use of estrogen replacement therapy

    c.   High alcohol or caffeine consumption

    d.   Advancing age in women

31. Which statement regarding calcitonin is *false*?

    a.   It is obtained from salmon.

    b.   It is currently available only in oral form.

    c.   It increases bone density and reduces the incidence of vertebral fractures.

    d.   It is indicated for Paget's disease and hypercalcemia.

32. Selective estrogen receptor modulators (SERMs) are contraindicated in clients with all of the following conditions *except* which one?

    a.   Thromboembolism

    b.   Pregnancy or lactation

    c.   Hormone replacement

    d.   Postmenopause

33. Which of the following is *not* a symptom of osteomalacia and/or rickets?

    a.   Hypocalcemia

    b.   Convulsions

   c.   Muscle weakness

   d.   Bowlegs and a pigeon breast

34. After analgesic and anti-inflammatory drugs have been tried, which of the following therapies may be used to alter the course of rheumatoid arthritis progression?

   a.   Bisphosphonates

   b.   Calcitonin therapy

   c.   Disease-modifying drugs

   d.   Uric acid inhibitors

35. What percentage of clients with gout are women?

   a.   10%

   b.   15%

   c.   50%

   d.   90%

36. Sodium hyaluronate is a therapy for clients with moderate osteoarthritis. Which statement about this drug is *false*?

   a.   It is injected directly into the knee joint.

   b.   It coats the articulating cartilage surface.

   c.   Clients should avoid strenuous activity for 48 hours after it is administered.

   d.   It is used prior to treatment with COX-2 inhibitors and NSAIDs.

37. Which of the following clients is *least* likely to present with gout?

   a.   Pacific Islander

   b.   Male

   c.   Female

   d.   Client using a thiazide diuretic

MAKING CONNECTIONS

38. Methotrexate can be used to treat rheumatoid arthritis. What other condition is it used for?

   a.   Cancer

   b.   Pernicious anemia

   c.   Cardiac dysrhythmia

   d.   Renal failure

39. Promethazine is a phenothiazine that is used to treat which of the following?

   a.   Dysrhythmia

   b.   Hypertension

   c.   Inflammation

   d.   Motion sickness

40. In addition to treating rheumatoid arthritis, hydroxychloroquine is also used for which of the following?

    a. Cancer

    b. Pernicious anemia

    c. Malaria

    d. Renal failure

41. Isoniazid can affect serum calcium by causing hypercalcemia. A client receiving this drug is being treated for which disease?

    a. Peptic ulcers

    b. Tuberculosis infection

    c. Viral infection

    d. Inflammation

42. Diazepam (Valium) is used as an antianxiety agent in many hospitalized clients. What other condition is it used for?

    a. Muscle spasms

    b. Osteomyelitis

    c. Parkinson's disease

    d. Immune disorders

CALCULATIONS

43. The nurse is giving colchicine in 0.5 mg tablets for an acute attack of gout. The dose is to be repeated every hour until the client develops GI symptoms or the pain is relieved. The maximum dose is 4 mg. How many doses can the nurse give before the maximum dose is reached?

44. Hydroxychloroquine sulfate (Gen-Hydroxychloroquine) 400 mg daily is ordered for a client with rheumatoid arthritis. It is available in 200 mg tablets.
How many tablets should be given?

CASE STUDY APPLICATIONS

45. Your client is a 74-year-old male who has primary gout and has just started taking allopurinol (Apo-Allopurinol) 100 mg daily. He is reporting symptoms of gastric upset and intermittent episodes of extreme pain in the joints.

    a. What education should the nurse provide regarding these symptoms and their treatment?

    b. What education should the nurse provide regarding possible adverse effects?

    c. What laboratory tests should the nurse monitor to determine the longer-term effects of allopurinol?

46. Ms. S is a 28-year-old client with type 1 diabetes with renal failure on hemodialysis. You bring her morning medications, which include Rocaltrol and calcium tablets.

    a. She asks you why she is receiving vitamin D and calcium, because she does not have a bone disease and is too young for osteoporosis. How do you explain this to her?

    b. What client teaching regarding vitamin D therapy would you give Ms. S?

    c. What information regarding calcium supplements should you give her?

47. Mrs. R is 78 years old and has been admitted to the hospital with a vertebral compression fracture. Now that her pain has been controlled, she is asking you questions about prevention of further problems of this nature.

   a.   Mrs. R wants to know what causes the bones to come brittle in elderly people. What explanation will you give her?

   b.   What drug therapy is likely to be prescribed to treat Mrs. R's osteoporosis?

   c.   What education will Mrs. R need regarding the use of her prescriptions for Fosamax and Evista?

CHAPTER 47
DRUGS FOR SKIN DISORDERS

FILL IN THE BLANK

From the textbook, find the correct word(s) to complete the statement(s).

1. Drugs used to promote the shedding of old skin are called _____ agents.

2. Mites cause a skin disorder called _____.

3. Vitamin A–like compounds that provide resistance to bacterial infection by reducing oil production and the occurrence of clogged pores are called _____.

4. _____ (with UVA and/or UVB) is used in cases of severe psoriasis.

5. Itching associated with dry, scaly skin is called _____.

6. The onset of rosacea usually occurs between the ages of _____ and _____.

7. A skin disorder with symptoms resembling an allergic reaction is called atopic dermatitis, or _____.

MATCHING

For questions 8 through 14, match the drug in column I with the classification in column II.

Column I

8. _____ Benzoyl peroxide (Benzacin, Benzamyclin, others)

9. _____ Fluticasone (Flonase)

10. _____ Cyclosporine (Apo-Cyclosporine)

11. _____ Azelaic acid (Azelex, Finacea, others)

12. _____ Lindane (Hexit)

13. _____ Lidocaine (Solarcaine, others)

14. _____ Sulfacetamide sodium (PMS-Sulfacetamide)

Column II

a. Scabicide/pediculicide

b. Sunburn / minor irritation agent

c. Acne and acne-related agent

d. Topical glucocorticoid

e. Psoriatic agent

For questions 15 through 19, match the symptom in column I with the description in column II.

Column I

15. _____ Erythema

16. _____ Pruritus

17. _____ Sunburn

18. _____ Open comedones

19. _____ Closed comedones

Column II

a.   Blackheads

b.   Whiteheads

c.   Intense itching

d.   Redness

e.   "First-degree" injury

MULTIPLE CHOICE

20. Drugs to treat oily skin would most likely be used for which of the following disorders?

   a.   Atopic dermatitis

   b.   Contact dermatitis

   c.   Seborrheic dermatitis

   d.   Stasis dermatitis

21. Which of the following medications is also used for the treatment of wrinkles?

   a.   Benzoyl peroxide (Benzacin)

   b.   Tretinoin (Retin-A)

   c.   Calcipotriene (Dovonex)

   d.   Hydroxyurea (Gen-, Apo-Hydroxyurea)

22. Which of the following medications is administered topically for psoriasis?

   a.   Calcipotriene (Dovonex)

   b.   Acitretin (Soriatane)

   c.   Hydroxyurea (Gen-, Apo-Hydroxyurea)

   d.   Methotrexate (Apo-, Ratio-Methotrexate)

23. _____ is the systemic drug most often prescribed for severe psoriasis.

   a.   Lidocaine (Solarcaine)

   b.   Calcipotriene (Dovonex)

   c.   Tetracaine HCl (Pontocaine)

   d.   Methotrexate (Apo-, Ratio-Methotrexate)

24. Which of the following treatments would *not* be used to promote the shedding of old skin?

   a.   Resorcinol

   b.   Salicylic acid

   c.   Sulfur

   d.   Benzoyl peroxide

25. Which of the following statements about benzocaine is true?

    a.   When applied to the ear, mouth, or throat, it produces minor irritation.

    b.   It is more appropriate for sunburn than for pruritus or insect bites.

    c.   Drug sensitivity is rare.

    d.   It should not be applied to an open wound.

26. Which of the following is an over-the-counter medication for acne?

    a.   Adapalene (Differin)

    b.   Azelaic acid (Azelex)

    c.   Benzoyl peroxide (Benzacin)

    d.   Sulfacetamide sodium (PMS-Sulfacetamide)

27. Exposure to perfume, cosmetics, detergents, or latex is associated with which of the following disorders?

    a.   Atopic dermatitis

    b.   Contact dermatitis

    c.   Seborrheic dermatitis

    d.   Stasis dermatitis

28. Topical glucocorticoids are a common treatment for all of the following *except* which one?

    a.   Psoriasis

    b.   Rosacea

    c.   Pruritus

    d.   Dermatitis

29. Which of the following is contraindicated in conjunction with phototherapy for the treatment of psoriasis?

    a.   Tar and anthralin

    b.   Keratolytic pastes

    c.   Psoralens

    d.   Cyclosporine

30. Lindane is contraindicated in all of the following clients *except* which one?

    a.   Children aged 2 to 10 years

    b.   Children less than 2 years

    c.   Children with seizures

    d.   Children who have abrasions, rash, or dermatitis

31. Use of Accutane is contraindicated in clients with all of the following conditions *except* which one?

    a.   Rosacea

    b.   Severe depression and suicidal tendencies

    c.   Seizures treated with carbamazepine

    d.   Diabetes treated with oral agents

32. Which vitamin is synthesized by the skin?

    a. Vitamin A

    b. Vitamin D

    c. Vitamin E

    d. Vitamin K

MAKING CONNECTIONS

33. Methotrexate may be used to treat psoriasis. Which other condition is it used for?

    a. Gout and rheumatoid arthritis

    b. Rheumatoid arthritis and certain cancers

    c. Systemic fungal infections and certain cancers

    d. Urinary tract infections and peptic ulcers

34. Topical metronidazole (Flagyl) is used to treat rosacea. What is it used for when given PO or IV?

    a. Crohn's disease

    b. High lipid levels in the blood

    c. Anti-infective therapy

    d. Dysrhythmia

35. What drug is used as a local anesthetic and an antidysrhythmic?

    a. Warfarin

    b. Propranolol

    c. Infliximab

    d. Lidocaine

36. Which is among the first-line drugs used for allergic rhinitis?

    a. NSAIDs

    b. Sympathomimetics

    c. Glucocorticoids

    d. Cytokines

CASE STUDY APPLICATIONS

37. AM is a 9-year-old brought to the pediatrician by her mother for an immunization. As you give the injection, you notice that the child has nits clinging to her hair. A quick assessment tells you that the child appears to be clean and well cared for. When you point out the problem to her mother, she confesses that she has used an OTC treatment for the lice, which her daughter got at a friend's sleepover. She is obviously uncomfortable and blurts out, "We're not like that—we are clean people." A prescription for lindane (Hexit) is given to the mother.

    a. What teaching must you do regarding the use of lindane?

    b. Whom must the mother notify of her daughter's pediculosis?

    c. What information can you give mother and daughter to prevent this problem from recurring?

38. You are working at a walk-in clinic in Ottawa. A 20-year-old college student visiting from Victoria over the August long weekend presents with complaints of severe sunburn.

    a. What other assessments would you need?

    b. What interventions might help the pain and other symptoms of sunburn?

    c. Promotion of wellness is one goal in your care plan. What information should be given to the young man regarding prevention and sequelae of sunburn?

39. TJ, a 17-year-old, stops by the school nurse's office to "hang out." After some preliminary conversation, he confides to you that he is worried about his complexion and that nothing he has tried has cleared up his severe acne. He is afraid he will be "scarred for life" and asks if there are any other medications to help him. He also wants to know why he has such a bad case of acne, and his friend has hardly any.

    a. What can you tell TJ about the causes of acne?

    b. What assessments must be made prior to starting Accutane?

    c. What other information should be assessed regarding TJ's lifestyle and hygiene habits?

CHAPTER 48

DRUGS FOR EYE AND EAR DISORDERS

FILL IN THE BLANK

From the textbook, find the correct word(s) to complete the statement(s).

1. In clients who have glaucoma, increased intraocular pressure is most often caused by a _____ in the _____ of aqueous humour.

2. A type of slower developing glaucoma in which the iris does not cover the trabecular meshwork is referred to as _____.

3. Drugs that cause the pupils to constrict are called _____.

4. Drugs that cause the pupils to dilate are referred to as _____.

5. Drugs that cause relaxation of ciliary muscles are called _____.

6. Swimmer's ear is sometimes referred to as _____.

7. Inflammation of the middle ear is called _____.

8. Inflammation of the mastoid sinus is called _____.

MATCHING

For questions 9 through 14, match the antiglaucoma drug in column I with the drug action in column II.

Column I

9. _____ Pilocarpine (Miocarpine, Spersacarpine)

10. _____ Timolol (Apo-Timop, Timoptic, Timoptic XE)

11. _____ Acetazolamide (Acetazolam)

12. _____ Mannitol (Osmitrol)

13. _____ Epinephrine (Epinal, Eppy/N)

14. _____ Latanoprost (Xalatan)

Column II

a. Increases the outflow of aqueous humour

b. Decreases the formation of aqueous humour

For questions 15 through 22, match the antiglaucoma drug in column I with the classification in column II.

Column I

15. _____ Pilocarpine (Miocarpine, Spersacarpine)

16. _____ Acetazolamide (Acetazolam)

17. _____ Isosorbide (PMS-Isosorbide)

18. _____ Epinephrine (Epinal, Eppy/N)

19. _____ Demecarium bromide (Humoursol)

20. _____ Latanoprost (Xalatan)

21. _____ Betaxolol (Betaoptic)

22. _____ Apraclonidine (Iopidine)

Column II

a. Miotic, direct-acting cholinergic agonist

b. Miotic, acetylcholinesterase inhibitor

c. Sympathomimetic

d. Prostaglandin

e. Beta-adrenergic blocker

f. Alpha$_2$-adrenergic agonist, direct acting

g. Carbonic anhydrase inhibitor

h. Osmotic diuretic

MULTIPLE CHOICE

23. Which of the following types of medications may contribute to the development of glaucoma?

    a. Beta-blockers

    b. Glucocorticoids

    c. Antibiotics

    d. Calcium channel blockers

24. Which of the following best describes closed-angle glaucoma?

    a. Chronic, simple glaucoma

    b. Develops when the iris is pushed over the area where the aqueous fluid normally drains

    c. Develops more slowly than open-angle glaucoma

    d. Best treated by drugs that decrease the formation of aqueous humour

25. Which of the following classes of drugs for eye procedures should *not* be used for clients with glaucoma?

    a. Mydriatic (sympathomimetic) drugs

    b. Cycloplegic (anticholinergic) drugs

    c. Osmotic diuretics

    d. Carbonic anhydrase inhibitors

26. When used for glaucoma, one drawback of prostaglandins is that they do which of the following?

    a. Change pigmentation of the eye

    b. Reduce blood pressure

    c. Increase urine output

    d. Block sympathetic impulses

27. Which of the following medications is converted to epinephrine in the eye?

    a. Pilocarpine (Miocarpine, Spersacarpine)

    b. Physostigmine sulfate (Eserine Sulfate)

c.   Dipivefrin (Apo-Dipivefrin, Propine)

d.   Bimatoprost (Lumigan)

28. Which class of drugs used for eye examinations has the potential to produce unfavourable CNS effects?

a.   Osmotic diuretics

b.   Sympathomimetic drugs

c.   Anticholinergic drugs

d.   Cholinergic agonists

29. Major risk factors associated with glaucoma include all *except* which one?

a.   Hypertension

b.   Migraine headaches

c.   Ethnic origin

d.   Epilepsy

30. Which of the following statements regarding closed-angle (acute) glaucoma is *false*?

a.   It is usually unilateral.

b.   The iris is pushed over the area where the fluid normally drains.

c.   It is frequently seen in persons of European ethnicity.

d.   It constitutes an emergency situation.

31. Which of the following statements regarding beta-blocking agents is *false*?

a.   They are contraindicated in persons who are allergic to sulfa.

b.   They are the most frequently used antiglaucoma drug.

c.   The mechanism by which they work is not fully understood.

d.   They may produce systemic side effects such as bronchoconstriction, bradycardia, and hypotension.

32. In which client would the use of acetazolamide (Acetazolam), a carbonic anhydrase inhibitor, be contraindicated?

a.   A client with asthma-producing bronchospasms

b.   A client with an allergy to sulfonamides

c.   A client with open-angle glaucoma

d.   A client with a history of third-degree AV block

33. You are teaching an elderly client to instill her own eye drops. How will you explain the procedure?

a.   Tilt the head back and toward the side of the affected eye.

b.   Tilt the head back and toward the side of the unaffected eye.

c.   Instill the drops to the centre of the cornea, blink, and wipe the eye.

d.   Lift the upper lid by the lashes, and drop the medication into the sac.

34. When teaching a family member to instill eye drops for an elderly client, you will include all *except* which one?

    a. Apply gentle pressure for 30 seconds to the inner canthus after instilling.

    b. Wait 5 minutes before instilling another type of drop.

    c. There is no need to remove the client's contact lenses.

    d. Eye medication should be refrigerated.

35. What is the basic course of treatment for ear infection?

    a. Antibiotics

    b. Corticosteroids

    c. Earwax removal agents

    d. Irrigation with a bulb syringe

36. Which of the following regarding chloramphenicol ear drops is *false*?

    a. They are used primarily in cases of ruptured eardrum.

    b. They are indicated if the client has hypersensitivity to the drug.

    c. They are the most commonly used topical antibiotic.

    d. Side effects include burning, redness, rash, and swelling.

37. When instilling ear drops, all of the following are correct *except* which one?

    a. Run warm water over the bottle to warm the drops.

    b. In an adult client, the pinna should be held up and back.

    c. The client should lie on the side opposite the affected ear for 5 minutes after instillation.

    d. The area should not be massaged, to prevent systemic drug effects.

MAKING CONNECTIONS

38. Cholinergic agonists exert an effect in the body through which type of receptor?

    a. Nicotinic

    b. Muscarinic

    c. Dopaminergic

    d. Serotonergic

39. Beta-blockers are examples of which class of antidysrhythmic drugs?

    a. Class I

    b. Class II

    c. Class III

    d. Class IV

40. What is one important respiratory effect of beta-blockers?

    a. Bronchospasm

    b. Bronchodilation

    c. Increased release of surfactant

    d. Hyperventilation

41. What is the most serious adverse effect of taking potassium-sparing diuretics and salt substitutes at the same time?

    a. Hyperkalemia

    b. Hypokalemia

    c. Edema

    d. Dehydration

42. In addition to glaucoma, the carbonic anhydrase inhibitor acetazolamide (Acetazolam) is also prescribed for which of the following?

    a. Seizures

    b. Coagulation disorders

    c. Psoriasis

    d. Malaria

CALCULATIONS

43. The client has an order for acetazolamide (Acetazolam) 250 mg PO tid.
What is the total amount of Acetazolam the client will receive in 24 hours?

44. A client has acute glaucoma. Pilocarpine has been ordered 1 drop every 5 minutes for 6 doses.
Would the nurse question this order? Why or why not?

CASE STUDY APPLICATIONS

45. Mr. M was recently diagnosed with open-angle glaucoma. Intraocular pressure is currently being controlled with miotic medications, including latanoprost (Xalatan). Mr. M wants to know if there is a permanent cure and if continued treatment will be necessary.

    a. Your care plan includes interventions related to client education. What client teaching must you do for Mr. M regarding his disease?

    b. One of Mr. M's nursing diagnoses reads "Knowledge deficit related to therapeutic regimen as evidenced by client's inability to identify indications and side effects of antiglaucoma medications." What specific information regarding the use of latanoprost must you give Mr. M?

    c. List some general nursing interventions that would be important for a client with glaucoma.

    d. How would the nurse evaluate the effectiveness of Mr. M's glaucoma medications?

46. Five-year-old BJ is brought to the pediatrician's office by his mother, who states that he has been crying, running a temperature of 39°C, and complaining of an earache. Your assessment reveals bulging, reddened eardrums and bloody drainage in the left ear. The mother states that she has been using chewable baby Aspirin for his fever and that she has another child at home using "ear drops, and he hates those cold things going into his ears." A diagnosis of otitis media is made by the doctor, and an oral antibiotic is prescribed.

    a.   What other assessments must you make regarding the use of antibiotics by this client?

    b.   BJ's mother obviously has a lack of knowledge about her son's medications and treatments. What interventions could you include in your care plan to address this client problem?

47. Mrs. I has come to the clinic with complaints of mild hearing loss and a sensation of fullness with intermittent ringing of the ears. Upon assessment with the otoscope, you observe a dark mass in the ear canal.

    a.   What other assessments should be made prior to treating this problem?

    b.   How would the problem be treated?

ANSWER KEY

Chapter 1

1. 1800s
2. chemists, complex mixtures
3. synthesize
4. suffering, quality of life
5. medicines
6. disease, suffering
7. administration
8. biological
9. Biologics

10. b	11. c	12. a	13. d	14. b	15. a
16. d	17. c	18. c	19. c	20. b	21. d
22. a	23. d	24. d	25. b	26. b	27. a

28. a. It is important to cover the following points in a teaching plan for a client with mild constipation:
    1. Natural alternatives usually cost less than OTC drugs.
    2. Natural alternatives tend to produce fewer side effects.
    3. Mild constipation can also be treated with diet changes: Try using high-fibre products and increasing water consumption.
    4. If constipation persists, the client needs to make an appointment for assessment with a health care provider.

    b. A nursing history would include the client's medical history, including bowel health, nutritional history, and medication history. It is important to evaluate what OTC medications have been taken in the past and what prescription drugs are being taken. Remember to assess both current and past herbal and alternative therapies. Also assess social history, including use of alcohol, tobacco, and street drugs.

29. a. A client can have a drug reaction to OTC, generic, or trade-name medications. The important nursing action is to assess what reaction the client is having and how life threatening it is for her. Life-threatening reactions may involve the heart and lungs. If the client has difficulty breathing or a blood pressure or heart abnormality, then she needs to seek emergency care. All drug reactions should be taken seriously. A nurse should be consulted for all drug reactions.

    b. It is important for Ms. B to know that all prescription drugs are put through several levels of rigorous testing. Medications are approved for marketing in Canada only after Health Canada has evaluated their safety, efficacy, and quality.

Chapter 2

1. usefulness
2. pharmacological
3. prototype
4. chemical, generic, trade
5. chemical
6. combination drugs
7. bioavailability
8. expensive

9. b	10. a	11. d	12. c	13. a	14. c
15. a	16. d	17. b	18. a	19. a	20. d
21. c					

22. a. Generic drugs are expected to have a similar effect as their brand-name counterparts. Generic and trade products have identical doses; however, the added ingredients in the generic product may be slightly different. Generic medications are less expensive. Part of the increased cost of brand-name drugs helps to pay for drug development, as well as marketing and promotion of the trade name.

    b. Tylenol is a non-narcotic analgesic. It is not a controlled substance. In Canada, controlled substances are drugs whose use is restricted by the 1997 Controlled Drugs and Substances Act.

Chapter 3

1. exposure
2. 24
3. naloxone
4. influenza, tuberculosis, cholera, HIV
5. Public Health Agency of Canada, Health Canada
6. A

7. a	8. c	9. b	10. b	11. a	12. c
13. b	14. a	15. b	16. d	17. c	18. e
19. e	20. b	21. d	22. c	23. a	24. d

25. b   26. b   27. b   28. c   29. d   30. a
31. d
32. a. Because Mrs. M has not been exposed to anthrax, antibiotic use is not recommended. The antibiotic is expensive, can cause significant side effects, and, most importantly, can promote the development of bacterial strains that are resistant to antibiotics.

b. Anthrax vaccine is available. It takes 18 months to complete the six injections. At this point, the CDC recommends vaccination only for laboratory personnel who work with anthrax, military personnel in high-risk areas, and those who deal with animal products imported from areas where the disease is endemic.

33. a. Assessments include checking for history of eczema, atopic dermatitis, and other exfoliative skin conditions or present disease; checking for an alteration in immunity (HIV-AIDS, leukemia, lymphoma, immunosuppressive drugs); pregnancy or breastfeeding; age of the client; and previous allergic reaction to any component of the vaccine.

b. Information given in a pamphlet may include the following:

1. The vaccine provides high-level protection if given prior to exposure or up to 3 days after.
2. Protection may last from 3 to 5 years.
3. The vaccine is contraindicated in people with serious skin conditions, immunocompromised persons, pregnant or lactating women, children under the age of 1 year, and anyone allergic to its components unless there is a documented face-to-face contact with an infected person.
4. This vaccine is known for serious side effects. Of every 1 million people vaccinated, 250 could die from the vaccine.

34. a. Potassium iodide prevents damage to the thyroid gland only after radiation exposure. It does not protect any other body tissues. It will not prevent radiation sickness or other cancers that may develop as a result of the exposure.

b. Potassium iodide will be absorbed by the thyroid gland and prevent the radioactive iodine from being absorbed by the gland. This lessens the gland's exposure to radiation and prevents the cancer. KI is effective even if taken 3 to 4 hours after exposure.

Chapter 4

1. absorption, distribution, metabolism, excretion
2. blood-brain, fetal-placental
3. Metabolism
4. first-pass effect
5. Absorption
6. bone marrow, teeth, eyes, adipose tissue
7. excretion
8. Toxic concentration
9. therapeutic range
10. loading
11. a   12. b   13. a   14. b   15. a   16. b
17. c   18. b   19. c   20. a   21. a   22. c
23. d   24. a
25. a. Because Mr. P is obese, the medications may be dissolved in the fat and accumulate there and then slowly be released. Hypertension and diabetes can alter drug distribution as these disorders are associated with compromised renal function. When renal function is compromised, drug dosing must be reduced to account for changes in metabolic and excretion function.

b. Mr. P's anxiety should be reduced. Half-life of the drug should be considered by the nurse. If the client is experiencing side effects of the anti-anxiety drugs, then the nurse should consider renal and hepatic function as a potential problem, increasing the plasma half-life.

c. The primary site of excretion for all medications is the kidney. The nurse should be checking intake and output of this client.

26. a. Mr. A has been abusing alcohol, which will affect hepatic function. He is 60 years old and therefore has some degree of vessel narrowing.

b. Because of the history of alcohol abuse and the age of the client, medication dosing may be reduced to lessen the chance of toxicity.

c. The nurse should assess the renal system. If renal blood flow has been impaired, then excretion of medications will be slow and side effects or toxic effects may be seen in the post-procedure period.

Chapter 5

1. Pharmacodynamics
2. frequency distribution
3. 50
4. lethal
5. therapeutic index
6. lower
7. Efficacy
8. Potency, efficacy
9. receptor
10. Antagonists
11. b   12. a   13. b   14. a   15. a   16. b
17. a   18. a   19. a   20. c   21. d   22. b
23. c   24. c   25. d
26. a. Determine the age of the client. Identify how often the analgesic is used for pain relief and how efficacious the medication has been. Identify if the dosage is standard and safe. Evaluate the therapeutic index for this drug.

b. Chronic pain related to history of migraine headaches.

c. Has there been enough time for the medication to be absorbed and distributed? Does the client need a more potent drug? Is the agonist/antagonist formulation of this drug not appropriate for this client? Are drug-drug interactions occurring? Are drug-food interactions occurring?

27. a. What antibiotics are the clients taking? Are the doses standard, safe, and potent? Have the clients taken the drugs long enough to consider the slow results unreasonable? Is this an efficacy issue?

b. The client exhibits the following signs of wound healing: well-approximated wound edges, no drainage 48 hours after wound is closed, no inflammatory response present beyond day 5 post-injury.

c. Wound edges opening, drainage, inflammation, pain, fever.

Chapter 6

1. biophysical, psychosocial, ethnocultural, and spiritual
2. development
3. growth
4. prenatal, embryonic, fetal
5. increases, excretion
6. decreases, decrease
7. preschool
8. polypharmacy

9. a	10. e	11. c	12. b	13. d	14. b
15. a	16. a	17. b	18. c	19. d	20. c
21. b	22. c	23. d	24. b	25. a	26. c
27. b	28. c	29. c	30. d	31. c	

32. The skeleton and all major organs are developed by week 8. Because substance abuse is teratogenic, all or some of the major organs and/or the skeletal system could be affected.

b. The woman may deliver a neonate that has multiple developmental anomalies.

c. Drugs and other chemicals ingested by the mother may cross the placental barrier and affect the developing fetus.

33. a. Middle-age adults are sometimes called the "sandwich generation" because they are caring for children and aging parents.

b. They must opt for lifestyle changes such as limiting lipid intake, maintaining optimum weight, and exercising to improve overall health.

c. Cardiovascular disease, hypertension, obesity, arthritis, cancer, and anxiety.

34. a. Polypharmacy.

b. The chances for drug interactions and adverse reactions dramatically increase.

c. Although the nurse should avoid preconceived ideas that all elderly clients are physically and cognitively impaired, a careful assessment of hearing, vision, and mental status is necessary.

Chapter 7

1. health history
2. chief complaint
3. observation
4. nursing process

5. f	6. e	7. d	8. c	9. g	10. h
11. a	12. c	13. d	14. b	15. a	16. a
17. b	18. d	19. b	20. a	21. a	22. b
23. c	24. a	25. d	26. b	27. d	28. c
29. a					

30. a. At this age, adolescents want to be liked by their peers, as displayed in their dress and lifestyle.

b. Yes, related to non-adherence to treatment of a potentially life-threatening condition with potentially long-term adverse effects to major organs of the body.

c. Non-adherence to treatment related to failure to follow treatment regimen, blood glucose levels over 20 mmol/L.

31. a. The priority intervention is to establish the need for and use of an interpreter to communicate with the client. This will enable the nurse to communicate a plan of care to the client and to reduce the chances of legal implications.

b. Language, culture, lifestyle, education, low income, healthcare beliefs.

32. a. The potential exists for withdrawal effects from the substance abuse and the requirement of additional medication for pain relief. Also, there is a potential for non-adherence to treatment related to drug dependency.

b. The client will follow an established plan of care as an inpatient and outpatient. The client will enrol in a substance abuse recovery program and be in compliance with goals of the program. The desired outcome will be for a complete recovery from the trauma and substance abuse.

Chapter 8

1. enteral
2. topical
3. seven rights
4. oral
5. Sublingual
6. Suppositories, enemas
7. intravenous
8. intramuscular
9. transdermal
10. Transmucosal

11. a	12. b	13. b	14. a	15. c	16. b
17. c	18. a	19. b	20. a	21. b	22. d
23. d	24. c	25. d	26. a	27. b	28. b
29. b	30. d	31. d	32. b	33. d	34. c

35. a. The nurse must take a detailed personal, family, and sexual health history when assisting the client in a choice of contraception.

b. Oral contraceptive agents are effective and convenient; however, missing a daily dose means risking pregnancy. Therefore, for an active lifestyle, this may not be the most desirable approach. On the other hand, an oral medication may be less bothersome than injections, patches, or vaginal inserts. Injections or implants may last a long time, but they may be initially painful or subject to infection. In addition, these approaches may be uncomfortable, as may vaginal inserts. Vaginal inserts might be used less routinely because they are sometimes messy, inconvenient, and less reliable. The nurse should help the client weigh every disadvantage against the convenience of taking medication less frequently.

36. a. As the client is nauseated and has diarrhea, oral medications or suppositories would probably not be recommended unless the nausea and diarrhea were not severe enough to interfere with the drug therapy. The source of discomfort is the gastrointestinal tract. Therefore, topical drugs would most likely do little good to relieve discomfort; also, in elderly clients, the skin is usually sensitive. Alternatives might be drugs administered by the parenteral route, for example, by an intramuscular or subcutaneous injection.

b. Effectiveness of the route of medication can be evaluated by collecting data about the resolution of presenting symptoms.

Chapter 9

1. medication errors, adverse drug reactions
2. non-maleficence
3. reasonable and prudent action
4. clarified, administered
5. MedEffect
6. b   7. d   8. d   9. c   10. c   11. b
12. d   13. d   14. a   15. b   16. c   17. c
18. c   19. c   20. a   21. c   22. d   23. a
24. d   25. c   26. b   27. a   28. d   29. c
30. d

31. a. Assessment is the first step of the nursing process. Subjective data (complaining of a headache) and objective data (vital signs) are both used.

b. The ethical principle of beneficence would ensure that only good would be done and would be included in the nursing actions for this client.

32. a. Risk for injury related to excessive anticoagulation as evidenced by increased dosage of anticoagulant medication.

b. Implementation would include monitoring the client for signs and symptoms of increased clotting time and elevated prothrombin time.

33. a. The nurse needs to find out when the client took her last dose of lithium, what her prescribed dose is,

and her current lithium level. When a client is experiencing a period of sodium depletion (e.g., use of diuretics, dehydration), the proximal tubule of the kidney will reabsorb sodium and lithium in an effort to prevent the depletion of these salts. Consequently, lithium serum levels rise and may lead to lithium toxicity. Finding out the serum lithium level would provide important information about possible toxicity. Therapeutic levels of lithium are 0.5 to 1.2 mEq/L. Toxic levels are most serious when serum lithium levels exceed 2 mEq/L.

b. Yes. If the client's lithium level is elevated, administering another dose of lithium would increase the symptoms of toxicity. Nurses should always review recent laboratory data and other information in the client's chart before administering medications, especially those drugs, such as lithium, that have a narrow margin of safety.

c. You should question the order. If you administer the dose and the client develops more serious symptoms, most likely both you and the healthcare provider are liable. The standard by which the nurse is judged is whether the actions taken were those that a reasonable and prudent nurse would have taken when faced with a similar dilemma.

d. Deficit in fluid volume: The client will verbalize an understanding of sodium and fluid requirements when taking lithium. Risk for poisoning related to lithium toxicity: The client will maintain a therapeutic serum level by regular monitoring of blood lithium levels.

e. Teaching would include information about changing sodium intake, taking new medications, and other changes that may cause lithium toxicity or increased excretion of lithium.

34. a. While this is a deviation from the precise order, most nurses would not consider the change in time a medication error. However, incorrect documentation is a medication error. Also, taking ferrous sulphate with food can decrease absorption by up to 70%. The times were likely chosen specifically to avoid meal times. Nurses who practise in clinical agencies need to understand and follow policies and procedures governing medication administration for the organization in which they practise. These policies and procedures establish the standards of care for that particular hospital or organization, and it is important that nurses adhere to those established policies and procedures. Common errors relate to failing to administer a medication at the prescribed time. For example, an agency policy may identify that it is permissible to give a medication 30 minutes early or 30 minutes late for medications taken four times a day. The standards of care and the agency's policy manual are designed to help the nurse reduce medication errors and maintain client safety.

b. To make allowances without consulting the prescribing healthcare provider is not wise. It would be better for the nurse to consult with the healthcare provider who ordered the medication and have the order changed. The nurse should also indicate on the medication administration record that the medication was given at 8 AM and omitted at 10 AM.

Chapter 10

1. holistic
2. individuality, totality
3. spiritual
4. values, beliefs, practices
5. Western medicine
6. c 7. e 8. f 9. g 10. b 11. a
12. d 13. c 14. d 15. c 16. b 17. c
18. a 19. b 20. d 21. a 22. d 23. c
24. a 25. b 26. b 27. c

28. a. Assess Mrs. B's cultural background, level of income, lifestyle, religious beliefs, use of non-prescription drugs and whether there are other environmental factors (such as the husband's alcoholic parents living with her) that may contribute to her child's future alcohol abuse or influence her well-being. This client should also be assessed for the possibility of domestic violence.

b. Alcoholism has both social and biological components. Some persons are more sensitive to alcohol based on their genetic makeup. Alcoholism may develop in people who are exposed to socially accepted drinking. It may be influenced by culture, environment, poverty, and traumatic experiences.

c. Referrals for this client may include a community group such as AA or a local church. She also needs to enlist the support of her non-alcoholic family. If the assessment for domestic violence is positive, make appropriate referrals.

29. a. Side effects of the antihypertensives should be assessed—especially whether they are causing impotence. Also, the client's knowledge of the use of the medications and how to take them should be evaluated.

b. He should be instructed in the correct dosage schedule and side effects that may occur. The client needs to know that abruptly discontinuing antihypertensives has been known to cause strokes.

30. a. Other types of pain-relieving measures that may be acceptable to this client include guided imagery, biofeedback, acupuncture, therapeutic massage, heat, cold, and use of TENS.

b. Find out the client's religion and offer her the option of a consultation with a minister regarding the use of stronger medications. Find out what she has done in the past to relieve her pain, and do this, if possible.

c. Possibly a non-narcotic pain reliever would give some relief. Acetaminophen, ASA, and ibuprofen do not cause the drowsiness often associated with narcotics.

Chapter 11

1. healing power
2. reduce, medications
3. judgmental
4. woody tissue, stems, bark
5. active chemicals
6. Natural Health Products Directorate (NHPD)
7. e 8. d 9. d 10. a 11. b 12. b
13. b 14. d 15. e 16. c 17. d 18. c
19. a 20. c 21. c 22. d 23. c 24. b
25. c 26. b 27. a 28. d 29. b 30. a
31. a 32. d 33. a 34. b

35. a. The nurse should find out what herbs the client is planning on using and determine whether he is aware of possible side effects and herb-drug interactions.

b. Many herbal supplements cause increased effects from warfarin and digoxin. The client should be informed that he may experience increased tendency to bleed and possibly digitalis toxicity. Herbal preparations should not be taken without consulting his physician. Since the client may take the herbals in spite of the nurse's warning, he should be instructed in signs and symptoms to report. Symptoms of bleeding include bruises, bleeding gums, and hematuria. Digoxin toxicity symptoms include anorexia, nausea, and seeing yellow halos around objects.

c. Some clients may be allergic to one of the many chemicals in herbals. Clients should start by using the smallest amount possible until it is determined whether they have an allergy to any component of the substance.

36. a. The client may be experiencing serotonin syndrome caused by the combination of the Prozac and the St. John's wort.

b. Combining St. John's wort with tricyclic antidepressants such as Elavil or Tofranil may cause serotonin syndrome. MAO inhibitors in combination with St. John's wort may cause hypertensive crisis.

37. a. You would want to monitor liver function studies (AST, ALT) because the combination of Echinacea and methotrexate may result in hepatotoxicity.

b. Since this client is already combining a prescription drug with an herbal that is known to have an adverse interaction, the possibility of herb-drug interactions should be stressed. The client should also be made aware that herbal supplements are not approved by Health Canada and may not do what they claim to do. He should be made aware of the possibility of an allergic reaction to an ingredient in the preparation.

c. This goal is probably not realistic as the client is already using an herbal preparation, although he is not happy with the results at the present time. The nurse should attempt to understand what the client is trying to accomplish by using the herbal preparation and be prepared to offer him alternatives to meet his needs.

He may need a new prescription or possibly wish to combine herbals with prescription medications. Open communication and a non-judgmental attitude on the part of the nurse will encourage the client to explore possibilities and decide what is best for his situation. A more realistic goal might be to have the client verbalize possible herb-drug interactions related to the Echinacea prior to discharge.

Chapter 12

1. Substance abuse
2. opium, marijuana, cocaine
3. dose, length of therapy
4. physical dependence, psychological dependence
5. Substance dependence
6. crack cocaine
7. benzodiazepine
8. methadone
9. tolerance
10. withdrawal

11. a	12. c	13. c	14. d	15. b	16. b
17. d	18. a	19. c	20. a	21. a	22. b
23. a	24. a	25. b	26. a	27. b	28. b
29. c	30. a	31. d	32. d	33. c	34. d
35. a	36. d	37. d			

38. a. Marijuana can cause lung damage and increases the likelihood of a client developing lung cancer and other lung disorders.

b. Marijuana causes psychological dependence. Long-term use may result in personality changes. Marijuana is also considered the "gateway" drug. This means that it increases the risk of taking other drugs.

c. Marijuana smoke introduces four times more particulates into the lungs than tobacco smoke.

39. a. Substance addiction depends on many complex and interacting variables. While some factors related to substance abuse are genetic (such as issues of metabolic enzymes and innate tolerance), there are also environmental factors that impact one's risk. Having a close family member with a history of substance abuse should make the client seriously consider whether he or she wants to continue using alcohol on a regular basis.

b. When did the client last consume alcohol? How much alcohol is usually consumed in a day or week? Has the client ever had withdrawal symptoms? Has the client ever been to an alcohol treatment program? Does the client believe that he or she could stop drinking if he or she wanted to? What is the client's current mental status? What is the client's nutritional status? What is skin integrity like? What is the client's sleeping pattern? Does the alcoholic parent live with the client?

c. There are many potential nursing diagnoses that will be further informed by the assessment. Here are some examples of nursing diagnosis that you might find with someone who is a regular user of alcohol: One potential nursing diagnosis is denial related to fear, anxiety, or lack of knowledge. The client outcome is that the client is able to realistically assess alcohol intake and create achievable plans to reduce or cease alcohol consumption. A related nursing diagnosis may be defensiveness related to perceived threat to positive self-regard. The expected client outcome is that the client excepts responsibility for his or her own behaviour, adequately describes his or her current health status and alcohol use, and participates in a plan to reduce or cease alcohol consumption. Another potential nursing diagnosis is compromised family coping related to substance abuse. The client outcome is the that family will understand the behaviours needed to support a drug-free family environment and cope with the recovery process. A final nursing diagnosis is knowledge deficient related to lack of understanding of the use and abuse of alcohol. The expected outcome is that the client will be able to correctly identify the causes and treatment of addiction and will be able to express the prevention behaviours necessary to reduce or cease alcohol consumption.

Chapter 13

1. central, peripheral
2. autonomic
3. fight-or-flight, rest-and-digest
4. Norepinephrine, acetylcholine
5. adrenergic, cholinergic
6. parasympathetic, sympathetic
7. Adrenergic
8. adrenergic (or sympathetic)
9. Cholinergic

10. e	11. b	12. c	13. d	14. a	15. c
16. b	17. e	18. e	19. d	20. b	21. c
22. a	23. d	24. c	25. d	26. d	27. a
28. d	29. a	30. d	31. c	32. a	33. b
34. b	35. a	36. b	37. a	38. c	39. a
40. c	41. a	42. a	43. d	44. c	

45. $\left(\dfrac{20 \text{ mg}}{1} \times \dfrac{5 \text{ cc}}{10 \text{ mg}} \right) = \dfrac{100}{10} = 10 \text{ cc}$

$\dfrac{10 \text{ cc}}{\text{dose}} \times 4 \text{ doses} = 40 \text{ cc } 6 \text{ day}$

46. $\left(\dfrac{0.3 \text{ mg}}{1} \times \dfrac{1 \text{ mL}}{0.6 \text{ mg}} \right) = \dfrac{0.3}{0.6} = 0.05 \text{ mL}$

47. a. Potential nursing diagnoses would include the following:

  1. Ineffective airway clearance due to drying of secretions caused by Benadryl and interference

with bronchodilation when Inderal is given with Ventolin.

2. Possible altered urinary elimination: retention or hesitancy related to use of Minipress and Benadryl.

3. Possible altered cardiac output: decrease related to use of Minipress and Inderal.

b. Nursing interventions that can be done to decrease possible problems or interactions include the following:

1. Identify interactions and review with physician when appropriate.

2. Increase hydration to 3 L/day to decrease risk of drying of secretions causing altered airway clearance.

3. Monitor for signs of orthostatic hypotension and possible decreases or increases in BP or pulse.

4. Monitor intake and output to be sure client maintains urine output and experiences no urinary dysfunction due to adverse medication effects.

48. a. The nurse should inform Ms. W of the following information regarding pilocarpine (Salagen): Advise her to be near bathroom facilities after taking the drug, that blurred vision is a possible side effect, and that she should not drive until the effects of the drug are known. She should also be instructed to avoid abrupt changes in position and prolonged time standing in one place.

Chapter 14

1. generalized anxiety disorder (GAD)
2. limbic, reticular activating
3. Anxiolytics, hypnotics
4. GABA receptor–chloride
5. benzodiazepines
6. Barbiturates
7. Respiratory depression
8. IV, III
9. Antidepressants

10. b	11. a	12. c	13. a	14. d	15. d
16. f	17. b	18. a	19. c	20. b	21. b
22. d	23. a	24. d	25. c	26. d	27. c
28. a	29. b	30. b	31. b	32. b	33. c
34. b	35. b	36. d	37. d	38. d	
39. a					

40. $\dfrac{1.5 \text{ mg}}{\text{dose}} \times \dfrac{1 \text{ g}}{1000 \text{ mg}} \times \dfrac{1 \text{ mL}}{0.001 \text{ g}} = \dfrac{1.5}{1} = \dfrac{1.5 \text{ mL}}{\text{dose}}$

41. $\dfrac{1 \text{ mg}}{\text{dose}} \times \dfrac{1 \text{ mL}}{5 \text{ mg}} = \dfrac{1}{5} = \dfrac{0.2 \text{ mL}}{\text{dose}}$

42. a. Nursing assessments prior to giving lorazepam include the following: Allergies to benzodiazepines or chemically similar drugs; Liver and renal function; History of organic brain disease, narrow-angle glaucoma, and chronic respiratory conditions; History of depression, alcohol, or drug abuse; Medications taken routinely (including digoxin) and when taken last; Herbal supplement use.

b. Nursing interventions would include the following: Resuscitation equipment and airway; Flumazenil as benzodiazepine receptor antagonist; Ventilator; Someone to take client home after the procedure; Monitor vital signs q5–15 min, especially respiratory rate and depth; Monitor client's level of consciousness and responsiveness.

c. To evaluate the effectiveness of intervention, the nurse would use the following: The client has no injury related to the administration of lorazepam. The client has normal vital signs during the administration of lorazepam.

43. a. Sleep pattern disturbance related to situational anxiety.

b. Interventions include the following: Explore potential contributing factors (noise, interruptions, etc.); Maintain bedtime routine as per client preference; Recommend the following non-pharmacological interventions to induce sleep: Back rub; Light bedtime snack; Establish a regular time to sleep; Avoid napping during the day; Decrease caffeine, chocolate, nicotine, and other stimulants in the second half of the day; Limit alcohol consumption; Exercise at least 2–3 hours before bedtime; Hot bath 1 hour before sleep; Comfortable sleeping environment; Use stress reduction and relaxation just prior to sleep; Relief of pain or discomfort prior to sleep

c. The nurse will teach that benzodiazepines are the first drug of choice for sleep. However, all of these drugs will cause interruption of REM sleep and, therefore, should not be continued for more than 1 week. OTC drugs (normally anticholinergics) also interrupt REM sleep, can cause a hangover, and should not be used for more than 1 week.

Chapter 15

1. acute, chronic
2. infection, trauma, metabolic disorders, vascular diseases, neoplastic disorders
3. barrier methods or other contraceptive measures
4. folate
5. sleep, strobe, flickering
6. Febrile, 3, 5, fever (or temperature)
7. carbamazepine (Tegretol)
8. Partial, complete
9. valproic acid (Depakene)
10. diazepam (Valium), lorazepam (Ativan)
11. Status epilepticus, respirations (or breathing)
12. airway
13. abnormal, suppress

14. 3, months

15. f   16. e   17. b   18. a   19. c   20. g

21. d   22. a   23. a   24. b   25. a   26. b

27. c   28. d   29. c   30. b   31. d   32. a

33. d   34. a   35. d   36. d   37. c   38. b

39. a   40. b   41. d   42. c   43. c   44. a

45. a

46. $\dfrac{60 \text{ mg}}{\text{dose}} \times \dfrac{5 \text{ mL}}{20 \text{ mg}} = \dfrac{300}{20} = \dfrac{15 \text{ mL}}{\text{dose}}$

47. $\dfrac{1200 \text{ mg}}{4 \text{ doses}} = 300 \text{ mg/dose}$

48. a. Possible risk of injury related to medication administration: Inappropriate administration of Dilantin IV can lead to emboli, hypoventilation, hypotension, venous irritation, seizures, or decreased level of consciousness.

 b. Nursing interventions for administration of Dilantin IV: Use saline only to mix Dilantin. Infuse no faster than 50 mg/min. Use IV line with filter. Check for infiltration often as it is a soft tissue irritant. Use large vein or central venous catheter only. Never use Dilantin IM. Avoid hand veins to prevent local vasoconstriction. Prime IV line with saline if hanging piggyback. Monitor for LOC changes after seizure. Keep side rails up and padded. Have emergency equipment available. Monitor for hypotension or depressed respirations during administration.

49. a. The first priority diagnosis would be knowledge deficit related to new medical condition and new medication for management of seizures as evidenced by client asking questions.

 b. Interventions: Assess what the client knows about epilepsy, seizures, and management. Assess for any misunderstandings about medication and treatment regimen. Provide information to client regarding the following: Medications will be dosed at the lowest dosage to prevent seizures, which will decrease the amount of side effects expected. The medication dosages will be increased as needed if seizures continue. Other medications might be added or drugs might be changed as needed to control seizures. Seizures will be controlled best if clients adhere to the medication schedule. Clients will need to return for lab appointments and follow-up physician visit to evaluate therapeutic effect. Side effects that might be expected initially include dizziness, ataxia, diplopia, and a change of urine colour to pink, red, or brown. The dizziness and drowsiness will decrease as the medication is continued. More serious side effects should be reported to the physician. Drugs to avoid: Many meds interact with phenytoin. The client must inform the physician that he is on phenytoin before any medications are added. The pharmacist might also be consulted before OTC medications and herbals or supplements are added. No foods need to be avoided, but supplements of folic acid, calcium, and vitamin D will impair the effect of Dilantin. The nurse should give the client a list of foods that contain folic acid, calcium, and vitamin D. These foods should not be taken in large quantities, although they do not need to be avoided.

Chapter 16

1. major depressive disorder, bipolar disorder

2. Major depressive disorder

3. tricyclic antidepressants (TCAs), selective serotonin reuptake inhibitors (SSRIs), monoamine oxidase (MAO) inhibitors

4. SSRIs

5. TCAs

6. lithium

7. attention deficit–hyperactivity disorder (ADHD)

8. CNS stimulants

9. mood stabilizers, mania, depression

10. f   11. e   12. d   13. b   14. c   15. a

16. a   17. c   18. b   19. e   20. d   21. d

22. c   23. e   24. b   25. a   26. d   27. b

28. d   29. d   30. d   31. d   32. d   33. c

34. c   35. b   36. d   37. b   38. a   39. c

40. b   41. d   42. c   43. a   44. b   45. a

46. d

47. $\dfrac{1.2 \text{ g}}{\text{day}} \times \dfrac{1000 \text{ mg}}{1 \text{ g}} \times \dfrac{1 \text{ capsule}}{300 \text{ mg}} = \dfrac{1200}{300} = 4 \text{ capsules}$

$\dfrac{4 \text{ capsules}}{4 \text{ doses}} = \dfrac{1 \text{ capsule}}{\text{dose}}$

48. $\dfrac{45 \text{ mg}}{\text{day}} \times \dfrac{5 \text{ mL}}{20 \text{ mg}} = \dfrac{225}{20} = \dfrac{11.25 \text{ mL}}{\text{day}}$

49. a. Risk for injury related to adverse effects of lithium.

 b. The nurse should assess for the following: Knowledge of side effects: dizziness, drowsiness, nausea, metallic taste, tremors, vomiting, and diarrhea; Lab studies: renal and kidney function, blood levels of lithium; Interactions: diuretics and low-sodium diet possibly leading to lithium toxicity; History: allergies or previous renal or cardiac conditions; Mental and emotional status: previous suicide attempts or present intent; Knowledge of whom to notify in case of adverse or toxic effects of lithium; Knowledge of adverse and toxic effects of lithium.

 c. The goal is to demonstrate the following: Understanding of drug effects and precautions; Improvement in mood stability; Ability to notify or seek help when questions or problems arise; No injury related to adverse effects of lithium.

50.

Goals for Client	Evaluation
Client will show (or report):	
Improved affect or mood	No longer has suicidal ideation
	Engages in normal daily activities
Improved sleep patterns	Can sleep through the night, stays asleep, and falls asleep easily
Decreasing episodes of side effects	Decreased headaches, nausea, drowsiness since beginning medications
Continuation of medication regimen	Continues to take medications as ordered

Chapter 17

1. schizophrenia
2. hours to days, months to years
3. positive, negative
4. cause (etiology), brain damage, medication overdose, depression, alcoholism, genetics, illicit drug use
5. hallucinations, delusions, disorganized thoughts, disorganized speech patterns
6. interest, motivation, responsiveness, pleasure
7. antipsychotic
8. dopamine (D_2)
9. schizophrenia, extrapyramidal

10. b	11. a	12. a	13. a	14. c	15. a
16. c	17. b	18. b	19. c	20. f	21. b
22. d	23. g	24. a	25. e	26. c	27. h
28. i	29. b	30. c	31. d	32. b	33. d
34. b	35. b	36. c	37. b	38. a	39. c
40. a	41. c	42. d	43. d		

44. $\dfrac{15 \text{ mg}}{\text{dose}} \times \dfrac{1 \text{ mL}}{25 \text{ mg}} = \dfrac{15}{25} = \dfrac{0.6 \text{ mL}}{\text{dose}}$

45. $\dfrac{200 \text{ mg}}{\text{day}} \times \dfrac{1 \text{ tablet}}{50 \text{ mg}} = \dfrac{200}{50} = \dfrac{4 \text{ tablets}}{\text{day}}$

$\dfrac{4 \text{ tablets}}{2 \text{ doses}} = \dfrac{2 \text{ tablets}}{\text{dose}}$

46. a. Interventions used for the diagnosis of knowledge deficit: Assess client's readiness to learn based on the emotional response of the client. Provide health teaching related to Clozaril: can cause drowsiness, dry mouth, hypotension. Does not cause as many problems with EPS as Apo-Chlorpromazine does. Get up slowly to prevent dizziness and falls due to orthostatic hypotension. Avoid activities requiring mental alertness until effects of medication are known. Avoid alcohol and other CNS depressants. Weekly labs are required to monitor for agranulocytosis. Report any evidence of infection: sore throat and mild fever. Instruct client on best time to take the medication and what to do for missed doses.

b. Evaluation will include the following: Client will report to lab and physician appointments as requested for lab work. Client will not experience injury (falls) related to dizziness, sedation, ataxia. Client remains compliant with therapeutic regimen prescribed. Client verbalizes understanding of medical regimen, adverse effects of medication, and need to be compliant.

47. Assessments include the following: Vital signs: temp, pulse, blood pressure, and body weight; Behaviour and appearances: dietary intake, activities of daily living, and socialization with others; Symptoms of condition: hallucinations, delusions, enjoyment of life, personal hygiene, speech patterns, and motor movement; Monitoring for side effects and adverse effects of medications such as akathisia, abnormal movements, dizziness, drowsiness, constipation, photosensitivity, or orthostatic hypotension; Let client know that side effects will decrease with time on the medication; Any past history of seizures since medication can influence the seizure threshold; Assess plans for pregnancy or if any contraceptives are being used; Monitor for fluid volume deficit by monitoring intake and output and weight, daily; Teach client to increase oral intake to maintain hydration; Monitor for improvement in symptoms of condition; Worsening of the condition should be reported immediately; Monitor compliance with medication regimen; Assess present medications or herbs that may interact with the new medication.

Chapter 18

1. dopamine, acetylcholine
2. Alzheimer's disease
3. Alzheimer's disease
4. acetylcholine
5. genetic
6. antipsychotic, extrapyramidal
7. hypotension, tachycardia, muscle twitching, mood changes
8. cognitive, behavioural, daily activities
9. Acetylcholinesterase inhibitors, functioning

10. b	11. a	12. c	13. a	14. b	15. c
16. a	17. a	18. b	19. c	20. i	21. h
22. g	23. e	24. f	25. a	26. c	27. d
28. b	29. a	30. d	31. d	32. a	33. a
34. c	35. a	36. b	37. a	38. d	39. c
40. c	41. a	42. c	43. b	44. d	45. b
46. a					

47. You require 4 tablets per day × 7 days = 28 tablets. You have 25 tablets. Yes, you need to reorder.

48. $\dfrac{7.5 \text{ mg}}{3 \text{ doses}} = \dfrac{2.5 \text{ mg}}{\text{dose}}$

49. a. The nursing diagnosis is risk for injury related to drug effects and unresolved symptoms of parkinsonism. This diagnosis relates to sedation as a side effect of anticholinergics and of interactions with other possible CNS depressants such as Zoloft. The tremors and involuntary movements also cause possible balance problems. Orthostatic hypotension is also a side effect that causes instability of balance.

b. The client will have no injury related to the side effects of medications or the condition (Parkinson's disease).

50. a. The priority diagnosis at this point would be risk of injury related to possible adverse effects of drugs and interactions.

b. Interventions would include the following: Assess for interactions between medications in the regimen. Tricyclics and benzodiazepines can potentiate their CNS depression, causing sedation and sleep deprivation; Assess for side effects of the medications: sedation, vomiting, diarrhea, obstructed urine flow, insomnia, abnormal dreaming, aggression, syncope, depression, headache, irritability, fatigue, urinary incontinence, and restlessness; Provide instructions for proper administration: give at bedtime and once daily. Maintain a regular medication schedule. Provide assistance to the client when memory is impaired; Assess for contraindicated conditions or medications: hypotension, bradycardia, hyperthyroid, peptic ulcer disease; Teach safety precautions for side effects of medications: no hot showers, arise slowly, have something to hold on to during ambulation when needed; Include family and client in management of the client's condition; Collaborate with other departments as needed: PT, OT, home healthcare; Assess for caregiver strain; Monitor for improvement with the client's short-term memory or behaviours while on medications.

Chapter 19

1. opioids (narcotics), non-opioids (non-narcotics)
2. anti-inflammatory, antipyretic
3. tension
4. aura
5. nociceptor
6. anxiety, depression, fatigue
7. character, nature
8. stop, prevent
9. triptans, ergot alkaloids, serotonin
10. intracranial vessels, orally, parenterally, nasally

11. d	12. c	13. a	14. b	15. e	16. d
17. a	18. e	19. c	20. a	21. e	22. e
23. f	24. d	25. a	26. c	27. b	28. e
29. a	30. c	31. c	32. d	33. b	34. a
35. c	36. d	37. a	38. d	39. a	40. b
41. c	42. c	43. b	44. d	45. b	46. c

47. a   48. b

49. $\dfrac{400 \text{ mg}}{\text{dose}} \times \dfrac{5 \text{ mL}}{100 \text{ mg}} = \dfrac{2000}{100} = \dfrac{20 \text{ mL}}{\text{dose}}$

50. $\dfrac{0.4 \text{ mg}}{\text{dose}} \times \dfrac{1 \text{ mL}}{0.02 \text{ mg}} = \dfrac{0.4}{0.02} = \dfrac{20 \text{ mL}}{\text{dose}}$

51. a. Interventions include the following: Assess the psychosocial situation of the client because anxicty, fatigue, and pain will increase the sensation of pain; Analyze the cultural aspects of the client's pain; Assess the client's knowledge related to addiction, the use of narcotic analgesic, and his prior experience with them; Teach the client non-pharmacological aspects of pain control: relaxation, massage, thermal packs, biofeedback; Discuss the source of pain and the therapeutic management for the client's pain, including using narcotic pain reliever only after less potent medications are attempted first; Teach the client to assess levels of pain with objective methods to quantify pain in order to better evaluate management of pain; Teach the client to journal to identify triggers for the pain.

b. The outcomes are that the client will report less pain after interventions and more relief from pain management techniques, both pharmacological and non-pharmacological.

52. a. Interventions include the following: Assess the medication regimen used by the client; Educate the client on possible non-pharmacological approaches: relaxation, biofeedback, massage, thermal therapy; Educate the client on triggers that can cause migraines; Help the client identify triggers that might apply; Teach the client appropriate administration techniques of the medications: take Percocet as aura begins and do not wait until headache is severe; Teach the client to evaluate the level of pain and evaluate the improvement using pain scale of choice; Encourage the client to revisit the physician if no improvement has been made with present medications; Encourage the client to request or ask if additional medications might be helpful.

b. Goals include the following: Client will identify triggers to migraines and eliminate the triggers; Client will gain comfort by using non-pharmacological approaches to treating migraine discomfort; Client will identify a decrease in discomfort after medication is taken; Empower the client to seek medication or measures in addition to those previously named.

Chapter 20

1. sensation, consciousness
2. infiltration (or field block)
3. consciousness
4. IV, inhaled
5. pain following surgery
6. General anesthetics, sleeping

7. location, extent

8. sensation, motor activity

9. opiates, anxiolytics, barbiturates, neuromuscular blockers

10. balanced, lowered

11. e	12. a	13. b	14. c	15. e	16. b
17. b	18. e	19. e	20. d	21. c	22. e
23. e	24. a	25. d	26. e	27. b	28. e
29. c	30. h	31. g	32. f	33. d	34. d
35. a	36. b	37. c	38. d	39. c	40. b
41. c	42. a	43. a	44. d	45. b	46. b
47. d	48. a	49. b	50. b		

51. $\dfrac{\frac{1}{6}\,gr}{dose} \times \dfrac{60\,mg}{1\,gr} \times \dfrac{1\,mL}{15\,mg} = \dfrac{\frac{60}{6}}{15} = \dfrac{10}{15} = \dfrac{0.67\,mL}{dose}$

52. $\dfrac{100\,mg}{dose} \times \dfrac{2\,cc}{200\,mg} = \dfrac{200}{200} = \dfrac{1\,mL}{dose}$

53. a. Knowledge deficit related to upcoming surgery and unknown medication regimen.

b. Interventions include preoperative surgical preparation and teaching: Preoperative medications are given to relieve anxiety and provide sedation; Anticholinergics are given to dry secretions to prevent pneumonia and aspiration; Pain medications are given to aid in pain control; An IV medication is given to cause rapid unconsciousness; After IV medications take effect, the client is given an inhaled anesthesia; Muscle relaxants are given to provide relaxation during which time the client will breathe with use of a ventilator; Postoperative medications will include analgesics for the client, and antiemetics if needed to prevent vomiting; Assess the client's understanding of the information given; Ask for client questions.

54. a. The nursing diagnosis is anxiety related to anticipated pain of invasive procedure as evidenced by inability to concentrate; appearance of nervousness, apprehension, and tension; restlessness; and hyperattentiveness.

b. Assessment data include rapid pressured speech, tremulousness, restlessness, scanning of room, and asking questions.

c. Interventions are as follows: Assist client to reduce level of anxiety by reassurance and staying with the client; Speak slowly and calmly when giving information; Ask about any physical problems and past history as well as present medications; Give clear, concise information when teaching about the medications to be used; Discuss alternate methods of relaxation; Help establish short-term goals and reinforce positive responses to questions and actions; Initiate health teaching in short, concise statements and move at the client's own pace; Monitor vital signs and any evidence of shortness of breath or chest pain.

d. Goals for the client may include the following: The client will demonstrate a decrease in anxiety as shown by slower speech patterns, decreased vital signs, and the ability to repeat instruction-and-answer questions in a focused method; The client will relate information offered during the teaching session relating to the upcoming procedure; The client will relate information that has been taught throughout the teaching session.

e. Vital signs are normal. The client repeats instructions and answers questions appropriately.

Chapter 21

1. increases

2. increasing peripheral resistance

3. relax, decreasing

4. angiotensin II, aldosterone

5. Reflex tachycardia

6. fight-or-flight

7. Diuretics

8. f	9. c	10. d	11. a	12. b	13. c
14. g	15. d	16. a	17. b	18. d	19. c
20. a	21. c	22. d	23. a	24. a	25. b
26. b	27. d	28. a	29. b	30. a	31. d
32. a	33. c	34. c	35. d	36. a	

37. $\dfrac{15\,mg}{1} \times \dfrac{2\,mL}{20\,mg} = 1.5\,mL$

38. $\dfrac{60\,mg}{1} \times \dfrac{1\,tablet}{120\,mg} = \frac{1}{2}\,tablet$

39. a. Assessment data include smoking, weight, elevated lipids, and anxiety.

b. Nursing diagnoses are as follows:

1. Imbalanced nutrition: Mmore than body requirements (Outcome: Client demonstrates accurate knowledge of dietary regimen to lower dietary fats.)

2. Deficient knowledge: purpose, precautions, and side effects of antihypertensive drugs (Outcome: Client will verbalize accurate understanding of the purpose, precautions, and side effects of drugs used to treat hypertension.)

3. Health-seeking behaviours: relaxation techniques to effectively reduce stress (Outcome: Client reports subjective relief of stress after using relaxation techniques.)

c. The nurse will consider adding a second antihypertensive drug class if the first drug has proven to be inadequate in treatment of hypertension. It is common to prescribe two antihypertensives concurrently to manage resistant hypertension.

40. a. Orthostatic hypotension may be causing the dizziness. Explaining to Ms. F that she should sit on the side of the bed a few minutes before standing might solve this problem.

b. Cardiac rhythm abnormalities are one sign of possible hyperkalemia. When switched to a potassium-sparing diuretic such as spironolactone, Ms. F should not supplement her diet with excess potassium.

c. It may not be necessary to change this client's medications, because they seem to be keeping blood pressure within normal limits. Client teaching may be all that is necessary to resolve Ms. F's complaints.

Chapter 22

1. hyperlipidemia
2. plaque
3. triglycerides, phospholipids, steroids
4. cholesterol, triglycerides, phospholipids
5. statin
6. b   7. d   8. c   9. a   10. c   11. b
12. b   13. d   14. d   15. d   16. b   17. b
18. a   19. d   20. c   21. b   22. c   23. a
24. c   25. c
26. 2 tablets at bedtime which is usually 2100 hours

$$\frac{40 \text{ mg}}{1} \times \frac{1 \text{ tablet}}{40 \text{ mg}} = \frac{40}{40} = 1 \text{ tablet}$$

27. 2 tablets, divide the dose, give one in the morning 30 minutes before breakfast, and 1 tablet 30 minutes before the evening meal

$$\frac{1.2 \text{ g}}{1} \times \frac{1000 \text{ mg}}{1 \text{ g}} \times \frac{1 \text{ tablet}}{600 \text{ mg}} = \frac{1200}{600} = 2 \text{ tablets}$$

28. a. Data assessment includes obesity; history of two heart attacks; and history of hypertension, elevated LDL, elevated triglycerides.

b. Therapy with a statin drug is highly indicated because the client has a history of heart disease and hypertension with elevated lipid levels.

c. Reduce dietary intake of lipids and encourage a safe exercise program.

29. a. Ascertain if the client is taking the drugs as prescribed. If she is taking the drugs, then dietary habit changes are important to discuss, especially lipid-rich foods. Many clients believe that if they are taking lipid-lowering agents, they do not have to watch their dietary fat intake.

b. Teach risk factor modification, which includes diet restrictions related to fats, calorie assessment, exercise assessment, stress assessment, knowledge, and understanding of when to take statin drugs. Remind her that it is best to take statin drugs in the evening as the body produces the most cholesterol during the night.

Chapter 23

1. angina pectoris
2. plaque
3. stable

4. organic nitrates
5. transdermal patch
6. anticoagulants
7. c   8. a   9. b   10. b   11. c   12. a
13. c   14. a   15. a   16. c   17. b   18. a
19. d   20. b   21. c   22. c   23. a   24. d
25. a   26. d   27. d   28. b   29. b   30. a
31. c   32. c   33. c   34. c   35. c   36. d
37. d   38. b   39. c   40. a   41. c

42. $\dfrac{50 \text{ mg}}{250 \text{ mL}} \times \dfrac{1000 \text{ } \mu g}{1 \text{ mg}} \times \dfrac{1 \text{ mL}}{60 \text{ gtt}} \times \dfrac{15 \text{ gtt}}{1 \text{ min}} =$

$\dfrac{750\,000}{15\,000} = \dfrac{50 \text{ } \mu g}{\text{min}}$

43. $\dfrac{100 \text{ mL}}{125 \text{ mg}} \times \dfrac{60 \text{ gtt}}{1 \text{ mL}} \times \dfrac{10 \text{ mg}}{1 \text{ hr}} \times \dfrac{1 \text{ hr}}{60 \text{ min}} =$

$\dfrac{60\,000}{7500} = \dfrac{8 \text{ gtt}}{\text{min}}$

44. a. His advancing age has put him at risk for atherosclerosis. His heavy tobacco use has predisposed him to vascular disease. His weight has increased the stress on the cardiovascular system. His life may be considered stressful based on the size of his family. He may have led a sedentary life because of his career path as an accountant.

b. Symptoms include slurred speech and weakness on the left side.

c. Retavase will dissolve the cerebral thrombosis. Lasix will control blood pressure and decrease the chances of further clot movement. Heparin prevents further thrombus development.

d. Hydrochlorothiazide is a diuretic that will treat Mr. M's hypertension. It is a safer drug for use at home as it does not lower potassium like Lasix. Warfarin is taken orally and will be used to provide anticoagulation. This drug is used to prevent further thrombus development and therefore prevent an embolus event. Warfarin is a good discharge anticoagulant because it can be given by mouth. Diltiazem is a calcium channel blocker that is an effective drug to be used at home to stabilize hypertension.

45. a. Nursing diagnoses are as follows: Altered tissue perfusion related to vascular disease (Outcome: Client will experience relief of chest pain.) Pain (headache) related to adverse effects of medication (Outcome: Client will experience relief of headaches.) Decreased cardiac output related to loss of myocardial muscle function (Outcome: Client has adequate cardiac output within 24 hours of treatment as evidenced by BP < 160/90 mm Hg, respiration < 20/min.)

b. Client presents with some worsening signs of heart failure. Respiration is elevated to 28/min. Lower extremities are edematous, chest pain is not relieved, and client is gaining weight.

c. The following reasons may be suspected:

1. Possibly Mrs. R is not taking the medications correctly. Review the medication delivery systems used to treat her chest pain and determine if she is using the medications correctly.

2. Mrs. R's medical situation may be worsening. Her coronary arteries may be obstructed and cardiac failure is occurring based on coronary occlusion.

3. Mrs. R. may be resistant to the nitrates; therefore, new agents may be necessary to treat her chest pain or current agents may need to be increased in dosage.

4. The combination treatment (nitrate, beta-blocker, calcium channel blocker) may not be the best combination to treat this client.

Chapter 24

1. Frank-Starling
2. 60
3. preload, afterload
4. increase, strength
5. forcefully, slowly
6. digoxin immune Fab (Digibind)
7. increasing

8. c	9. e	10. d	11. c	12. b	13. c
14. a	15. c	16. e	17. d	18. a	19. c
20. d	21. b	22. a	23. b	24. c	25. a
26. d	27. b	28. a	29. c	30. b	31. c
32. c	33. a	34. d	35. d	36. a	37. c
38. b	39. d	40. a			

41. 6.25 mg/day × 3.125 mg/1 pill = 2 pills/day

2 pills/dose × 2 doses/day = 4 pills/day

4 pills/day × 14 days = 56 pills

42. $\frac{40 \text{ mg}}{1} \times \frac{2 \text{ mL}}{20 \text{ mg}} = \frac{80}{20} = 4 \text{ mL}$

43. a. Hydrochlorothiazide and lisinopril will lower blood pressure, thus reducing the workload on the heart. Atorvastatin will help reduce blood cholesterol levels, which are associated with hypertension and heart disease.

b. Mr. L is showing a need to control his life and manage his disease. He is 60 years old, and he is determined to manage his disease without prescriptions. However, Mr. L should be encouraged to take the drugs as prescribed. He needs to understand that heart failure is a progressive disorder and that he is in the early stages. He can limit the progression with knowledge and attention to symptoms. He should be advised to try alternative therapies in addition to his medications, not in place of them.

c. Mr. L should be advised to continue his walks and develop a complete exercise and dietary program, under the direction of his nurse.

44. a. Laboured and rapid respiration, coarse breath sounds with wheezing, rapid weight gain, and rapid heart rate support a diagnosis of heart failure.

b. The digoxin is given IV for fast uptake and action. The 0.5 mg dose with a repeat in 4 hours is considered a loading dose. It is common to give an adult 0.25 mg/day by mouth of digoxin to treat heart failure.

c. This client needs the renal system evaluated frequently. The output is of extreme importance as retention of fluid will increase the heart failure. This client had a 4.5 kg weight gain in 3 days. The nurse should be asking about the hourly urinary output.

Chapter 25

1. sodium
2. supraventricular
3. sudden death
4. atrial fibrillation
5. arterial embolism (or small blood clots)
6. heart block, severe bradycardia, AV block
7. a. SA node
   b. AV node
   c. bundle of His
   d. bundle branches
   e. Purkinje fibres
   f. P wave
   g. QRS complex
   h. T wave

8. a	9. b	10. d	11. d	12. a	13. c
14. a	15. a	16. e	17. a	18. d	19. c
20. b	21. d	22. b	23. c	24. a	25. d
26. d	27. c	28. b	29. a	30. b	31. b
32. d	33. d	34. c	35. b	36. c	37. a
38. c	39. d	40. c	41. b		

42. $\frac{100 \text{ mL}}{125 \text{ mg}} \times \frac{20 \text{ mg}}{1 \text{ hr}} = \frac{2000}{125} = \frac{16 \text{ mL}}{\text{hr}}$

43. $\frac{250 \text{ mL}}{900 \text{ mg}} \times \frac{0.5 \text{ mg}}{1 \text{ min}} \times \frac{60 \text{ min}}{1 \text{ hr}} =$

$\frac{7500}{900} = \frac{8.33 \text{ mL}}{\text{hr}} \text{ or } \frac{8 \text{ mL}}{\text{hr}}$

44. a. Since propranolol decreases heart rate and slows conduction through the AV node, the nurse should document heart rate and rhythm before giving propranolol. The nurse should also assess for the presence of heart block, bradycardia, AV block, and asthma. A blood pressure assessment is essential before the delivery of propranolol.

b. Quinidine is an antidysrhythmic drug. It will slow the conduction and prolong the refractory period. The client should be placed in the supine position because hypotension can result following administration.

c. Quinidine can cause diarrhea. It can also cause dysrhythmias or worsen existing ones. The nurse must therefore assess cardiac rhythm frequently. The nurse must also assess for dehydration and fluid and electrolyte imbalance because of the loss of fluid from diarrhea. A common side effect of propranolol is hypotension and bradycardia. The nurse must be alert for the client's complaints of dizziness and fatigue.

45. a. Assess cardiac rhythm. Do not give if client is demonstrating heart block, severe hypotension, severe congestive failure, or cardiogenic shock. Make sure vital signs and ECG are documented before drug is given. Note shortness of breath, presence of cough, chest pain, and urinary output.

b. Teach client about heart rate and the need to notify the nurse if rate goes below 60 bpm. Watch for orthostatic hypotension, confusion, and chest pain. Do not give with grapefruit juice as it may increase the level of Isoptin. Hawthorne, an herbal supplement, can cause hypotension if given with Isoptin.

c. Nursing diagnoses include the following: Altered tissue perfusion related to cardiac conduction abnormality; Knowledge deficit related to medication regimen; Risk for injury related to medication adverse effects.

Chapter 26

1. a. prothrombin activator
b. thrombin
c. fibrinogen
2. a. plasmin
b. plasminogen activator
3. anticoagulants
4. thrombolytics
5. Antifibrinolytics
6. prothrombin time (PT), international normalized ratio (INR)

7. a	8. e	9. b	10. c	11. f	12. e
13. g	14. d	15. a	16. a	17. c	18. b
19. d	20. a	21. d	22. c	23. c	24. a
25. a	26. c	27. d	28. d	29. c	30. b
31. b	32. d	33. b	34. a	35. b	36. a
37. d	38. c				

39. $\dfrac{2500 \text{ U}}{1 \text{ hr}} \times \dfrac{1000 \text{ mL}}{50\,000 \text{ U}} = \dfrac{2\,500\,000}{50\,000} = \dfrac{50 \text{ mL}}{\text{hr}}$

40. $\dfrac{20\,000 \text{ U}}{500 \text{ mL}} \times \dfrac{30 \text{ mL}}{1 \text{ hr}} = \dfrac{1200 \text{ U}}{\text{hr}}$

$\dfrac{1200 \text{ U}}{1 \text{ hr}} \times \dfrac{24 \text{ hr}}{1 \text{ day}} = \dfrac{28\,800 \text{ U}}{\text{day}}$

41. a. Ms. S should use caution when engaged in activities that can cause bleeding, such as shaving, brushing teeth, trimming nails, and using kitchen

knives. A soft toothbrush and an electric razor are safe choices. Contact activities, because of their high risk for injury, should be avoided.

b. Ms. S should report unusual bruising or bleeding such as nosebleeds, bleeding gums, black or red stools, heavy menstrual periods, or spitting up blood.

c. ASA or other medications containing salicylates should never be taken. Acetaminophen could be used for headaches. Feverfew, garlic, ginger, and arnica also should be avoided.

42. a. Alcohol is a major irritant for GI ulcer formation. The chronic use of alcohol might contribute to ulceration. The use of warfarin also prolongs bleeding time, thus the bright red blood during vomiting.

b. Nursing diagnoses are as follows: Altered tissue perfusion related to blood loss (Outcome: The client will experience a stable blood pressure and pulse. The client will have no signs and symptoms of anoxia.) Knowledge deficit related to alcohol consumption (Outcome: The client will demonstrate understanding of the long-term effects of alcohol consumption.) Knowledge deficit related to warfarin treatment (Outcome: The client will demonstrate understanding of the drug's action by accurately describing drug side effects and precautions.)

c. Immediate IM administration of vitamin K could reverse the anticoagulation effects of warfarin. Administration of an antifibrinolytic, such as aminocaproic acid (Amicar), might reduce excessive bleeding from the ulcer site.

Chapter 27

1. sympathetic
2. alpha
3. alpha, beta
4. $beta_1$
5. basic life support
6. Whole blood
7. circulatory overload
8. PT, PTT, bleeding time

9. a	10. b	11. a	12. c	13. b	14. c
15. a	16. b	17. c	18. d	19. a	20. c
21. b	22. d	23. c	24. a	25. b	26. d
27. d	28. b	29. d	30. a	31. c	32. b

33. 13.86 mL/hr: 369.6 μg/min

$\dfrac{92.4 \text{ kg}}{1 \text{ min}} \times \dfrac{4 \text{ μg}}{1 \text{ kg}} \times \dfrac{1 \text{ mg}}{1000 \text{ μg}} \times \dfrac{250 \text{ mL}}{400 \text{ mg}} \times \dfrac{60 \text{ min}}{1 \text{ hr}}$

$= \dfrac{5\,544\,000}{400\,000} = 13.86 \text{ mL/hr}$

$\dfrac{400 \text{ mg}}{250 \text{ mL}} \times \dfrac{1000 \text{ μg}}{1 \text{ mg}} \times \dfrac{1 \text{ hr}}{60 \text{ min}} \times \dfrac{13.86 \text{ mL}}{1 \text{ hr}}$

$= \dfrac{5\,544\,000}{15\,000} = \dfrac{369.60 \text{ μg}}{\text{min}}$

34. $$\frac{99.4 \text{ kg}}{1 \text{ min}} \times \frac{5 \text{ } \mu g}{1 \text{ kg}} \times \frac{1 \text{ mg}}{1000 \text{ } \mu g} \times \frac{250 \text{ mL}}{500 \text{ mg}} \times \frac{60 \text{ min}}{1 \text{ hr}}$$

$$= \frac{7\,455\,000}{500\,000} = \frac{14.91 \text{ mL}}{hr}$$

35. a. Assessment data include auto accident, wandering, confusion, weak pulse, dysrhythmias, changing blood pressure, pulse, and unresponsiveness.

b. Altered tissue perfusion related to changing pulse and blood pressure.

c. Dextran is an IV colloid given to expand fluid volume. If blood pressure rises, the nurse can assume the drug is effective. Norepinephrine is a potent vasoconstrictor used to reverse the severe hypotension. If blood pressure rises, then the nurse can assume the drug is effective. Dobutamine will help the heart beat with more force so that vital organs can receive blood and nutrients. When pulse becomes strong and blood pressure rises, the nurse can assume that the drug is effective. Lidocaine was likely given to correct the dysrhythmia. When heart rate and rhythm return to pre-incident levels, then the nurse can assume the medication was effective.

36. a. With a closed head injury, neurogenic shock must be considered. The fact that the client is comatose, has slow respirations, low blood pressure and pulse, and has unresponsive pupils supports this diagnosis.

b. Vasoconstrictors such as norepinephrine will likely be needed to maintain the client's blood pressure; a cardiotonic agent such as dopamine may be useful in strengthening the force of the myocardial contraction.

c. Blood pressure, pulse, and respirations return to normal. The client regains consciousness. No CPR is necessary, and no tissue hypoxia to the brain or kidneys results.

Chapter 28

1. erythropoiesis, erythropoietin
2. epoetin alfa (Epogen, Eprex)
3. iron
4. size, colour
5. Ferritin, hemosiderin
6. recycled

7. c	8. a	9. b	10. a	11. b	12. a
13. c	14. d	15. d	16. c	17. b	18. a
19. a	20. c	21. a	22. b	23. d	24. b
25. a	26. d	27. c	28. a	29. c	30. a
31. b					

32. $$\frac{57 \text{ kg}}{1 \text{ day}} \times \frac{5 \text{ } \mu g}{1 \text{ kg}} = \frac{285}{1} = \frac{285 \text{ } \mu g}{\text{day}}$$

33. No;

$$\frac{30 \text{ kg}}{1 \text{ day}} \times \frac{20 \text{ } \mu g}{1 \text{ kg}} = \frac{600}{1} = \frac{600 \text{ } \mu g}{\text{day}}$$

34. a. Renal failure causes a decrease in the production of the hormone erythropoietin. This leads to anemia and a decreased production of RBCs.

b. Hypertension is the most likely side effect to occur. It is related to the increased hematocrit and also to the renal failure. Others include CVA, MI, and thrombophlebitis, all related to the increased hematocrit. It would be important to ask the client during your assessment if he had any blurred vision, slurred speech, transient weakness, chest pain, or calf pain.

c. Topics to cover include the importance of keeping physician appointments so that blood pressure can be monitored, how to self-administer SC injections, used needle disposal, reportable BP changes, and how to take his own blood pressure at home. Signs and symptoms of thrombophlebitis should be discussed. The client should also be taught to maintain adequate dietary intake of iron, folate, and B_{12} and to maintain his renal diet.

35. a. He should tell you that the cause of pernicious anemia is lack of intrinsic factor, in this case probably caused by his chronic gastritis. Since oxygen is carried by the RBCs and he is anemic, the body cells are not getting adequate oxygen. This causes the tired, lethargic feeling.

b. The client should be told to inform other nurses that he uses vitamin B_{12}, particularly in view of its interaction with colchicine. The importance of monitoring potassium levels should be stressed. Instruction on self-administration may be needed. If the client gives it parenterally, signs of anaphylaxis should be taught.

c. An iron preparation would be used in cases of inadequate hemoglobin or inadequate RBCs. The problem in megaloblastic anemia is that the RBCs are not maturing properly. B_{12} will treat this problem.

36. a. Assessments include health history, allergies, history of bacterial or fungal infections, vital signs, and WBC count with differential.

b. The client should be told that filgrastim may cause an elevation in liver enzymes. It may cause an allergic reaction. Due to the stimulation of bone marrow cells, it may produce bone pain.

c. She needs to wash hands frequently; limit contact with crowds and people with colds; cook all foods; avoid fresh fruits, vegetables, and plants; limit exposure to children and animals; empty the bladder frequently; drink more; and cough and deep breathe several times daily.

Chapter 29

1. ventilation
2. nebulizer
3. emphysema, chronic bronchitis
4. dextromethorphan

5. MDI

6. bronchial

7. 2 full minutes

8. bitter

9. viral, upper respiratory tract

10. e   11. b   12. a   13. b   14. e   15. e

16. d   17. c   18. e   19. d   20. c   21. b

22. d   23. a   24. b   25. b   26. a   27. b

28. c   29. a   30. a   31. d   32. c   33. b

34. c   35. a   36. b

37. $\dfrac{50\ \text{kg}}{1\ \text{hr}} \times \dfrac{0.25\ \text{mg}}{1\ \text{kg}} = \dfrac{12.50\ \text{mg}}{1\ \text{hr}} \times \dfrac{6\ \text{hr}}{1} = 75\ \text{mg}$

38. $\dfrac{4\ \text{mg}}{\text{dose}} \times \dfrac{5\ \text{mL}}{2\ \text{mg}} = \dfrac{20}{2} = \dfrac{10\ \text{mL}}{\text{dose}}$

39. a. Green thick mucus. Increased incident of wheezing and shortness of breath and wheezing worsening over 2 weeks.

   b. Assess respiratory status, respiratory rate, vital signs, auscultation of breath sounds, pulmonary function studies (peak flow, arterial blood gasses, and O_2 saturation). Fluids: IV if necessary, PO if possible, 2–3 L per day.

   Head of bed elevated. O_2 as needed to maintain oxygen saturation levels at a satisfactory level. Administer beta$_2$-agonist and monitor for improvement and side effects. Client teaching to include: preventive inhaler (beclomethasone). Notify physician for any increased dyspnea, wheezing, fever, change in sputum colour or consistency. Encourage compliance with meds and discuss side effects and ways to decrease side effects: Avoid environmental antigens that trigger asthma responses such as pollen, animal dander, dust, smoke, cold air; Eat regularly, but smaller meals more frequently; Receive yearly vaccines to prevent respiratory infections; Decrease or eliminate intake of caffeine; Avoid smoking.

   c. Beclomethasone is a glucocorticoid used to decrease inflammation and prevent asthma attacks. Theophylline is a methylxanthine used to provide bronchodilation.

   d. Lorazepam is a CNS depressant that is used as an antianxiety agent to decrease the dyspnea due to stress and anxiety. Metaproterenol is a beta$_2$-agonist that will dilate bronchioles and relieve the dyspnea.

40 a. Knowledge deficit related to medication change evidenced by questions asked by client.

   b. Assess client knowledge of the medications that she has been taking and of her condition.

Chapter 30

1. humoral, antibodies

2. active

3. passive

4. cytokines

5. biological response modifiers

6. superinfections

7. glucocorticoids, antimetabolites, antibodies, calcineurin inhibitors

8. c   9. a   10. d   11. e   12. f   13. b

14. c   15. c   16. b   17. c   18. a   19. c

20. a   21. c   22. a   23. c   24. a   25. d

26. c   27. c   28. b   29. a   30. d

31. 72 hours = 12 240 mg

   $\dfrac{81.6\ \text{kg}}{\text{dose}} \times \dfrac{150\ \text{mg}}{1\ \text{kg}} = \dfrac{12\ 240}{\text{dose}}$

   2, 4, 6, 8 weeks = 8160 mg

   $\dfrac{81.6\ \text{kg}}{\text{dose}} \times \dfrac{100\ \text{mg}}{1\ \text{kg}} = \dfrac{8160}{\text{dose}}$

   12, 16 weeks = 4080 mg

   $\dfrac{81.6\ \text{kg}}{\text{dose}} \times \dfrac{50\ \text{mg}}{1\ \text{kg}} = \dfrac{4080}{\text{dose}}$

32. $\dfrac{45.3\ \text{kg}}{\text{dose}} \times \dfrac{0.15\ \text{mg}}{1\ \text{kg}} = \dfrac{6.795\ \text{mg}}{\text{dose}}$

   $\dfrac{6.795\ \text{mg}}{\text{dose}} \times \dfrac{2\ \text{doses}}{1} = \dfrac{13.59\ \text{mg}}{24\ \text{hr}}$

33. a. The immunostimulant therapy may cause a spontaneous abortion.

   b. Complications or adverse reactions include encephalopathy, depression, bone marrow depression, nausea, and stomatitis.

   c. Side effects include hematuria, petechiae, tarry stools, bruising, fever, sore throat, jaundice, dark-coloured urine, clay-coloured stools, feelings of sadness, and nervousness.

34. a. Immunosuppressants are used to dampen the immune response to reduce the possibility of rejection. The client will need to take the medication as long as the organ is viable.

   b. This class of drugs was developed to suppress the normal cell-mediated immune response. In lay terms, the medication you are taking keeps your body from rejecting your new kidney.

   c. Adverse reactions include superimposed infections, bone marrow depression, alopecia, arthralgia, respiratory distress, edema, nausea, vomiting, paresthesia, fever, blood in urine, black stools, increased pigmentation, and feelings of sadness.

35. a. Vaccinations have eradicated smallpox and poliovirus. They have reduced diphtheria and measles to a fraction of their occurrence prior to vaccinations. They keep our children healthy and reduce the chance of disability or death from infectious diseases.

   b. AJ may have a red area and a sore spot where the shot was given, but this is normal. Severe reactions are rare and usually occur at the time of the shot, when help is readily available.

Chapter 31

1. to rid the body of antigens
2. Mast
3. H_2-receptors
4. non-steroidal anti-inflammatory drugs (NSAIDs)
5. Glucocorticoids
6. Cushing's
7. Reye's
8. c   9. a   10. a   11. c   12. b   13. d
14. c   15. a   16. a   17. d   18. c   19. a
20. c   21. d   22. b   23. b   24. d   25. b
26. d   27. a   28. c   29. c
30. $\dfrac{30 \text{ gtt}}{\text{dose}} \times \dfrac{1 \text{ mL}}{15 \text{ gtt}} = \dfrac{30}{15} = \dfrac{2 \text{ mL}}{\text{dose}}$

   $\dfrac{2 \text{ mL}}{\text{dose}} \times \dfrac{6 \text{ doses}}{1} = \dfrac{12 \text{ mL}}{24 \text{ hr}}$

   $\dfrac{30 \text{ gtt}}{\text{dose}} \times \dfrac{6 \text{ doses}}{1} = \dfrac{180 \text{ gtt}}{24 \text{ hr}}$

31. $\dfrac{500 \text{ mg}}{\text{dose}} \times \dfrac{1 \text{ tablet}}{250 \text{ mg}} = \dfrac{500}{250} = \dfrac{2 \text{ tablets}}{\text{dose}}$

   $\dfrac{500 \text{ mg}}{\text{dose}} \times 4 \text{ doses} = \dfrac{2000 \text{ mg}}{24 \text{ hr}}$

   Not a recommended dose. 1000 mg is recommended in a 24-hour period.

32. a. A.C. & C tablets are a combination of ASA and codeine. ASA is an anti-inflammatory/pain reliever and codeine is an opioid used for moderate pain. Ketoprofen is also an anti-inflammatory/pain reliever, but with higher anti-inflammatory properties than ASA.

    b. Glucocorticoids are contraindicated when an active infection is present.

    c. ASA is irritating to the stomach lining and with its anticoagulant effect may cause gastric bleeding. Codeine may cause constipation, nausea, and vomiting. Ketoprofen may also cause nausea and vomiting.

33. a. The drug classification is non-steroidal anti-inflammatory drug (NSAID).

    b. They have no GI side effects and do not affect blood coagulation.

    c. The nurse should assess for heart failure, fluid retention, hypertension, renal disease, and liver dysfunction.

34. a. Children under the age of 19 years should not be given Aspirin (ASA).

    b. Children under 1 year should be given infant drops related to variations in the strengths in the preparations listed as "children's liquid."

    c. Aspirin when given to children under the age of 19 may cause the potentially fatal condition Reye's syndrome.

Chapter 32

1. antibiotics, anti-infectives
2. mutations
3. broad spectrum
4. Superinfection
5. penicillinase (or beta-lactamase)
6. Cephalosporins
7. Macrolide
8. aminoglycosides
9. a   10. f   11. b   12. e   13. e   14. d
15. c   16. b   17. g   18. f   19. b   20. d
21. f   22. b   23. e   24. c   25. a   26. c
27. c   28. d   29. b   30. c   31. d   32. c
33. d   34. d   35. d   36. b   37. b   38. b
39. a   40. d   41. a   42. a   43. c   44. b
45. d
46. $\dfrac{500 \text{ mg}}{1} \times \dfrac{1 \text{ g}}{1000 \text{ mg}} = \dfrac{1 \text{ tablet}}{1 \text{ g}} = \dfrac{500}{1000} =$

   $\dfrac{\frac{1}{2} \text{ tablet}}{\text{dose}} = \dfrac{\frac{2}{1} \text{ dose}}{1} = \dfrac{1 \text{ tablet}}{12 \text{ hr}}$

47. $\dfrac{500 \text{ mg}}{\text{dose}} \times \dfrac{1 \text{ tablet}}{250 \text{ mg}} = \dfrac{500}{250} = \dfrac{2 \text{ tablets}}{\text{dose}}$

   $\dfrac{2 \text{ tablets}}{\text{dose}} \times \dfrac{4 \text{ doses}}{1} = \dfrac{8 \text{ tablets}}{24 \text{ hr}}$

48. a. The widespread use of antibiotics often leads to resistant strains of bacteria.

    b. The longer the antibiotic is used, the higher the percentage of resistant strains.

    c. She may develop acquired resistance.

    d. It will most likely become ineffective in treating her infection.

49. a. Broad-spectrum antibiotics are prescribed until the culture and sensitivity tests can be performed and the actual microbe can be identified.

    b. Culture and sensitivity tests are performed to identify the microbe.

    c. Specific drug therapy can be selected based on which antibiotic would be most effective.

50. a. Adverse effects are formation of crystals in the urine, hypersensitivity reactions, nausea and vomiting, aplastic anemia, hemolytic anemia, and agranulocytosis.

    b. The nurse must carefully monitor the client's condition and provide client education.

    c. Encourage 3000 mL of fluid every 24 hours to reduce the possibility of the formation of crystals in the urine.

Chapter 33

1. Fungi
2. Clotrimazole

3. Canadian Malaria Network, atovaquone/proguanil (Malarone)
4. mycoses
5. dermatophytic
6. lungs, brain, digestive organs
7. superficial, systemic
8. azoles, ergosterol
9. Amphotericin B
10. orally

11. a 12. b 13. a 14. a 15. b 16. a
17. c 18. a 19. d 20. b 21. e 22. f
23. d 24. d 25. d 26. c 27. a 28. a
29. d 30. b 31. a 32. c 33. a 34. b
35. d 36. a 37. b 38. a 39. a 40. d

41. $\dfrac{150\ lb}{1} \times \dfrac{1\ kg}{2.2\ lb} = 68.18\ kg$

$\dfrac{150\ lb}{day} \times \dfrac{1\ kg}{2.2\ lb} \times \dfrac{0.25\ mg}{1\ kg} = \dfrac{37.50}{2.2} = \dfrac{17.05\ mg}{day}$

42. 100 mg/50 mg × 1 = 2 tablets/dose

43. a. The client should consult her obstetrician concerning the best choice for her drug regimen. Antifungals with less adverse reactions are more commonly used for vaginal candidiasis, such as terconazole and tioconazole.

b. The foremost importance is to treat the problem without harm to the fetus. Therefore, the drug of choice would be the antifungal with the least adverse reactions and the least potential for harm to the fetus.

44. a. These are not the usual symptoms of malaria. Fever and chills usually appear 14 to 25 days after infection.

b. The symptoms are likely caused by dehydration and exhaustion due to extended travel in a short period of time.

c. Malaria prevention includes taking prophylactic medication, staying in from dusk until dawn, wearing long-sleeved shirts and pants, sleeping under a mosquito net, and using a DEET-based repellent.

45. a. The client will receive metronidazole (Flagyl) 250 to 750 mg tid.

b. Adverse reactions include anorexia, nausea, diarrhea, dizziness, headache, dryness of the mouth, and metallic taste in the mouth.

c. Amebiasis involves the large intestine.

Chapter 34

1. capsid, ribonucleic acid (RNA), deoxyribonucleic acid (DNA)
2. intracellular parasites
3. latent
4. antiretrovirals
5. highly active antiretroviral therapy (HAART)
6. neuroaminidase inhibitors

7. protease inhibitors
8. DNA, contaminated blood, body fluids
9. Acyclovir
10. hepatitis C virus

11. c 12. d 13. b 14. e 15. a 16. b
17. d 18. a 19. a 20. c 21. c 22. a
23. a 24. b 25. c 26. a 27. b 28. a
29. c 30. d 31. d

32. $\dfrac{100\ mg}{dose} \times \dfrac{1\ tablet}{50\ mg} = \dfrac{100}{50} = \dfrac{2\ tablets}{dose}$

$\dfrac{2\ tablets}{dose} \times \dfrac{2\ doses}{day} = \dfrac{4\ tablets}{day}$

33. Mr. X had 14 pills on hand. He will require 21 pills to fill the new order. Therefore, he requires 7 more pills.

34. a. The combination drug regimen is called highly active antiretroviral therapy (HAART). The goal of HAART is to reduce the plasma level of HIV to its lowest possible level and to allow the client to live symptom-free longer. HAART also reduces the probability that a virus will become resistant to treatment.

b. Classes include nucleoside reverse transcriptase inhibitors (NRTIs), non-nucleoside reverse transcriptase inhibitors (NNRTIs), protease inhibitors, and reverse transcriptase inhibitors (RTIs).

c. NRTIs build their own DNA, preventing the viral DNA chain from lengthening. NNRTIs bind directly to the viral enzyme reverse transcriptase and inhibit its function. RTIs inhibit viral replication because reverse transcriptase is not found in animal cells. Protease inhibitors block the viral enzyme protease, which is responsible for the final assembly of the HIV virions.

35. a. The vaccination may prevent the client from getting influenza or reduce the severity of the symptoms.

b. The vaccination lasts several months to 1 year.

c. Amantadine (Symmetrel) is the drug of choice.

36. a. Transmission occurs through exposure to contaminated blood and body fluids.

b. Symptoms include fever, chills, fatigue, anorexia, nausea, and vomiting.

c. Symptoms include prolonged fatigue, jaundice, liver cirrhosis, and ultimately liver failure.

37. a. Judicious use of drug therapy is still warranted during pregnancy.

b. Acyclovir is the drug of choice.

Chapter 35

1. surgery, radiation therapy, chemotherapy
2. alkylating agents
3. folic acid
4. intravenously
5. plant extracts or natural products
6. hormones, hormone

7. Biological response

8. d   9. e   10. g   11. a   12. b   13. c

14. a   15. b   16. e   17. b   18. c   19. e

20. d   21. f   22. a   23. b   24. d   25. d

26. a   27. c   28. a   29. c   30. b   31. c

32. d   33. b   34. c   35. a   36. d   37. a

38. b   39. a   40. d   41. b   42. d

43. $\dfrac{20 \text{ mg}}{\text{dose}} \times \dfrac{1 \text{ tablet}}{10 \text{ mg}} = \dfrac{20}{10} = \dfrac{2 \text{ tablets}}{\text{dose}}$

44. $\dfrac{25 \text{ mg}}{\text{dose}} \times \dfrac{2 \text{ mL}}{50 \text{ mg}} = \dfrac{50}{50} = \dfrac{1 \text{ mL}}{\text{dose}}$

$\dfrac{1 \text{ mL}}{\text{dose}} \times \dfrac{4 \text{ doses}}{1} = \dfrac{4 \text{ mL}}{\text{day}}$

45. a. Tumours should be treated at an early stage with multiple drugs and using several methods such as chemotherapy, radiation, and surgery when possible. If Mr. U had not sought medical treatment early enough, the remaining cancer cells could decrease the chance of recovery.

b. Drugs from different antineoplastic classes can be given during a course of chemotherapy. Different classes might affect different stages of the cancer cell's life cycle, thereby increasing the percentage of cancer cell death.

c. Administer drugs on a specific schedule to give normal cells time to recover from the adverse effects of the drugs.

46. a. Medications include antiemetics, benzodiazepines, serotonin receptor antagonists, and corticosteroids.

b. The client should avoid crowds, unsanitary conditions, and other potentially infectious situations. Proper hygiene is strongly recommended.

c. Anorexia can be reduced by providing the client with her favourite foods. A well-balanced diet should be implemented, including consultation with a registered dietitian.

47. a. Tamoxifen causes initial "tumour flare," an idiosyncratic increase in tumour size and bone, but this is an expected therapeutic event.

b. Tamoxifen is a selective estrogen receptor modulator (SERM).

c. The drug is effective against breast tumours that require estrogen for their growth.

d. Tamoxifen is one of the few antineoplastics given to *prevent* cancer, as well as to *treat* cancer.

e. No, this medication is a pregnancy category D and has been determined to have adverse effects on the fetus. It should be given only if the benefits to the mother outweigh the risks to the fetus.

Chapter 36

1. alimentary, accessory
2. transport, enzymes, digestion, absorption
3. villi, microvilli, food/medications

4. peristalsis, smooth
5. cardiac sphincter, esophageal reflux
6. chief, parietal, intrinsic factor
7. acidic, 1.5 to 3.5
8. erosion, mucosal, duodenum
9. peptic ulcer disease, glucocorticoids, ASA, NSAIDs
10. *Helicobacter pylori*

11. e   12. c   13. a   14. g   15. f   16. d

17. b   18. d   19. b   20. a   21. d   22. c

23. b   24. d   25. c   26. d   27. b   28. b

29. d   30. c   31. d   32. a

33. $\dfrac{60 \text{ gtt}}{1 \text{ mL}} \times \dfrac{100 \text{ mL}}{30 \text{ min}} \times \dfrac{60 \text{ min}}{1 \text{ hr}} = \dfrac{360\,000}{30}$

$= \dfrac{12\,000 \text{ gtts}}{\text{hr}}$

$\dfrac{100 \text{ mL}}{30 \text{ min}} \times \dfrac{60 \text{ min}}{1 \text{ hr}} = \dfrac{6000}{30} = \dfrac{200 \text{ mL}}{\text{hr}}$

34. 1000, 1400, 1900, 2200 hours

$30 \text{ mL} \times 4 = 120 \text{ mL}$

$120 \text{ mL} \times 7 = 840 \text{ mL}$

35. a. Nursing diagnoses include risk for injury and knowledge deficit.

b. Risk for injury would be the priority due to the existing confusion. Knowledge deficit is related to OTC medication.

36. a. Short-term goals are client will be free from injury and will exhibit less confusion.

b. Liver function tests need to be monitored since cimetidine and ranitidine are hepatotoxic drugs.

37. a. Nursing diagnosis is knowledge deficit due to new medications.

b. Do not take OTC meds before checking with a healthcare provider due to drug-drug interactions.

c. Antacids should be given 2 hours before or 2 hours after other medications because of drug-drug interactions and the effect of antacids on the gastric pH.

Chapter 37

1. stress, sights, sounds, smells
2. anticholinergics, antihistamines
3. pH, alkalosis
4. Anorexiants, moderate
5. frequency, bowel movements
6. food intake, dietary fibre
7. impaction, obstruction
8. laxative, defecation
9. monitoring, education
10. esophageal obstruction, intestinal obstruction, fecal impaction, bowel

11. b   12. g   13. e   14. a   15. d   16. f

17. c   18. c   19. c   20. a   21. d   22. c

23. a   24. a   25. d   26. b   27. b   28. c
29. c   30. b   31. c   32. c   33. a   34. c

35. $\dfrac{10\ mg}{dose} \times \dfrac{2\ mL}{25\ mg} = \dfrac{20}{25} = \dfrac{0.8\ mL}{dose}$

3-mL syringe

For average size adult, 20–21 gauge, 1 to 1-1/2 inch needle.

36. $\dfrac{2.5\ mg}{dose} \times \dfrac{4\ doses}{day} = \dfrac{10\ mg}{day}$

37. a. Risk for injury and knowledge deficit are two important nursing diagnoses for this client.

b. Client will be free from physical injury related to frequency of stools and physical weakness. Client will understand the signs and symptoms of complications and report them appropriately.

c. Nursing actions include providing a clutter-free environment with commode at bedside and a call bell within reach and monitoring for stools—amount and character.

d. Criteria include abdominal assessment for presence of bowel sounds, palpation for softness of and pain-free abdomen, and act of defecation.

38. a. Initial assessment will include vital signs, evidence of weakness or confusion, and abdominal assessment.

b. Objective data include vital signs, abdominal assessment, number of stools visualized, with colour and character of stool.

c. Safety issues are call bell within reach, ability to follow directions and call for help, commode at bedside, clutter-free environment with slippers available.

39. a. Initial assessment will include vital signs, adequate nutrition, absence of vomiting, stable laboratory studies, and lack of uterine contractions.

b. The primary goal is a full-term pregnancy without harm to fetus or mother.

c. Compazine is pregnancy category C, so the risks must be weighed against the benefits since fetal harm in animals has been noted.

d. Outcome criteria will include (1) VS and weight (no further loss of weight), (2) laboratory results (stable electrolytes), Hgb, and Hct, and (3) intake and output (adequate nutrition and hydration).

40. a. Low-fat diet should be maintained while on Xenical, and fat-soluble vitamin supplements should be added to the diet.

b. Supplemental multivitamins with D, E, K, and beta carotene should be taken daily; psyllium may be taken at bed time to decrease GI side effects.

c. Psychological support and client education reinforcing the difference between hunger and appetite accompanied by diversional therapy. Nutritional consult is needed to assess for healthy foods among those the client likes.

Chapter 38

1. amounts, homeostasis
2. D, synthesize
3. prothrombin, blood clotting
4. lipid soluble, A, D, E, K
5. Fat-soluble, intestines, liver
6. Dietary Reference Intake, average, deficiency
7. Hypervitaminosis, A, C, D, E, B_6, niacin, folic acid
8. Alcohol abuse, thiamine
9. ergocalciferol
10. Vitamin E, free radicals, membranes
11. e   12. d   13. a   14. b   15. g   16. c
17. f   18. d   19. a   20. d   21. a   22. a
23. c   24. b   25. a   26. d   27. a   28. a
29. a   30. a   31. c   32. c

33. $\dfrac{200\ \mu g}{month} \times \dfrac{ml}{100\ \mu g} = \dfrac{200}{100} = \dfrac{2\ mL}{month}$

34. $\dfrac{250\ mL}{4\ hr} = \dfrac{62.50\ mL}{hr}$

35. a. Pulmocare is specialized for respiratory clients.

b. Protein and albumin levels will need to be monitored as well as electrolytes, glucose, and kidney function tests.

c. The four types of enteral feedings are oligomeric, polymeric, modular, and specialized.

d. The overall goal for this client is to have his nutritional status meet body requirements.

e. Nursing interventions include monitoring daily weights, intake and output, and lab values to determine success of the care plan.

f. Evaluative criteria will include respiratory assessment (especially the right middle lobe to note clearing or absence of adventitious sounds) and daily weights with maintenance of body weight and adequate intake and output.

36. a. Client will receive hyperalimentation with high-caloric intake, supplemented by vitamins and trace minerals.

b. Impaired swallowing post stroke is the reason for the TPN. A central line is necessary for TPN longer than 2 weeks to avoid phlebitis in peripheral veins secondary to the delivery of a hyperosmolar solution administered intravenously.

c. The short-term goal is the client will be free from hyper- and hypoglycemic reactions.

d. The long-term goal is the client will receive adequate nutrition allowing for change to enteral feedings.

e. The nurse will monitor the following: hyper- and hypoglycemic reactions and blood glucose, respiratory status, vital signs, insertion site for signs of infection, daily weight, and intake and output.

f. Client will not experience difficulty breathing, will remain infection-free, and will maintain moderate weight gain.

37. a. For long-term therapy, peripheral veins are not sufficient because of phlebitis.

b. This type of feeding will be necessary for 6 weeks or more; client will be infection free and maintain stable lab results.

c. The client can go home with home care support in the community.

Chapter 39

1. Hormones
2. electrolyte
3. IV
4. cardiovascular
5. anxiety
6. with
7. infection

8. c	9. d	10. e	11. a	12. b	13. c
14. b	15. a	16. d	17. d	18. c	19. b
20. a	21. a	22. b	23. d	24. c	25. d
26. d	27. a	28. a	29. b	30. c	31. b
32. a	33. d	34. c			

35. $\dfrac{10\text{ U}}{\text{dose}} \times \dfrac{1\text{ mL}}{20\text{ U}} = \dfrac{10}{20} = \dfrac{0.5\text{ mL}}{\text{dose}}$

36. $\dfrac{200\text{ mg}}{\text{dose}} \times \dfrac{1\text{ tablet}}{50\text{ mg}} = \dfrac{200}{50} = \dfrac{4\text{ tablets}}{\text{dose}}$

37. a. Thyroid preparations increase metabolic activity. They may elevate body temperature, increase heart rate, and reduce the client's weight. The effects of thyroid medications increase when a client is also taking insulin.

b. The nurse should take a thorough health history, communicate findings with the prescribing physician, and teach the client to report adverse effects promptly.

38. a. Propylthiouracil may cause vital sign changes. The client should be taught how to monitor these and to report changes promptly. This may require the purchase of necessary equipment. Risk of infection increases with the use of propylthiouracil. The client must understand the importance of avoiding crowds and individuals with known illnesses. This may lead to feelings of isolation.

b. The nurse can assist by encouraging alternative methods of communication such as the telephone and computer when susceptibility is increased. As drowsiness may occur with the use of this medication, teaching concerning safety is of importance. The nurse should instruct the client to avoid being near environmental hazards, driving, and operating machinery.

Chapter 40

1. type 1 diabetes mellitus, type 2 diabetes mellitus
2. oral antihyperglycemics
3. resistant
4. blood glucose

5. a	6. b	7. b	8. d	9. c	10. b
11. a	12. e	13. a	14. c	15. c	16. d
17. d	18. d	19. b	20. a	21. b	22. c
23. c	24. b	25. a	26. b	27. a	

28. 35 U + 20 U = 55 U

29. $\dfrac{10\text{ mg}}{\text{dose}} \times \dfrac{1\text{ tablet}}{5\text{ mg}} = \dfrac{10}{5} = \dfrac{2\text{ tablets}}{\text{dose}}$

30. a. Pharmacotherapy for type 2 diabetes is usually oral antihyperglycemic agents, and lifestyle changes such as proper diet and increased level of activity will be necessary.

b. People with type 2 diabetes mellitus are advised to maintain blood glucose levels between 4.0 and 6.0 mmol/L before meals or while fasting; 2 hours after meals, blood glucose levels should be between 5.0 and 8.0 mmol/L.

31. a. The following are hypoglycemic signs observed in clients with either type 1 or type 2 diabetes: polyuria—excessive urination; polyphagia—increase in hunger; polydipsia—increased thirst; glucosuria—high levels of glucose in the urine; change in weight; fatigue.

b. Initially, the following general areas should be monitored and reviewed: Obtain complete health history including allergies, drug history, and possible drug interactions. Review lab tests for any abnormalities. Obtain accurate history of alcohol use. Monitor blood glucose. Monitor for signs and symptoms of illness or infection. Monitor weight, weighing at the same time of day each time. This should be done for a time necessary to determine a pattern of weight loss or weight gain. Monitor activity level. Assess appetite and presence of symptoms that indicate client may not be able to consume or retain the next meal. Monitor blood pressure and other vital signs. Assess lifestyle habits that might affect client's physical condition and approaches for pharmacotherapy (smoking, eating patterns, substance misuse or abuse).

c. Client education as it relates to oral antihyperglycemic drugs would include goals for pharmacotherapy, importance of diet and exercise, reasons for obtaining baseline data such as vital signs and cardiac and renal function tests, and recognizing symptoms of hypoglycemia. Once a specific approach for pharmacotherapy has been determined, the following are additional points the nurse should include when teaching clients: Always carry a source of simple sugar in case of hypoglycemic reactions. Wear a medic alert bracelet to alert emergency personnel of the diabetes. Notify caregivers, coworkers, and others who may be able to render assistance. Avoid the use of alcohol to avoid an antabuse-like reaction. Maintain specified diet and exercise regimen while on antidiabetic drugs as these activities will help to keep blood glucose within a normal range. Swallow tablets whole and do not crush sustained-release tablets. Take medication 30 minutes before breakfast, or as directed by the healthcare provider.

Chapter 41

1. Follicle-stimulating hormone, luteinizing hormone
2. menopause
3. amenorrhea
4. progestins
5. prolactin, oxytocin

6. d   7. c   8. b   9. a   10. b   11. c
12. a   13. e   14. d   15. d   16. d   17. d
18. b   19. b   20. a   21. c   22. a   23. c
24. c   25. c   26. c   27. d   28. b   29. a
30. b   31. c

32. $\dfrac{100\ cc}{2\ hr} \times \dfrac{15\ gtt}{1\ cc} \times \dfrac{1\ hr}{60\ min} = \dfrac{1500}{120} = \dfrac{12.50\ gtt}{min} = \dfrac{13\ gtt}{min}$

33. $\dfrac{100\ mg}{dose} \times \dfrac{1\ mL}{400\ mg} = \dfrac{100}{400} = \dfrac{0.25\ mL}{dose}$

34. a. Ms. M has a knowledge deficit related to the prescribed drug regimen. The desired outcome is for Ms. M to understand the drug regimen and manage it appropriately.

b. Estrogen replacement therapy may be prescribed short term to alleviate unpleasant symptoms occurring during and after menopause. Hot flashes, night sweats, vaginal dryness, susceptibility to infection, erratic menstrual cycle, and nervousness may be reduced. The short-term risks of estrogen replacement therapy are bloating, nausea, vaginal bleeding, breast tenderness, and other common menstrual symptoms. The long-term risks are ovarian cancer, gallbladder disease, and breast cancer.

35. a. The nurse must use this medication with caution and continuously monitor maternal and fetus status. Adverse effects of oxytocin include fetal dysrhythmias, neonatal jaundice, and intracranial hemorrhage related to possible fetal trauma. Maternal effects include cardiac arrhythmias, hypertensive episodes, water intoxication, uterine rupture or uterine hypotonicity, seizures, postpartum hemorrhage, and coma.

b. Changes in maternal and fetal vital signs must be reported immediately and the infusion stopped. Intake and output should be monitored closely. Contraction status during labour and fundal checks in the postpartum period are of utmost importance. The nurse must understand that uterine hypotonicity in the postpartum period is related to postpartum hemorrhage.

Chapter 42

1. Anabolic steroids
2. virilization
3. sildenafil (Viagra)
4. Benign prostatic hyperplasia (BPH)
5. Androgens
6. Finasteride (Proscar)

7. a   8. b   9. c   10. a   11. b   12. b
13. d   14. a   15. a   16. b   17. c   18. d
19. c   20. a   21. a   22. d   23. b   24. c
25. d   26. a   27. b

28. $\dfrac{150\ mg}{dose} \times \dfrac{1\ tablet}{100\ mg} = \dfrac{150}{100} = \dfrac{1.5\ tablets}{dose}$

29. $\dfrac{4\ mg}{dose} \times \dfrac{1\ capsule}{2\ mg} = \dfrac{4}{2} = \dfrac{2\ capsules}{dose}$

30. a. The nurse should teach Mr. E that the goal of finasteride (Proscar) therapy is to reduce urinary symptoms related to an enlarged prostate. Urinary symptoms such as hesitancy, difficulty starting the stream, decreased diameter of the stream, nocturia, dribbling, and frequency should be diminished. The nurse should explain to Mr. E that it may be necessary to take Proscar for the remainder of his life to keep the symptoms under control.

b. To evaluate effectiveness of therapy, the nurse should devise a method of follow-up to assess the resolution of urinary symptoms. Mr. E should also be encouraged to contact his nurse if symptoms worsen.

31. a. The nurse should obtain a list of herbs used by Mr. S. If he uses echinacea in conjunction with androgen therapy, his insulin requirements may decrease, necessitating a change in his insulin dosage.

b. Mr. S should be instructed to carefully monitor his blood glucose during androgen therapy and be encouraged to report symptoms of hypoglycemia such as sweating, tremors, anxiety, or vertigo.

Chapter 43

1. distal
2. distal, reabsorbed, secreted
3. a. efferent arteriole
   b. peritubular capillaries
   c. proximal tubule
   d. distal tubule
   e. collecting duct
   f. loop of Henle
   g. Bowman's capsule
   h. glomerulus

    i. afferent arteriole

4. a   5. b   6. c   7. b   8. e   9. c
10. d   11. a   12. d   13. b   14. b   15. a
16. d   17. c   18. d   19. a   20. b   21. c
22. b   23. d   24. a   25. c   26. a   27. d
28. a   29. d   30. d   31. d   32. d

33. $\dfrac{1\ mg}{dose} \times \dfrac{1\ tablet}{0.5\ mg} = \dfrac{1.0}{0.5} = \dfrac{2\ tablets}{dose}$

34. $\dfrac{1\ pill}{3\ days} = 0.33$ pills/day

    30 days $\times$ 0.33 = 10 pills

    The client should have at least 10 pills on hand.

35. a. Nursing diagnoses may include risk for injury, fatigue, and knowledge deficit.

    b. The nurse needs to monitor blood pressure and ask the client for recent blood pressure values. Inquire about the client's medication regimen. Review potassium levels if available. Obtain more information about presenting symptoms such as onset, alleviating and aggravating factors, and intensity. Inquire about other symptoms of hyperkalemia, including irritability, anxiety, and abdominal cramping. Obtain a 24-hour nutrition history, including beverages.

36. a. It is important for the nurse to communicate to Ms. F the health complications related to untreated hypertension. Assessment of Ms. F's lifestyle and stressors is also vital information needed to create an adequate plan of care.

    b. Lifestyle activities to reduce blood pressure should be communicated to Ms. F. Many factors may contribute to high blood pressure. These factors are often difficult to manage, and most clients require assistance to make the changes necessary to improve their health. Ms. F should be advised of the health hazards related to smoking, lack of exercise, obesity, stress, and alcohol consumption. The nurse should choose teaching methods appropriate for Ms. F's busy lifestyle. Handouts and written material will reinforce teaching and allow Ms. F to refer to the information at a later date. Follow-up appointments can be used to document progress in making lifestyle changes. Support groups may provide Ms. F with encouragement and accountability.

Chapter 44

1. Crystalloids
2. 7.35
3. 7.35 to 7.45
4. alkaline content
5. Hypertonic
6. Hypotonic
7. Isotonic
8. a   9. b   10. b   11. a   12. b   13. d
14. b   15. b   16. a   17. d   18. b   19. a

20. d   21. c   22. a   23. c   24. a   25. c
26. a   27. c   28. d   29. a   30. b

31. $\dfrac{1000\ cc}{8\ hr} = \dfrac{125\ cc}{hr}$

32. $\dfrac{8\ g}{day} \times \dfrac{1000\ mg}{1\ g} \times \dfrac{1\ tablet}{500\ mg} = \dfrac{8000}{500} = \dfrac{16\ tablets}{day}$

    $\dfrac{16\ tablets}{4\ doses} = \dfrac{4\ tablets}{dose}$

33. a. ASA and potassium may irritate the stomach mucosa. Also, an extremely low carbohydrate diet causes the body to burn fats for energy, creating keto acids. CNS depression may be caused by impending acidosis. Ms. S has a knowledge deficit of her drug regimen, requiring nursing intervention.

    b. Ms. S could benefit from a thorough nutritional assessment and resulting weight loss plan taking her drug regimen into consideration. Referral to a nutritionist may be necessary. The nurse should also ensure that Ms. S understands proper administration of her drug regimen.

34. a. Symptoms of hyponatremia include nausea, vomiting, muscle cramps, tachycardia, dry mucous membranes, and headache. The nurse should obtain a baseline set of vital signs and monitor values closely. The client should be asked about the onset and progression of symptoms. A diet history including beverages should be obtained.

    b. A hazard of working outdoors is sodium loss through profuse sweating. Fluid replacement is critical to avoid hyponatremia. Mr. W should be encouraged by the nurse to consume adequate amounts of water or electrolyte solutions such as sports drinks. The early symptoms of hyponatremia should serve as a signal to take refuge from the heat and concentrate on fluid replacement.

Chapter 45

1. movement
2. nervous, muscular, endocrine, skeletal
3. muscle spasms
4. analgesic, anti-inflammatory, centrally acting skeletal muscle relaxant
5. spasticity
6. dystonia
7. 3 to 6
8. a   9. b   10. b   11. a   12. a   13. b
14. a   15. a   16. b   17. a   18. b   19. d
20. b   21. c   22. a   23. a   24. b   25. a
26. c   27. b   28. a   29. d   30. b   31. b
32. b

33. $\dfrac{75\ mg}{dose} \times \dfrac{1\ tablet}{25\ mg} = \dfrac{75}{25} = \dfrac{3\ tablets}{dose}$

    $\dfrac{75\ mg}{dose} \times \dfrac{2\ doses}{day} = \dfrac{150\ mg}{day}$

34. $\dfrac{20\text{ mg}}{\text{dose}} \times \dfrac{1\text{ tablet}}{10\text{ mg}} = \dfrac{20}{10} = \dfrac{2\text{ tablets}}{\text{dose}}$

Yes, this is a safe dose.

35. a. Limiting use of the affected muscle, heat or cold packs, hydrotherapy, ultrasound, exercises, massage, and manipulation may help to decrease Ms. H's low back pain.

b. Ms. H needs to know that dizziness, dry mouth, rash, and a fast pulse rate with palpitations may be noted while using this drug. Another possible but rare reaction is swelling of the tongue. She should not take this drug with alcohol, phenothiazines, or MAO inhibitors because of unfavourable reactions.

c. Ask the client to rate her pain on a scale of 1 to 10 and see whether improvement is noted after using the drug. Monitor muscle tone, range of motion, and improved ability to do activities of daily living. These should increase if the drug is effective.

d. The client should be instructed in proper body mechanics while lifting, sitting, or engaged in other musculoskeletal movement activities.

36. a. Ms. B needs to know that Botox injections are indicated for moderate to severe frown lines. They are not for crow's feet. She also needs to know that they will, however, smooth the lines between the brows temporarily and must be repeated every 3 to 4 months. Although botulinum toxin is a poison in higher quantities, it is safe for use in tiny injections.

b. Side effects of Botox include headache, nausea, flu-like symptoms, temporary eyelid drooping, mild pain, erythema at the site of injection, and muscle weakness.

37. a. Mr. P should have a thorough assessment of his physical condition, especially vital signs, skin condition, mobility or lack of it, neurological function, self-care ability, and nutritional status. The nurse should also determine the adherence to his medication regimen, side effects, and what outcome the family expects.

b. Physical therapy exercises might decrease the severity of his symptoms. These include stretching to help prevent contractures, muscle-group strengthening exercises, and repetitive motion exercises. Surgery for tendon release or to sever the nerve-muscle pathway might be used in an extreme situation.

c. Mr. P and his family should be instructed to report any significant changes in his level of consciousness such as confusion, hallucinations, lethargy, and decreased speech ability. Also, palpitations, chest pain, dyspnea, visual disturbances, and unusual fatigue should be reported to the doctor. Treatment should not be discontinued abruptly. Taking the medications with food should decrease GI upset. Decreased urinary output, distended abdomen, and discomfort should be reported. Dry mouth may be treated with sips of water, sugarless candy, or gum if client is able to use this.

d. Family/client need to be instructed on gentle range of motion exercises and other physical therapy as indicated by the physician. Safety measures include rearranging the home to decrease the risk of falls or accidents and placing needed objects within Mr. P's reach.

Chapter 46

1. calcium
2. parathyroid, thyroid
3. vitamin D
4. rickets
5. osteoporosis, Paget's disease
6. parathyroid hormone, calcitonin
7. calcifediol, calcitriol
8. complexed, elemental
9. bisphosphonates
10. Disease-modifying drugs
11. uric acid-inhibiting drugs

12. b	13. a	14. e	15. c	16. d	17. e
18. c	19. c	20. a	21. b	22. d	23. e
24. c	25. b	26. d	27. d	28. a	29. c
30. b	31. b	32. d	33. b	34. c	35. a
36. d	37. c	38. a	39. d	40. c	41. b
42. a					

43. $\dfrac{4\text{ mg}}{\text{max dose}} \times \dfrac{1\text{ tablet}}{0.5\text{ mg}} = \dfrac{4}{0.5} = \dfrac{8\text{ tablets}}{\text{max dose}}$

44. $\dfrac{400\text{ mg}}{\text{dose}} \times \dfrac{1\text{ tablet}}{200\text{ mg}} = \dfrac{400}{200} = \dfrac{2\text{ tablets}}{\text{dose}}$

45. a. The symptoms the client is experiencing are normal for his condition. Allopurinol is used for gout flare-up and primary and secondary hyperuricemia.

b. To allay the pain, NSAIDs would probably be administered with anti-gout therapy. Medications could be administered with meals to minimize gastric upset. Other expected effects would include diarrhea and rash. Precautions would be taken to minimize these symptoms. Over a longer time, difficulty in urination may occur.

c. During drug therapy, laboratory tests (BUN and creatinine) would be ordered to monitor whether the kidneys are functioning properly. Fluid intake and output would be monitored. As allopurinol may cause bone marrow depression, blood cell counts would be taken regularly. Liver function tests would also be ordered.

46. a. Clients with kidney disease are unable to synthesize the active form of vitamin D from the precursors formed by the body or taken in through the diet. Calcium is not absorbed well from the GI tract unless there is adequate vitamin D, so the client may become hypocalcemic.

b. The client should be informed that periodic liver function tests will be necessary, as well as calcium, magnesium, and phosphate levels. The drug should be taken exactly as directed so that toxic levels do not develop. Fatigue, weakness, nausea, and vomiting should be reported. Alcohol and other liver-toxic drugs should be avoided. Exposure to 20 minutes of sunlight daily will help increase the amount of vitamin D available to the client.

c. Again, the importance of routine lab studies for calcium levels must be stressed. Oral calcium supplements should be taken with meals or within an hour after meals. The client should be advised to consume calcium-rich foods such as dark green, leafy vegetables and dairy products.

47. a. Osteoporosis occurs when the rate of bone replacement is less than the rate of bone breakdown. People at risk for osteoporosis include postmenopausal women, those who use excess alcohol or caffeine, those with anorexia nervosa, smokers, inactive persons, those who lack adequate vitamin D or calcium in their diets, and persons using corticosteroids, antiseizure medications, and immunosuppressive drugs. The disease can be detected through the use of bone density tests.

b. Medications used to treat osteoporosis include calcium and vitamin D, estrogen replacement therapy, estrogen receptor modulators, bisphosphonates, and calcitonin.

c. The client will need to be instructed that alendronate (Fosamax) decreases the breakdown of her bones. The usual side effects are GI problems such as nausea, vomiting, abdominal pain, and esophageal irritation. The drug should be taken on an empty stomach once a week. To prevent the esophagus from becoming irritated, the client should not lie down for 30 minutes after taking the medication. Client teaching for raloxifene (Evista) should include the need for periodic bone density scans. Sudden chest pain, dyspnea, pain in calves, and swelling in the legs should be reported promptly. The client should not take estrogen replacement therapy while using this drug. In addition, safety measures regarding falls should be discussed, as well as the need for weight-bearing activity and adequate dietary consumption of calcium and vitamin D.

Chapter 47

1. keratolytic
2. scabies
3. retinoids
4. Phototherapy
5. pruritus
6. 30, 50
7. eczema

8. c	9. d	10. e	11. c	12. a	13. b
14. c	15. d	16. c	17. e	18. a	19. b
20. c	21. b	22. a	23. d	24. d	25. d
26. c	27. b	28. b	29. d	30. a	31. a

| 32. b | 33. b | 34. c | 35. d | 36. c |

37. a. Lindane should be used cautiously in children under 10 years of age, and only if other pediculicides fail. Since this is the case here, the mother needs to know that lindane might cause local skin irritation and adverse CNS effects such as restlessness, dizziness, tremors, or convulsions. This usually occurs after misuse or ingestion. This shampoo must be kept out of the reach of smaller children in the household. It should not be applied to open skin lesions or used if the child has seizures. Mother should wear gloves while applying the shampoo, particularly if she is pregnant. The shampoo should remain on the hair for at least 5 minutes. Use of tepid water will decrease itching.

b. The child's teacher should be notified, as well as the parents of the child with whom she spent the night and any other children who attended the sleepover. Anyone else with whom the child has had close contact (grandparents, for example) should be notified as well.

c. Children in school should not swap clothing or towels. Coat and hat racks at school may need to be eliminated to prevent the spread from one child to another. Combs or other hygiene supplies should not be shared, and bodily contact with an infected person should be avoided. Also, the child should not sleep with brothers or sisters until the problem is resolved. The nurse should stress that this is not a problem of social class, but simply an event that occurs when there is close contact.

38. a. You would ask the client if he has had nausea, vomiting, chills, and headache, as well as assessing the amount of pain and extent of the erythema. Also ask about sunburn and tanning history, the amount of time the client usually spends in the sun before beginning to burn, and if he uses sunscreen products. An allergy history is also necessary.

b. Soothing lotions, rest, prevention of dehydration, and topical anesthetic agents may help. The topical anesthetics may be chilled prior to application to increase the cooling effect. In severe cases, ASA or ibuprofen may be used.

c. Medication should not be applied to broken skin. If this occurs, call the doctor. Prevent sunburn by decreasing exposure to sunlight or by increasing the SPF of the sunscreen. Wear a broad-brimmed hat, sunglasses with UV protection, and a long-sleeved shirt if extended exposure to sunlight is expected during peak hours of the day. Sunburn results from overexposure to UV light and is associated with light skin complexions. Chronic sun exposure can lead to eye injury, cataracts, and skin cancer.

39. a. Causes of acne are unknown, although some factors associated with it have been identified. Overproduction of sebum by oil glands, keratin that blocks oil glands, and certain bacteria grow within oil gland openings and change the sebum to an irritating

substance. This results in small, inflamed bumps on the skin. Other factors include male hormones, which regulate the activity of the sebaceous glands.

b. A mental health history should be taken to determine whether the client has had a history of depression or suicidal tendencies. Clients with seizures who use carbamazepine should be identified because there is an increased risk for seizures. Also, oral antidiabetic agents may not be as effective, so the nurse should assess for diabetes, heart disease, and elevated lipid levels. Before the drug is used, a patch test must be done to test for sensitivity.

c. He should be told to monitor foods and avoid those that seem to make his acne worse. He can be taught to keep a food log to help determine which ones these are. Products that will irritate the skin, such as cologne, perfumes, and other alcohol-based products, should be avoided. If severe inflammation occurs during therapy, the physician should be notified. Use of OTC agents should be avoided unless approved by the physician.

Chapter 48

1. blockage, outflow
2. open-angle glaucoma
3. miotics
4. mydriatics
5. cycloplegics
6. external otitis
7. otitis media
8. mastoiditis

9. a	10. b	11. b	12. b	13. a	14. a
15. a	16. g	17. h	18. c	19. b	20. d
21. e	22. f	23. b	24. b	25. b	26. a
27. c	28. d	29. d	30. c	31. a	32. b
33. a	34. c	35. a	36. a	37. d	38. b
39. b	40. a	41. a	42. a		

43. $\dfrac{250 \text{ mg}}{24 \text{ hr dose}} \times \dfrac{3 \text{ doses}}{1} = \dfrac{750 \text{ mg}}{24 \text{ hr}}$

44. No need to verify the order—this is the standard way to administer pilocarpine in an emergency situation. (Of course, if you are unsure of anything, it is always best to check it out before you go ahead!)

45. a. There is no permanent cure for glaucoma. Medications will have to be used indefinitely. Several classes of eye medications may be used alone or in combination to control the intraocular pressure problem characteristic of glaucoma.

b. Xalatan is used to decrease the IOP. Side effects may include conjunctival edema, tearing, dryness, burning, pain, itching, photophobia, or visual disturbances. The eyelashes on the treated eye may grow, thicken, and darken. The iris may have colour changes, as well as the skin around the eye. Generalized flu-like symptoms may occur. The client should remove contacts prior to administering and leave them out for 15 minutes. Wait 5 minutes between different eye medications.

c. The client should be instructed to report any visual changes and any changes in medications or new health-related problems. He should be taught the proper way to administer eye drops and be told to schedule them around his daily routines. Signs of side effects should be reported. He will need to know that measurements of intraocular pressure will be done periodically. For his safety, environmental lighting needs to be adjusted when dark and may need to be dimmed if there is photophobia.

d. Intraocular pressure should be measured using tonometry at regular intervals to determine the effectiveness of the medication.

46. a. Additional assessments needed include BJ's allergy history and whether his mother knows how to administer the drugs properly and is aware of potential side effects.

b. The mother needs teaching regarding the correct use of ear drops and the fact that Aspirin is contraindicated in young children because of the risk of Reye's syndrome. Teaching should include the following: Ear drops are contraindicated in cases where the eardrum has perforated. This is the most likely cause of the drainage in BJ's ear and may be seen on examination of the tympanic membrane. Explain that the bacteria present in the outer ear may be carried into the middle ear when the drops run in, thus increasing the chances of a further infection. The mother needs to be made aware that ear drops should be warmed by holding under warm water prior to administration. Also, the child should lie on the side opposite the affected ear for 5 minutes after the drops are put in. If the child is older than 3 years, the pinna should be pulled up and back; if less than 3 years, pull it down and back.

47. a. Mrs. I probably has impacted cerumen (earwax). This would explain the mild hearing loss and sensation of fullness with intermittent ringing of the ears. Other assessments to make would include whether she has a history of ruptured tympanic membranes, auditory canal surgery, or myringotomy tubes as these would contraindicate ear irrigation and the use of earwax softeners.

b. Initial nursing interventions would include removal by using mineral oil or an earwax softener preparation, followed by irrigation with a bulb syringe.